Common Core State Standards Edition

Everyday Mathematics®

The University of Chicago School Mathematics Project

Teacher's Guide to Activities

Kindergarten **K**

McGraw Hill Education

Chicago, IL • Columbus, OH • New York, NY

ii

Everyday Mathematics

Photo Credits
See page 430.

The University of Chicago School Mathematics Project (UCSMP)

Max Bell, Director, UCSMP Elementary Materials Component;
    Director, *Everyday Mathematics* First Edition
James McBride, Director, *Everyday Mathematics* Second Edition
Andy Isaacs, Director, *Everyday Mathematics* Third Edition
Amy Dillard, Associate Director, *Everyday Mathematics* Third Edition
Rachel Malpass McCall, Associate Director, *Everyday Mathematics*
    Common Core State Standards Edition

Authors

Jean Bell, Max Bell, David W. Beer*, Dorothy Freedman, Nancy Guile Goodsell†,
Nancy Hanvey, Deborah Arron Leslie, Kate Morrison

†*First Edition only*   **Third Edition only*

Third Edition Early Childhood Team Leaders

David W. Beer, Deborah Arron Leslie

Technical Art   Mathematics and Technology Advisor

Diana Barrie   James Flanders

Third Edition Teachers in Residence

Ann E. Audrain, Margaret Krulee, Barbara Smart

UCSMP Editorial   ELL Consultant

Patrick Carroll   Kathryn B. Chval
Lila K. Schwartz
Tiffany Nicole Slade

Contributors

Regina Littleton (Office Manager), Kriszta Miner (Project Manager), Deborah Adams,
Patrick Carroll, Moira Erwine, Carolyn Frieswyk, Serena Hohmann, Amy Rose, John Saller,
Sheila Sconiers, Ann Smelser, Penny Stahly, Izaak Wirszup, Nancy Roesing

everyday**math**.com

 **Education**

STEM McGraw-Hill is committed to providing instructional
materials in Science, Technology, Engineering, and Mathematics
(STEM) that give all students a solid foundation, one that
prepares them for college and careers in the 21st century.

Send all inquiries to:
McGraw-Hill Education
STEM Learning Solutions Center
P.O. Box 812960
Chicago, IL 60681

ISBN 978-0-07-657511-4
MHID 0-07-657511-X

Printed in the United States of America.

5 6 7 8 9 RMN 17 16 15 14 13 12

The **McGraw·Hill** Companies

The University of Chicago School Mathematics Project (UCSMP)

Acknowledgments

The first edition of *Everyday Mathematics* was made possible by sustained support over several years from the GTE Corporation and the National Science Foundation; additional help came from the Amoco Foundation through its support of the University of Chicago School Mathematics Project (UCSMP). Earlier projects supported by the National Science Foundation, the National Institute of Education, and the Benton Foundation provided us with insights into the surprising capabilities of young children.

Development of the second edition of *Everyday Mathematics* was funded by the Everyday Learning Corporation and the authors; development of the third edition was supported by Wright Group/McGraw-Hill, the University of Chicago, and the authors.

For all of these editions, many University of Chicago and UCSMP colleagues have been helpful. For this Common Core State Standards edition, Deborah Arron Leslie, Rachel Malpass McCall, Cheryl G. Moran, Mary Ellen Dairyko, Rebecca W. Maxcy, Denise Porter, and Sarah R. Burns formed a committee that provided invaluable guidance on many key issues. Rachel Malpass McCall's work as Associate Director of the Common Core State Standards Edition was especially important to the success of the project. We also acknowledge dedicated and resourceful assistance on production and technical tasks by many people at the University of Chicago and at the McGraw-Hill School Education Group.

Over the years that UCSMP has been working in schools, feedback and advice from teachers willing to take risks in trying development versions of our materials have been essential and enormously helpful. There are too many such teachers to list, but their contributions are gratefully acknowledged.

Andy Isaacs
Director, Third Edition and Common Core State Standards Edition

James McBride
Director, Second Edition

Max Bell
Director, First Edition

Contents

Everyday Mathematics

A Mission to Improve Mathematics

The University of Chicago School Mathematics Project

Everyday Mathematics was developed by the University of Chicago School Mathematics Project (UCSMP) in order to enable children in elementary grades to learn more mathematical content and become life-long mathematical thinkers.

◆ The National Science Foundation and Amoco, GTE, and other leading corporations supported the project through substantial, long-term funding.

◆ A strong partnership among researchers, mathematics educators, classroom teachers, students, and administrators was developed.

◆ A consistent, core author team at the University of Chicago School Mathematics Project collaborated on all grade levels to provide a cohesive and well-articulated Pre-K through Grade 6 curriculum.

◆ The *Everyday Mathematics* curriculum is completely aligned to the NCTM Curriculum Focal Points and the Connections to the Curriculum Focal Points for Grades Pre-K through 6.

> "We, our funders, and our users believe strongly that even the best curricula of decades ago are not adequate for today's youth."
>
> University of Chicago School Mathematics Project

Research Foundation

Everyday Mathematics began with the premise that students can, and must, learn more mathematics than has been expected from them in the past. This premise is based on research the UCSMP author team and others undertook prior to writing the curriculum. Following are some major findings of this research:

- The typical U.S. mathematics curriculum is arithmetic-driven, slow-paced, isolated in its instruction, and broad—rather than deep—in its content.

- International studies show that U.S. students learn much less mathematics than students in other countries.

- Children are capable of learning more mathematics in a richer curriculum.

- All children can be successful mathematical thinkers.

- Mathematics is meaningful to children when it is varied, rich, and rooted in real-world problems and applications.

Instructional Design

The *Everyday Mathematics* instructional design was carefully crafted to capitalize on student interest and maximize student learning. Among its features are the following:

- High expectations for all students
- Concepts and skills developed over time and in a wide variety of contexts
- Balance among mathematical strands
- Dynamic applications
- Multiple methods and strategies for problem solving
- Concrete modeling as a pathway to abstract understanding
- Collaborative learning in partner and small-group activities
- Cross-curricular applications and connections
- Built-in professional development for teachers

"Our teachers in Grades 6–8 tell me that students using the *Everyday Mathematics* program in earlier grades are arriving in their classrooms with a deeper understanding of mathematical concepts and are ready to start the year at a much higher level."

Principal Kenneth Tucker,
Pre-K to 8

Everyday
Mathematics

Meeting Standards, Achieving Results

The *Everyday Mathematics* program is celebrating more than 25 years of research and development. The program offers schools results unmatched by any other elementary mathematics program.

Research, Validation, Results

As part of the research for *Everyday Mathematics,* the authors at the University of Chicago School Mathematics Project examined successful curricula from around the world, researched how children learn mathematics, and studied the actual use of mathematics by people in their everyday lives. The results of this research were used to establish the scope and sequence for the mathematical content of the *Everyday Mathematics* program.

Field Testing

The program was written and field tested one grade-level at a time, beginning with Kindergarten. Field tests gathered information from classroom teachers and students in three main areas: teacher preparation of materials, student response to materials, and student achievement. Based on teacher and student feedback, the authors revised the curriculum before *Everyday Mathematics* was published.

Learner Verification

The best way to show the effectiveness of a program is to study it over time. Several independent research studies have been conducted which provide evidence for the effectiveness of *Everyday Mathematics.* For example, *Everyday Mathematics* was the focus of a five-year longitudinal study conducted by researchers at Northwestern University. Reports from this study and others are available through the University of Chicago School Mathematics Project or McGraw-Hill.

Tri-State Student Achievement Study

The ARC Center, a National Science Foundation (NSF) funded project, located at the Consortium for Mathematics and its Applications (COMAP), has carried out a study of the effects of standards-based mathematics programs on student performance on state-mandated standardized tests in Massachusetts, Illinois, and Washington.

The findings of the study are based on the records of over 78,000 students: 39,701 who had used the *Everyday Mathematics* curriculum for at least two years, and 38,481 students from comparison schools. The students were carefully matched by reading level, socioeconomic status, and other variables.

Results showed that the average scores of students in the *Everyday Mathematics* schools were consistently higher than the average scores of students in the comparison schools. (A complete report is available from COMAP or McGraw-Hill.)

What Works Clearinghouse

Everyday Mathematics is the only elementary math program found by the What Works Clearinghouse to have potentially positive effects on students' math achievement, among those with a medium to large extent of evidence. The studies of *Everyday Mathematics* cited in the What Works Clearinghouse findings included a total of approximately 12,600 students in Grades 3–5. The students were from a range of socioeconomic backgrounds and attended schools in urban, suburban, and rural communities in multiple states.

Closing the Gap

Many districts, by using the *Everyday Mathematics* program, have helped minority students increase achievement, reducing the minority/majority achievement gap while maintaining growth for all students. This helps schools and districts meet adequate yearly progress requirements set forth by No Child Left Behind legislation. District information is available by contacting McGraw-Hill.

A report based on 78,000 students showed that average standardized test scores were significantly higher for students in *Everyday Mathematics* schools than for students in comparison schools.

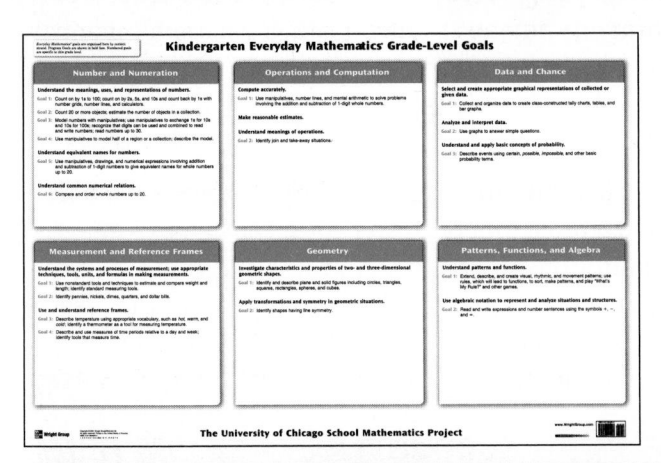

Everyday Mathematics Grade-Level Goals for Kindergarten

Program Goals and Grade-Level Goals

Everyday Mathematics structures content into Grade-Level Goals and Program Goals. Grade-Level Goals are then organized by content strand and are carefully articulated across the grades. The content in each grade provides all children with a balanced mathematics curriculum that is rich in real-world problem-solving opportunities. The success of this approach to teaching mathematics is evident in children's improved scores on standardized tests.

The Program Goals and Grade-Level Goals for Kindergarten are listed in the chart below.

Number and Numeration
Program Goal: Understand the meanings, uses, and representations of numbers.

Rote counting	**Goal 1** Count on by 1s to 100; count on by 2s, 5s, and 10s and count back by 1s with number grids, number lines, and calculators.
Rational counting	**Goal 2** Count 20 or more objects; estimate the number of objects in a collection.
Place value and notation	**Goal 3** Model numbers with manipulatives; use manipulatives to exchange 1s for 10s and 10s for 100s; recognize that digits can be used and combined to read and write numbers; read numbers up to 30.
Meanings and uses of fractions	**Goal 4** Use manipulatives to model half of a region or a collection; describe the model.

Number and Numeration (cont.)

Program Goal: Understand equivalent names for numbers.

Equivalent names for whole numbers	**Goal 5** Use manipulatives, drawings, and numerical expressions involving addition and subtraction of 1-digit numbers to give equivalent names for whole numbers up to 20.

Program Goal: Understand common numerical relations.

Comparing and ordering numbers	**Goal 6** Compare and order whole numbers up to 20.

Operations and Computation

Program Goal: Compute accurately.

Addition and subtraction facts	**Goal 1** Use manipulatives, number lines, and mental arithmetic to solve problems involving the addition and subtraction of single-digit whole numbers; demonstrate appropriate fluency with addition and subtraction facts within 5.

Program Goal: Understand meanings of operations.

Models for operations	**Goal 2** Identify join and take-away situations.

Data and Chance

Program Goal: Select and create appropriate graphical representations of collected or given data.

Data collection and representation	**Goal 1** Collect and organize data to create class-constructed tally charts, tables, and bar graphs.

Data and Chance (cont.)

Program Goal: Analyze and interpret data.

Data analysis	**Goal 2** Use graphs to answer simple questions.

Program Goal: Understand and apply basic concepts of probability.

Qualitative probability	**Goal 3** Describe events using *certain*, *possible*, *impossible*, and other basic probability terms.

Measurement and Reference Frames

Program Goal: Understand the systems and processes of measurement; use appropriate techniques, tools, units, and formulas in making measurements.

Length, weight, and angles	**Goal 1** Use nonstandard tools and techniques to estimate and compare weight and length; identify standard measuring tools.
Money	**Goal 2** Identify pennies, nickels, dimes, quarters, and dollar bills.

Program Goal: Use and understand reference frames.

Temperature	**Goal 3** Describe temperature using appropriate vocabulary, such as *hot*, *warm*, and *cold;* identify a thermometer as a tool for measuring temperature.
Time	**Goal 4** Describe and use measures of time periods relative to a day and week; identify tools that measure time.

Geometry

Program Goal: Investigate characteristics and properties of two- and three-dimensional geometric shapes.

Plane and solid figures	**Goal 1** Identify and describe plane and solid figures including circles, triangles, squares, rectangles, spheres, and cubes.

Program Goal: Apply transformations and symmetry in geometric situations.

Transformations and symmetry	**Goal 2** Identify shapes having line symmetry.

Patterns, Functions, and Algebra

Program Goal: Understand patterns and functions.

Patterns and functions	**Goal 1** Extend, describe, and create visual, rhythmic, and movement patterns; use rules, which will lead to functions, to sort, make patterns, and play "What's My Rule?" and other games.

Program Goal: Use algebraic notation to represent and analyze situations and structures.

Algebraic notation and solving number sentences	**Goal 2** Read and write expressions and number sentences using the symbols $+$, $-$, and $=$.

Common Core State Standards

Everyday Mathematics fully aligns with the national Common Core State Standards for Mathematics. Both are founded on cross-disciplinary skills such as critical thinking and problem solving. The Standards for Mathematical Practice, described in the Common Core State Standards, form a cohesive match with the already-proven instructional design of *Everyday Mathematics*. Both require children to:

◆ Make sense of problems and persevere in solving them.

◆ Reason abstractly and quantitatively.

◆ Construct viable arguments and critique the reasoning of others.

◆ Model with mathematics.

◆ Use appropriate tools strategically.

◆ Attend to precision.

◆ Look for and make use of structure.

◆ Look for and express regularity in repeated reasoning.

In *Everyday Mathematics*, the Grade-Level Goals, which state the core content that is assessed at each grade level, align with the Standards for Mathematical Content. *Everyday Mathematics* has a long track record of success resulting from constant revision based on evidence of what works. *Everyday Mathematics* is a world-class mathematics curriculum that fully meets the Common Core State Standards for Grades K–6.

> *Everyday Mathematics* fully meets all of the Common Core State Standards for Mathematics, Grades K–6.

Everyday
Mathematics
and the
COMMON CORE
STATE STANDARDS

COMMON CORE
100%
ALIGNMENT
STATE STANDARDS

Mc
Graw
Hill

Instruction and Planning

The *Teacher's Guide to Activities* includes a comprehensive correlation that shows the Kindergarten activities in *Everyday Mathematics* that cover each of the Common Core State Standards for Mathematics in Kindergarten. A complete correlation for all components is available at everydaymathonline.com.

Everyday Mathematics offers a variety of print and technology materials to meet instructional needs and to help incorporate these standards in the classroom curriculum.

Assessment

Everyday Mathematics provides many opportunities and tools for assessment. Assessment results show children's progress toward the *Everyday Mathematics* Grade-Level Goals and the Common Core State Standards.

Professional Development

Professional Development is offered at implementation, for continued support, and is built into the program materials to help teachers successfully implement the Common Core State Standards with the *Everyday Mathematics* program.

Everyday Mathematics

Common Core State Standards and *Everyday Mathematics*

The *Everyday Mathematics* curriculum is completely aligned to the *K-12 Common Core State Standards* for Kindergarten through Grade 6.

Common Core State Standards for Kindergarten	*Everyday Mathematics* Kindergarten Activities*
COUNTING AND CARDINALITY K.CC	
Know number names and the count sequence.	
K.CC. 1. Count to 100 by ones and by tens.	*Number of the Day Routine,* 1•3, 1•12, 2•1, 2•6, 2•9, 2•14, 3•4, 3•12, **3•15**, **4•2**, **4•6**, 4•13, 4•15, 5•7, 5•11, 6•5, **6•7**, **6•14**, **7•2**, **7•7**, **7•8**, **8•1**
K.CC. 2. Count forward beginning from a given number within the known sequence (instead of having to begin at 1).	*Number of the Day Routine,* 1•12, 2•1, 2•6, 2•9, 2•10, 2•14, 3•4, 3•12, **4•6**, 4•13, **5•5**, **7•7**
K.CC. 3. Write numbers from 0 to 20. Represent a number of objects with a written numeral 0-20 (with 0 representing a count of no objects).	*Number of the Day Routine, Monthly Calendar Routine,* 1•5, **1•6**, 1•7–1•10, **1•11**, **1•12**, **1•13**, **1•14**, **1•16**, 2•7, 2•8, 2•12, **3•1**, **3•3**, **3•5**, 3•7, **3•9**, 4•11, **4•12**, **4•16**, **5•3**, **7•10**, **8•6**, **8•9**, **8•15**

*Bold activity numbers indicate that the content from the standard is being taught in the Main Activity.
Activity numbers not in bold indicate that content from the standard is being reviewed or practiced in a Revisit Activity or Teaching Option.

Common Core State Standards for Kindergarten	Everyday Mathematics Kindergarten Activities
Count to tell the number of objects.	
K.CC. 4. Understand the relationship between numbers and quantities; connect counting to cardinality.	
K.CC. 4a. When counting objects, say the number names in the standard order, pairing each object with one and only one number name and each number name with one and only one object.	***Number of the Day*** and ***Attendance Routines,*** **1•3, 1•5, 1•6,** 1•7–1•10, **1•11, 1•12,** 1•13, **1•14, 1•16, 2•6–2•9, 2•11, 2•12, 3•3, 3•5,** 3•8, **3•9, 3•13, 3•16, 4•6, 4•7,** 4•8, **4•12, 5•1, 5•8, 6•11, 7•2, 7•5, 7•7,** 7•12, **8•1**
K.CC. 4b. Understand that the last number name said tells the number of objects counted. The number of objects is the same regardless of their arrangement or the order in which they were counted.	***Number of the Day*** and ***Attendance Routines,*** **1•3, 1•5, 1•6,** 1•7–1•10, **1•11, 1•12,** 1•13, **1•14, 1•16, 2•6–2•9, 2•11, 2•12, 3•3, 3•5,** 3•8, **3•9, 3•13, 3•16, 4•6, 4•7,** 4•8, **4•12, 5•1, 5•8, 6•11, 7•2, 7•5, 7•7,** 7•12, **8•1**
K.CC. 4c. Understand that each successive number name refers to a quantity that is one larger.	***Number of the Day Routine,*** **1•3, 1•5, 1•6,** 1•7–1•10, **1•11, 1•12,** 1•13, **1•14, 1•16, 2•6, 2•8, 2•9, 2•12, 3•13, 5•1,** 8•5
K.CC. 5. Count to answer "how many" questions about as many as 20 things arranged in a line, a rectangular array, or a circle, or as many as 10 things in a scattered configuration; given a number from 1-20, count out that many objects.	***Attendance*** and ***Weather Observation Routines,*** **1•5, 1•6, 1•8, 1•14, 1•16, 2•6–2•10,** 2•15, 2•16, **3•13, 3•14, 5•1,** 5•13, 6•6, **7•2, 7•7,** 7•12, **8•1**

Common Core State Standards for Kindergarten	***Everyday Mathematics* Kindergarten Activities**
Compare numbers.	
K.CC. 6. Identify whether the number of objects in one group is greater than, less than, or equal to the number of objects in another group, e.g., by using matching and counting strategies.	***Weather Observation Routine,* 1•6,** 1•8, **1•11, 1•14,** 1•15, **1•16, 2•7, 2•8, 2•10,** 2•16, **3•14,** 3•16, **4•2, 4•7,** 6•6, **6•11, 7•13**
K.CC. 7. Compare two numbers between 1 and 10 presented as written numerals.	**3•6, 4•2, 5•5,** 5•6, **6•11,** 6•12, **7•13, 7•14, 7•16, 8•4**
OPERATIONS AND ALGEBRAIC THINKING K.OA	
Understand addition as putting together and adding to, and understand subtraction as taking apart and taking from.	
K.OA.1. Represent addition and subtraction with objects, fingers, mental images, drawings, sounds (e.g., claps), acting out situations, verbal explanations, expressions, or equations.	**2•14,** 3•6, **3•8, 3•13,** 3•15, **4•1,** 4•3, **4•4,** 4•7, **4•8, 4•11, 4•15,** 5•1, 5•8, 5•15, 6•1, 6•2, **6•9,** 6•16, 7•2, **7•3,** 7•5, **7•6,** 7•11, **7•12, 7•16, 8•4, 8•9, 8•10,** 8•11, **8•13, 8•14, Project 3**
K.OA.2. Solve addition and subtraction word problems, and add and subtract within 10, e.g., by using objects or drawings to represent the problem.	**2•14,** 3•6, **3•8,** 3•15, 4•3, **4•4, 4•8, 4•11, 4•15,** 5•8, 5•15, **6•9,** 6•16, 7•2, **7•3,** 7•5, 7•6, **8•13, 8•14, Project 3**
K.OA.3. Decompose numbers less than or equal to 10 into pairs in more than one way, e.g., by using objects or drawings, and record each decomposition by a drawing or equation (e.g., 5 = 2 + 3 and 5 = 4 + 1).	**1•5,** 1•6, 1•7, 1•8, 1•9, 1•10, 1•11, 1•12, 1•13, 2•14, **4•8,** 5•8, 7•3, 7•5, 7•6, **7•9,** 7•11, 7•15, **7•16,** 8•8, **8•9, Project 3**
K.OA.4. For any number from 1 to 9, find the number that makes 10 when added to the given number, e.g., by using objects or drawings, and record the answer with a drawing or equation.	**1•16,** 2•8, 2•14, **3•13,** 5•1, 6•2, **7•12,** 7•15, **8•9, Project 3**
K.OA.5. Fluently add and subtract within 5.	**3•8, 3•13,** 3•15, 4•3, **4•8, 5•4,** 5•8, 5•9, 6•8, 7•5, **7•6,** 7•11, **7•12, 8•4, 8•5,** 8•7, 8•10, 8•11, **Project 3**

Common Core State Standards for Kindergarten	*Everyday Mathematics* Kindergarten Activities
NUMBER AND OPERATIONS IN BASE TEN K.NBT	
Work with numbers 11-19 to gain foundations for place value.	
K.NBT.1. Compose and decompose numbers from 11 to 19 into ten ones and some further ones, e.g., by using objects or drawings, and record each composition or decomposition by a drawing or equation (such as $18 = 10 + 8$); understand that these numbers are composed of ten ones and one, two, three, four, five, six, seven, eight, or nine ones.	**2•12, 3•16,** 4•7, 6•11, **7•8**
MEASUREMENT AND DATA K.MD	
Describe and compare measurable attributes.	
K.MD.1. Describe measurable attributes of objects, such as length or weight. Describe several measurable attributes of a single object.	1•6, **1•13,** 2•10, 2•12, 2•13, **3•4, 3•7, 3•12,** 3•14, 4•12, **4•13,** 5•4, **5•6, 5•7, 5•11, 5•14, 6•3,** 6•7, 7•3, 7•9, **8•15, Project 5**
K.MD.2. Directly compare two objects with a measurable attribute in common, to see which object has "more of"/"less of" the attribute, and describe the difference. *For example, directly compare the heights of two children and describe one child as taller/shorter.*	**1•1, 1•13,** 2•12, 2•13, **3•4, 3•7, 3•12,** 3•14, 4•12, 5•4, **5•7, 5•11, 8•15, Project 5**
Classify objects and count the number of objects in each category.	
K.MD.3. Classify objects into given categories; count the numbers of objects in each category and sort the categories by count.	*Weather Observation Routine, Recording Daily Temperature Routine, Survey Routine,* 1•6, 1•8, **1•11,** 2•1, 2•2, 2•3, **2•8,** 2•10, 2•16, **3•14,** 4•10, **4•13, 5•13, 6•5,** 6•6, 7•14, 8•2, 8•6

Common Core State Standards for Kindergarten	Everyday Mathematics Kindergarten Activities
GEOMETRY K.G	
Identify and describe shapes (squares, circles, triangles, rectangles, hexagons, cubes, cones, cylinders, and spheres).	
K.G.1. Describe objects in the environment using names of shapes, and describe the relative positions of these objects using terms such as *above, below, beside, in front of, behind,* and *next to.*	1•15, 1•16, **2•1,** 2•2, **2•3,** 2•11, 2•15, 3•10, 3•11, **6•3, 6•6,** 7•3, **8•3,** 8•13, **Projects 6, 7, and 8**
K.G.2. Correctly name shapes regardless of their orientations or overall size.	1•2, 1•15, 1•16, **2•1, 2•2,** 2•3, 2•5, 2•6, 2•11, 2•15, 3•10, 3•11, 4•1, **4•3,** 4•4, 4•8, **4•9, 4•10, 4•13,** 4•14, **5•3, 6•3, 6•6,** 7•3, **7•4, 8•3,** 8•13
K.G.3. Identify shapes as two-dimensional (lying in a plane, "flat") or three-dimensional ("solid").	**2•1, 2•2, 6•3, 6•6,** 7•3, **7•4, 8•3,** 8•13
Analyze, compare, create, and compose shapes.	
K.G.4. Analyze and compare two- and three-dimensional shapes, in different sizes and orientations, using informal language to describe their similarities, differences, parts (e.g., number of sides and vertices/"corners") and other attributes (e.g., having sides of equal length).	1•2, **2•1, 2•2,** 2•3, 2•5, 2•6, 2•11, 3•10, 3•11, 4•1, 4•8, **4•9, 4•10,** 4•14, **6•3, 6•6,** 7•3, **7•4, 8•3,** 8•13
K.G.5. Model shapes in the world by building shapes from components (e.g., sticks and clay balls) and drawing shapes.	1•15, **4•3,** 4•4, **4•9, 6•3,** 7•3, **7•4,** 8•3
K.G.6. Compose simple shapes to form larger shapes. *For example, "Can you join these two triangles with full sides touching to make a rectangle?"*	1•2, 1•15, 1•16, 2•2, 2•5, 2•6, 2•15, 3•10, 3•11, 4•1, **4•3,** 4•4, **7•4, 8•3**

Components at a Glance

The table below shows core materials that are used on a regular basis throughout *Kindergarten Everyday Mathematics.*

▶ Kindergarten Materials

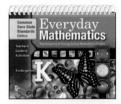

Teacher's Guide to Activities
Easy-to-follow classroom activities and ongoing daily routines that are the heart of the program.

My First Math Book
Consumable books provide support for classroom instruction. They provide a long-term record of each child's mathematical development.

Math Masters
Blackline masters for routines, activities, projects, Home Links, and games.

Assessment Handbook
Kindergarten-specific handbook that provides ideas for ongoing and periodic assessment. Includes blackline masters for tracking progress.

Resources for the Kindergarten Classroom
Curriculum support materials including optional theme-based activities; lists of books, games, songs, and software; and ideas for family letters.

Minute Math®
Brief activities for transition times and for spare moments throughout the day.

Kindergarten Center Activity Cards
Visually-oriented directions to children for Kindergarten center activities.

Teacher's Reference Manual
Comprehensive background information about mathematical content and program management for Early Childhood.

Mathematics at Home Books
Engaging activities for children to do at home with their families.

▶ Technology Components

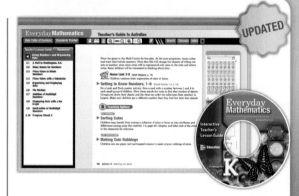

Interactive Teacher's Guide to Activities
Enables digital access to the *Everyday Mathematics Teacher's Guide to Activities* and all supporting components, including additional content support. Available online and on CD-ROM.

Assessment Management Spreadsheets
This electronic tool can be used to monitor and record children's progress. The Assessment Management Spreadsheets provide reports showing children's progress toward Grade-Level Goals.

Everyday Mathematics

Planning and Instructional Support

Kindergarten *Everyday Mathematics* organizes content into eight sections. Each Section Opener provides an overview of the content for the section. Also included is support for ongoing learning and practice, assessment, and differentiated instruction. Section Openers are useful for planning and advance preparation.

Overview

Describes the concepts and ideas that are the focus of the section.

Maintaining Ongoing Daily Routines

Describes ways to maintain daily routines appropriate to each section and keep them relevant throughout the year.

Learning in Perspective

Connections to prior and future content both within and across grade levels.

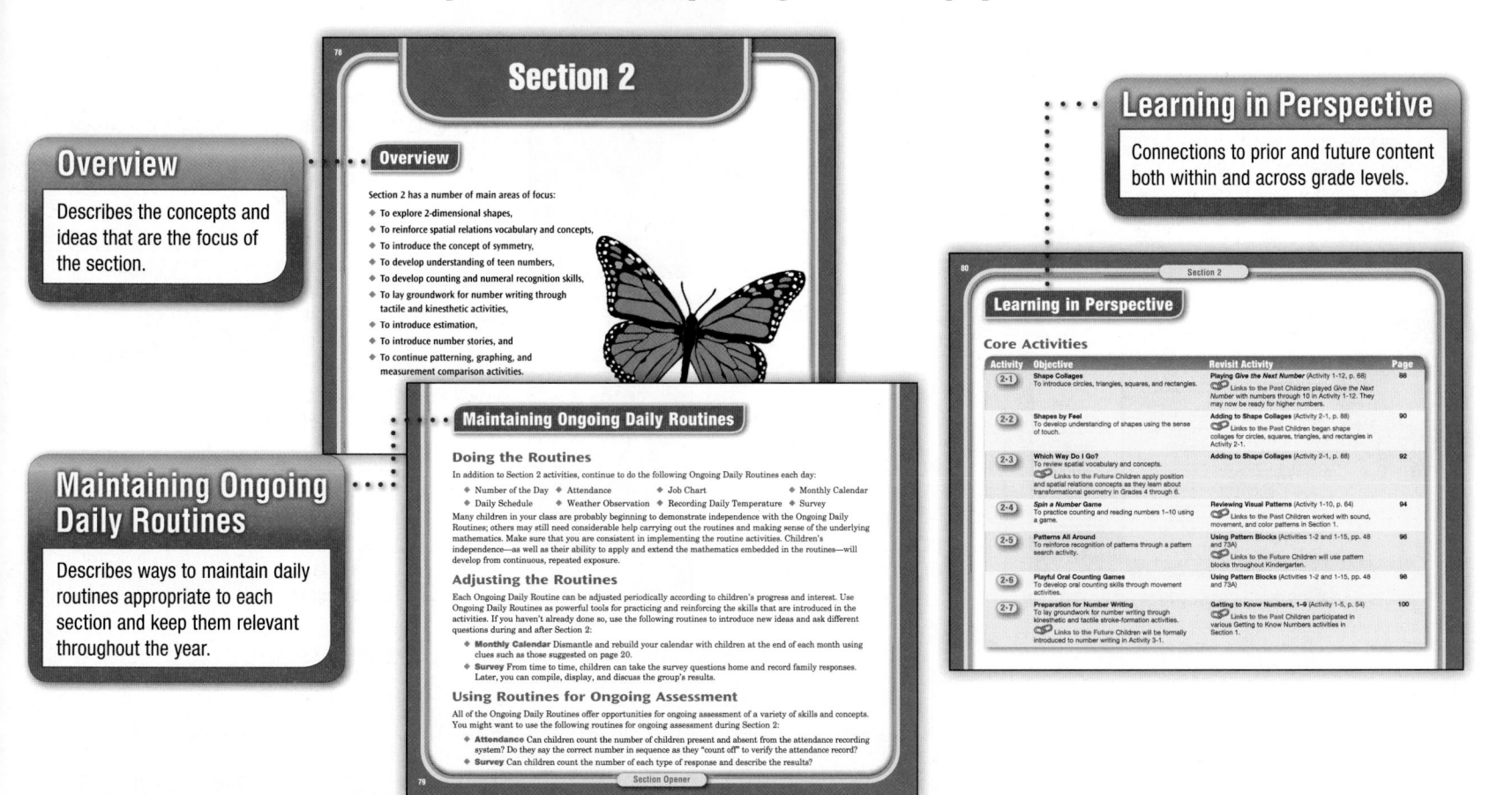

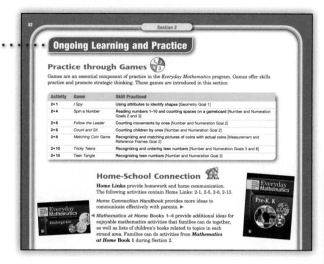

Ongoing Learning and Practice

Practice through Games

Games are an essential component of practice in the *Everyday Mathematics* program. Games offer skills practice and promote strategic thinking. These games are introduced in this section:

Activity	Game	Skill Practiced
2·1	I Spy	Using attributes to identify shapes [Geometry Goal 1]
2·4	Spin a Number	Reading numbers 1–10 and counting spaces on a gameboard [Number and Numeration Goals 2 and 3]
2·6	Follow the Leader	Counting movements by ones [Number and Numeration Goal 2]
2·6	Count and Sit	Counting children by ones [Number and Numeration Goal 2]
2·8	Matching Coin Game	Recognizing and matching pictures of coins with actual coins [Measurement and Reference Frames Goal 2]
2·10	Tricky Teens	Recognizing and ordering teen numbers [Number and Numeration Goals 3 and 6]
2·10	Teen Tangle	Recognizing teen numbers [Number and Numeration Goal 3]

Home-School Connection

Home Links provide homework and home communication. The following activities contain Home Links: 2-1, 2-5, 2-8, 2-13.

Home Connection Handbook provides more ideas to communicate effectively with parents. ▶

◀ *Mathematics at Home* Books 1–4 provide additional ideas for enjoyable mathematics activities that families can do together, as well as lists of children's books related to topics in each strand area. Families can do activities from *Mathematics at Home* Book 1 during Section 2.

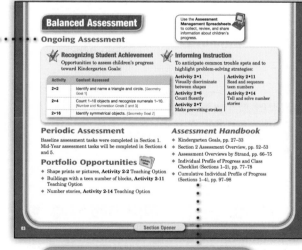

Balanced Assessment

Ongoing Assessment

Use the **Assessment Management Spreadsheets** to collect, review, and share information about children's progress.

Recognizing Student Achievement
Opportunities to assess children's progress toward Kindergarten Goals:

Activity	Content Assessed
2·2	Identify and name a triangle and circle. [Geometry Goal 1]
2·4	Count 1–10 objects and recognize numerals 1–10. [Number and Numeration Goals 2 and 3]
2·16	Identify symmetrical objects. [Geometry Goal 2]

Informing Instruction
To anticipate common trouble spots and to highlight problem-solving strategies:

Activity 2·1
Visually discriminate between shapes

Activity 2·6
Count fluently

Activity 2·7
Make prewriting strokes

Activity 2·11
Read and sequence teen numbers

Activity 2·14
Tell and solve number stories

Periodic Assessment

Baseline assessment tasks were completed in Section 1. Mid-Year assessment tasks will be completed in Sections 4 and 5.

Portfolio Opportunities

◆ Shape prints or pictures, **Activity 2-2** Teaching Option
◆ Buildings with a teen number of blocks, **Activity 2-11** Teaching Option
◆ Number stories, **Activity 2-14** Teaching Option

Assessment Handbook

◆ Kindergarten Goals, pp. 27–33
◆ Section 2 Assessment Overview, pp. 52–53
◆ Assessment Overviews by Strand, pp. 66–75
◆ Individual Profile of Progress and Class Checklist (Sections 1–2), pp. 77–78
◆ Cumulative Individual Profile of Progress (Sections 1–4), pp. 97–98

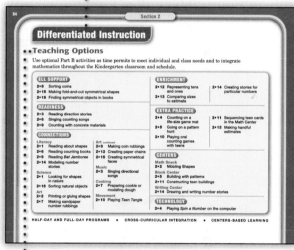

Differentiated Instruction

Teaching Options

Use optional Part B activities as time permits to meet individual and class needs and to integrate mathematics throughout the Kindergarten classroom and schedule.

ELL SUPPORT
2·8 Sorting coins
2·15 Making fold-and-cut symmetrical shapes
2·16 Finding symmetrical objects in books

READINESS
2·3 Reading direction stories
2·6 Singing counting songs
2·9 Counting with concrete materials

CONNECTIONS
Literacy
2·1 Reading about shapes
2·6 Reading counting books
2·9 Reading *Bat Jamboree*
2·14 Modeling number stories
Science
2·1 Looking for shapes in nature
2·16 Sorting natural objects
Art
2·2 Printing or gluing shapes
2·7 Making sandpaper number rubbings

Art continued
2·8 Making coin rubbings
2·12 Creating paper chains
2·15 Creating symmetrical faces
Music
2·3 Singing directional songs
Cooking
2·7 Preparing cookie or modeling dough
Movement
2·10 Playing Teen Tangle

ENRICHMENT
2·12 Representing tens and ones
2·13 Comparing sizes to estimate
2·14 Creating stories for particular numbers

EXTRA PRACTICE
2·4 Counting on a life-size game mat
2·5 Going on a pattern hunt
2·10 Playing oral counting games with teens
2·11 Sequencing teen cards in the Math Center
2·13 Making handful estimates

CENTERS
Math Snack
2·2 Nibbling Shapes
Block Center
2·5 Building with patterns
2·11 Constructing teen buildings
Writing Center
2·14 Drawing and writing number stories

TECHNOLOGY
2·4 Playing *Spin a Number* on the computer

HALF-DAY AND FULL-DAY PROGRAMS • CROSS-CURRICULAR INTEGRATION • CENTERS-BASED LEARNING

Online Learning and Practice

Highlights games and home activities for maintaining skills. These activities provide review and practice.

Ongoing Assessment

Includes assessment opportunities to assess progress toward Grade-Level Goals.

Differentiated Instruction

Highlights the many facets of differentiated instruction in each section, including English Language Learner support, Cross-Curricular Connections, Centers, Technology, and Readiness, Enrichment, and Extra Practice activities.

Teaching Options

Use these activities to meet individual and classroom needs throughout the Kindergarten day.

Assessment Support

Identifies useful pages in the *Assessment Handbook* for each section.

Everyday Mathematics®

Instructional Plan

Activity Support

 **A** Core Activities   **B** Teaching Options

346

Late-in-the-Year Counting

ACTIVITY 7·7

◎ **Objective** To reinforce and extend children's oral counting skills.

CCSS Mathematical Practices
SMP1, SMP2, SMP4, SMP5, **SMP6**, SMP7
Content Standards
K.CC.1, K.CC.2, K.CC.4a, K.CC.4b, K.CC.5

✔ Whole Group
✔ Small Group
☐ Partners
☐ Center

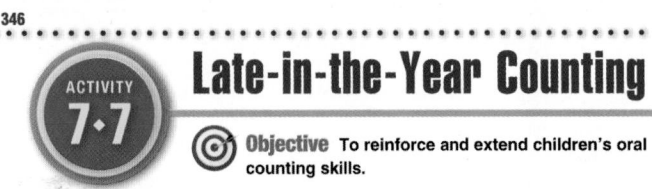

Key Concepts and Skills
• Count on from various numbers. [Number and Numeration Goal 1]
• Count backward from various numbers. [Number and Numeration Goal 1]
• Count beyond 100. [Number and Numeration Goal 1]
• Read numbers. [Number and Numeration Goal 3]
Materials Home Link Master (*Math Masters*, p. 52)

A Core Activities

▶ **Counting Forward and Backward from Higher Numbers**

Remind children that counting does not always begin with 1 and that they can count forward or backward. Using your signs or signals to start and stop counting, have children choral count forward or backward from various numbers, such as:

▷ the number of children in class

▷ the date on the calendar

▷ randomly-selected numbers on the number line or number grid

▷ the temperature

▷ 2-digit numbers generated by rolling two dice (or flipping two 0–9 number cards) to serve as the digits

Use several starting and stopping numbers (using both forward and backward prompts). To keep the activity interesting, incorporate movement, rhythm, a familiar tune, or a loud/soft pattern as children count. Encourage children to use the number line or number grid as a reference, as needed.

NOTE Also remember to regularly practice skip counting by 2s, 5s, and 10s with children. Take the counts beyond 100 so that children learn how the pattern continues with higher numbers.

Continue to engage the class in frequent oral counting practice as the year progresses, using the above suggestions as starting points for interrupted counts. Remember to keep the counts brief and playful. At least once a week, the class can choral count up to the number of the day on the Growing Number Line.

 Home Link 7·7 (*Math Masters*, p. 52)
Children practice counting skills at home.

▶ **Counting the Class Collection** (Revisit Activity 7·2, p. 332; *My First Math Book*, p. 15)
If they haven't done so recently, have the class count the items in the Class Collection that you began in Activity 7-2. Children should record the number of items that have been added since your last count and the total number of items in the collection on page 15 of their math books, as well as on your class chart. If you are keeping a class display of the growing total, update that too.

 B **Teaching Options**

ENRICHMENT

▶ **Skip Counting from Different Numbers**
Some children might enjoy using a number grid or number line to figure out how to skip count by 2s, 5s, and 10s from various numbers. Children can also use the "repeat" sequence on their calculators to skip count from different numbers.

EXTRA PRACTICE

▶ **Playing Counting Games**
Children can play *Give the Next Number* (Activity 1-12, page 68), *Count and Sit, Follow the Leader* (Activity 2-6, page 98), and any other counting games you may have introduced using higher numbers and/or backward counting. Use written numerals as starting points to provide practice with reading higher numbers.

347 **Activity 7·7** Late-in-the-Year Counting

Math Masters, p. 52

Ongoing Assessment:
Informing Instruction

Watch for children who cannot count higher than 70 or who can only count from 0. Provide extra opportunities for these children to practice their counting skills in small groups so you can determine where they are having difficulty and provide targeted support. Additional experiences with the numeration patterns on the number line or number grid might also be beneficial.

B **Teaching Options**

Includes activities to meet individual and classroom needs throughout the Kindergarten day. Teaching Options include English Language Learner support, Cross-Curricular Connections, Centers, Technology, and Readiness, Enrichment, and Extra Practice activities.

Everyday Mathematics

Assessment

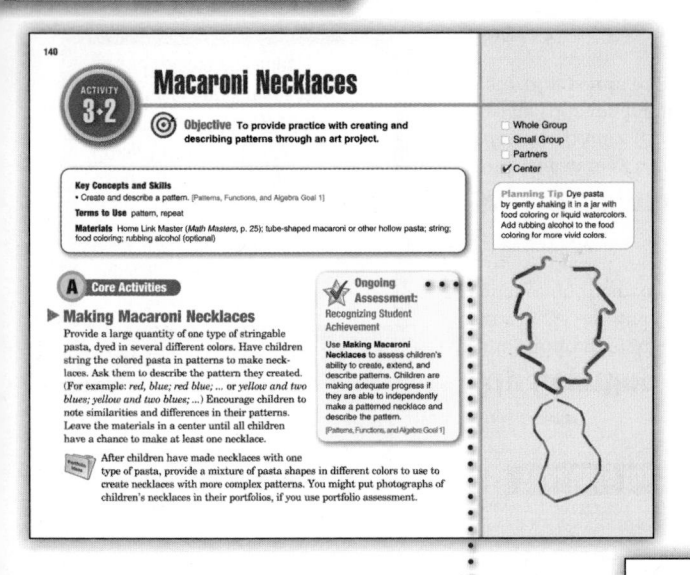

I n *Everyday Mathematics,* assessment is like a motion picture revealing the development of each child's mathematical understanding over time, while giving the teacher useful feedback about the instructional needs of both individual children and the class as a whole.

Purposes of Assessment

Formative Assessments provide information about children's current knowledge and abilities that can be used to plan, or inform instruction. Information from almost any assessment task in *Everyday Mathematics* might be useful for planning future instruction.

Summative Assessments measure children's growth and achievement and provide information that may be used to evaluate children's performance. Summative assessments in *Everyday Mathematics* include the Recognizing Student Achievement tasks.

Recognizing Student Achievement

Notes highlight tasks that can be used to monitor children's progress.

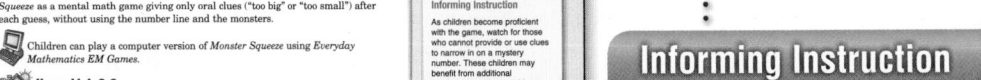

Informing Instruction

Notes suggest how to use kid-watching to effectively adapt instruction.

Class Checklists

Provided for Ongoing Assessment, Periodic Assessment, Baseline, Mid-Year, and End-of-Year assessments.

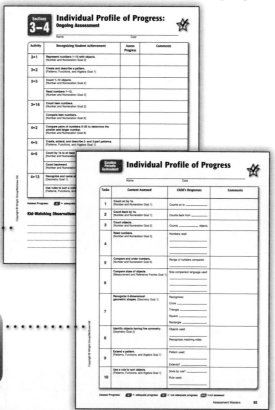

Types of Assessment

The *Assessment Handbook* provides ideas and tools for creating a complete picture of each child's progress and making assessment and instruction more manageable, productive, and exciting.

◆ **Ongoing Assessment** includes informal kid-watching and anecdotal record keeping, Recognizing Student Achievement tasks, and samples of children's work, such as sketches or drawings, activity pages, and number storybooks.

◆ **Periodic Assessment** includes Baseline, Mid-Year, and End-of-Year assessment activities. Digital checklists are available at www.everydaymathonline.com.

Class Progress Indicator

Provides space to compile and organize class data for any concept or skill.

Individual Profiles of Progress

Can be used in tandem with Class Checklists. Provided for both Ongoing Assessment and Periodic Assessment.

Everyday Mathematics

NCTM Curriculum Focal Points and *Everyday Mathematics*

The *Everyday Mathematics* curriculum is completely aligned to the NCTM Curriculum Focal Points and the Connections to the Curriculum Focal Points for Pre-Kindergarten through Grade 6.

NCTM Curriculum Focal Points for Kindergarten	*Everyday Mathematics* Kindergarten Activities
Number and Operations and Algebra: Representing, comparing, and ordering whole numbers and joining and separating sets	
Children use numbers, including written numerals, to represent quantities and to solve quantitative problems, such as counting objects in a set, creating a set with a given number of objects, comparing and ordering sets or numerals by using both cardinal and ordinal meanings, and modeling simple joining and separating situations with objects.	1•3, 1•4, 1•5, 1•11, 1•12, 1•14, 2•3, 2•4, 2•6, 2•8, 2•9, 2•10, 2•11, 2•12, 2•13, 2•14, 3•1, 3•3, 3•5, 3•6, 3•8, 3•9, 3•13, 3•15, 3•16, 4•1, 4•2, 4•4, 4•6, 4•7, 4•8, 4•11, 4•12, 4•15, 4•16, 5•1, 5•4, 5•5, 5•8, 5•9, 5•10, 6•1, 6•2, 6•4, 6•7, 6•8, 6•9, 6•10, 6•16 Routines 1, 2, 4, 6, 7, 8 Projects 2, 4, 5
Children choose, combine, and apply effective strategies for answering quantitative questions, including quickly recognizing the number in a small set, counting and producing sets of given sizes, counting the number in combined sets, and counting backward.	1•3, 1•4, 1•14, 2•13, 2•14, 3•8, 3•15, 3•16, 4•1, 4•4, 4•7, 4•8, 4•11, 4•15, 4•16, 5•4, 6•9, 7•2, 8•4, 8•13, 8•14 Routines 2, 6, 7
Geometry: Describing shapes and space	
Children interpret the physical world with geometric ideas (e.g., shape, orientation, spatial relations) and describe it with corresponding vocabulary.	2•3, 2•15, 2•16, 6•3, 6•6 Projects 2, 4, 6, 8
Children identify, name, and describe a variety of shapes, such as squares, triangles, circles, rectangles, (regular) hexagons, and (isosceles) trapezoids presented in a variety of ways (e.g., with different sizes or orientations), as well as such three-dimensional shapes as spheres, cubes, and cylinders. They use basic shapes and spatial reasoning to model objects in their environment and to construct more complex shapes.	1•2, 2•1, 2•2, 2•5, 4•5, 4•9, 4•10, 4•13, 5•3, 6•3, 6•6, 7•4

Measurement: Ordering objects by measurable attributes

Children use measurable attributes, such as length or weight, to solve problems by comparing and ordering objects.	1•1, 1•13, 3•4, 3•7, 3•12, 5•7, 8•15
Children compare the lengths of two objects both directly (by comparing them with each other) and indirectly (by comparing both with a third object), and they order several objects according to length.	1•1, 1•13, 3•7, 5•6, 5•7, 5•11 Project 2

NCTM Connections to the Curriculum Focal Points for Kindergarten	*Everyday Mathematics* Kindergarten Activities
Data Analysis	
Children sort objects and use one or more attributes to solve problems. For example, they might sort solids that roll easily from those that do not. Or they might collect data and use counting to answer such questions as, "What is our favorite snack?"	1•6, 1•8, 1•11, 1•13, 2•1, 2•8, 3•14, 4•13, 4•14, 5•3, 5•9, 5•13, 5•14, 6•5, 6•12 Routines 2, 6, 7, 8
Children re-sort objects by using new attributes (e.g., after sorting solids according to which ones roll, they might re-sort the solids according to which ones stack easily).	1•6, 2•16, 4•13, 4•14
Geometry	
Children integrate their understandings of geometry, measurement, and number. For example, they understand, discuss, and create simple navigational directions (e.g., "Walk forward 10 steps, turn right, and walk forward 5 steps").	2•3, 4•1, 5•7 Projects 2, 4, 6, 8
Algebra	
Children identify, duplicate, and extend simple number patterns and sequential and growing patterns (e.g., patterns made with shapes) as preparation for creating rules that describe relationships.	1•9, 1•10, 2•5, 3•2, 3•15, 4•3, 4•5, 5•2, 5•8, 5•15, 5•16, 6•10, 6•14, 6•15, 7•10, 7•15, 8•10 Routine 3 Projects 1, 4, 7

The Curriculum Focal Points identify key mathematical ideas for these grades. They are not discrete topics or a checklist to be mastered; rather, they provide a framework for the majority of instruction at a particular grade level and the foundation for future mathematics study.

Contents

Mathematical Strands

Contents

Activity	Title	Page	Number and Numeration	Operations and Computation	Data and Chance	Measurement and Reference Frames	Geometry	Patterns, Functions, and Algebra	This activity revisited in Activity* …
	Section 2 Opener	78							
2•1	Shape Collages	88					●		2-2, 2-3, 2-11, 3-10, 3-11
2•2	Shapes by Feel	90					●		4-8
2•3	Which Way Do I Go?	92					●		
2•4	*Spin a Number* Game	94	●						
2•5	Patterns All Around	96						●	3-13
2•6	Playful Oral Counting Games	98	●						2-14, 3-12, 4-15, 5-11
2•7	Preparation for Number Writing	100	●						4-11
2•8	*Matching Coin Game*	104	●		●	●			5-16
2•9	Number Board	106	●					●	
2•10	Tricky Teens	108	●						
2•11	Listen and Do (10–19)	110	●						
2•12	Teen Partners	112	●						
2•13	Estimation Jars	114	●						3-2, 4-5, 5-10, 6-10, 7-10
2•14	Number Stories: Stage 1	116		●					3-6
2•15	Symmetry Painting	120					●		6-3
2•16	Symmetry in Nature	122					●		4-9
	Project 2: Mathematics and Our Bodies	124							

Mathematical Strands (handwritten annotations: 4-2, 3-8, ✓ 2-4, 5-6)

Contents

Mathematical Strands

(handwritten annotations: 3•1 "3-4", 3•3 "3-11", 3•6 "3-12", 3•8 "2-5", 3•13 "5-11"*)*

(handwritten annotations: 4-12 next to 4•2; 4-4 and 5-2 next to 4•7/4•8; 3-3 circled next to 4•9; 6-8 next to 4•11)

Contents

Mathematical Strands

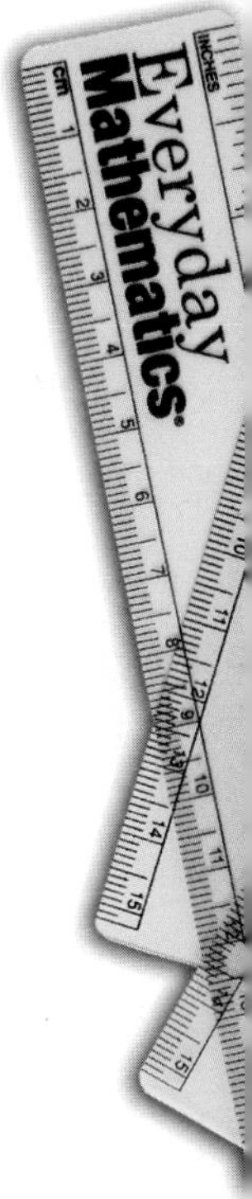

Contents

Welcome to *Everyday Mathematics*®, the elementary school mathematics curriculum developed by the University of Chicago School Mathematics Project (UCSMP). *Everyday Mathematics* offers you and your children a broad, rich, and balanced experience in mathematics.

Kindergarten Everyday Mathematics emphasizes the following content strands, skills, and concepts:

◆ **Number and Numeration** Counting; estimating; representing and comparing numbers; reading and writing numbers.

◆ **Operations and Computation** Exploring the meaning of addition and subtraction; developing and using concrete strategies to solve addition and subtraction problems.

◆ **Data and Chance** Collecting and organizing data; creating and analyzing tally charts, tables, and bar graphs; exploring basic probability concepts.

◆ **Measurement and Reference Frames** Using nonstandard tools to estimate and compare weight and length; identifying pennies, nickels, dimes, quarters, and dollar bills; exploring temperature and thermometers; using calendars and other tools to track or measure time.

◆ **Geometry** Exploring 2- and 3-dimensional shapes and line symmetry.

◆ **Patterns, Functions, and Algebra** Exploring visual, rhythmic, and movement patterns; using rules to sort by attributes, make patterns, and play games; learning about the +, −, and = symbols.

Throughout *Everyday Mathematics,* emphasis is placed on

◆ a realistic approach to problem solving in everyday situations, other applications, and purely mathematical contexts

◆ frequent and distributed practice of basic skills through ongoing program routines and mathematical games

- an instructional approach that revisits topics regularly to ensure full concept development and long-term retention of learning

- activities that explore a wide variety of mathematical content and offer opportunities for children to apply their skill and understanding to geometry, measurement, and algebra.

During your first year, you will become increasingly comfortable with the content, components, and strategies of *Kindergarten Everyday Mathematics*. You and your children will experience mathematical processes as a part of everyday work and play. These processes will gradually shape children's ways of thinking about mathematics and will foster the development of their mathematical intuition and understanding. By the end of the year, we think you will agree that the rewards are worth the effort.

Have an exciting year!

Professional Preparation

Components for *Kindergarten Everyday Mathematics*

Go to...	When you need...	
Teacher's Guide to Activities	• Ongoing Daily Routines • Daily activities • Section support information	• English language learners support • Projects
Early Childhood Teacher's Reference Manual	• Background on mathematical content	• Ideas for curriculum and classroom management in early childhood classrooms (Pre-K and K)
Assessment Handbook	• Suggestions for ongoing and periodic assessment • Grade-Level Goals across all grades	• Overview of the *Everyday Mathematics* assessment philosophy and tools and techniques for assessment
Minute Math® (Grade K)	• Quick mathematics activities and problems to use during transition times or spare moments in the day	
Resources for the Kindergarten Classroom	• Family letters and ideas for class newsletters • Optional theme-based activities and masters • Songs, rhymes, and fingerplays	• Lists of books, software, games, and other optional materials to support the Kindergarten program
Center Activity Cards	• Center-based mathematics activities that relate to select Teaching Options in the *Teacher's Guide to Activities*	
Content-by-Strand Poster	• Skills organized by content strand and paced by month	• Learning goals organized by section for the year
Early Childhood Home Connection Handbook	• Suggestions for home-school communication for Pre-K and K	• Masters for easy planning
Math Masters	• Blackline masters for routines, activities, projects, Home Links, and games	
My First Math Book	• Pages for children to use with particular activities beginning in the second half of the school year	• Blank writing and drawing pages for children to use in the Math Center, for math journaling, in conjunction with optional activities, or at other times
Mathematics at Home Books 1–4	• A variety of activities that children can do over the course of the school year with their families	

Suggested Reading and Other Preparation

In order to prepare for effective classroom and curriculum management, we suggest the following before you teach *Kindergarten Everyday Mathematics* for the first time.

☐ Review each component in your **Classroom Resource Package**, using the Professional Preparation table on page xxviii as a guide.

☐ Prepare to initiate the **Ongoing Daily Routines**. These will require some set-up before the first day, as well as some planning about how to begin them at the start of school. See page xxxi for a list of the Routines and their page numbers in the *Teacher's Guide to Activities*.

☐ Read the **Section Opener and the first several activities in Section 1** to help you plan for the first week of school. Section 1 begins on page 36 of this book.

☐ Read the **Management Guide** (Chapters 1–7) in the *Early Childhood Teacher's Reference Manual* for practical tips for getting started with the Kindergarten program.

☐ Photocopy the **Introductory Family Letter** on page 74 of *Resources for the Kindergarten Classroom* to distribute to children's families early in the school year. (Plan to send home the Routines Family Letter within a month or so.)

☐ Review the **baseline assessment tasks** on pages 40–41 in the *Assessment Handbook* and consider when and how you will administer these tasks.

☐ Find an easily accessible location for your ***Kindergarten Minute Math®*** book, one that will enable you to use the book during spare moments throughout the day.

☐ Set up your **Math Center**. Organize a variety of manipulatives so they are easy for children to access and maintain in good order. Add and rotate materials frequently.

☐ Consult the list of **classroom materials and supplies** on the next page to determine what you have and what you will need.

☐ Peruse the various sections in ***Resources for the Kindergarten Classroom***. If you do an All About Me or Families theme early in the school year, be sure to read the suggestions related to these themes in the Theme Activities section.

At the beginning of the year, include pattern blocks, counters, connecting cubes, measuring tools, sorting materials, games, and puzzles in your Math Center. Add new materials as they are introduced.

Manipulatives for *Kindergarten Everyday Mathematics*

The table below lists the materials that are used on a regular basis throughout *Kindergarten Everyday Mathematics*. Some activities call for simple additional materials that you or children can bring in at the appropriate time.

Item	Quantity	Item	Quantity
Attribute Blocks	set of 60	Pan Balance	1
Connecting Cubes	2 pkgs of 100	Pattern Blocks	2 sets of 250
Counters	pkg of 450	Pattern-Block Templates	pkg of 10
Craft Sticks	pkg of 1,000	Play Money, Coins	1 set of 88
Dice, Blank	pkg of 16	Rubber Bands	pkg of 400
Dice, Dot	3 pkgs of 12	Rulers, 12 in.	4 pkgs of 5
Dominoes, Double-9	2 sets of 55	Slates	25
Geoboards	4	Straws	pkg of 500
Inch Cubes	pkg of 10	Tape Measure, Retractable	pkg of 10
Metersticks, Dual Scale	5	Tape Measure, 30m/100ft	1
Number Line, −35 to 180	1	Thermometer, Classroom	1
Number Card Deck	pkg of 5	Timer	1

Collectibles

- Coins
- Buttons
- Various Materials for Sorting

All of these items are available from McGraw-Hill. They may be purchased either as a comprehensive classroom manipulatives kit or by individual components. The manipulatives kit provides appropriate quantities for a class of 25 and comes packaged in durable plastic tubs with labels.

* Calculators are available from McGraw-Hill for individual purchase only.

Instruction

The following pages introduce instructional procedures and suggestions for implementing *Everyday Mathematics.*

Ongoing Daily Routines

In *Everyday Mathematics,* children learn a great deal of mathematics through daily routines. Through the routines, mathematical concepts are reinforced on a daily basis so that children become aware of how mathematics pervades our everyday lives. Plan to initiate the routines at the beginning of the year. An introduction, beginning on page 2, explains the philosophy behind the routines and offers suggestions for implementing them.

Daily Activities

There are 128 **daily activities**, which are grouped into 8 sections. Each section includes 16 activities and an optional **Project**. (See page xxxiv for more information on the Projects.) Each group of activities begins with a **Section Opener** that summarizes the content of the section and provides useful information to help you plan.

Each daily activity in *Kindergarten Everyday Mathematics* includes two main parts:

◆ Required **Core Activities** (a Main Activity and a Revisit Activity)
◆ Additional **Teaching Options**

You will comfortably get through the entire *Teacher's Guide to Activities* if you do approximately **3 to 4 activities per week** (including the Main Activity, the Revisit Activity, and any Teaching Options you select) and complete **one section every 4 to 5 weeks (approximately one section per month)**. The Teaching Options can be used any time after the related Main Activity. Teachers in full-day programs will probably be able to use more Teaching Options than teachers in half-day programs. However all teachers will find many Teaching Options that fit into their classroom schedule and help them integrate more mathematics into daily activities.

The routines in *Kindergarten Everyday Mathematics* are

◆ Number of the Day (pages 8–11)
◆ Attendance (pages 12–15)
◆ Job Chart (pages 16–17)
◆ Monthly Calendar (pages 18–21)
◆ Daily Schedule (pages 22–23)
◆ Weather Observation (pages 24–27)
◆ Recording Daily Temperature (pages 28–31)
◆ Survey (pages 32–35)

OCTOBER 20__ __

SUNDAY	MONDAY	TUESDAY	WEDNESDAY	THURSDAY	FRIDAY	SATURDAY
	1	2	3	4	5	6
7	8	9	10	11	12	13
14	15	16	17	18	19	20
21	22	23	24	25	26	27
28	29	30	31			

Daily Activities: Format and Features

This diagram highlights important features of the Kindergarten activities. Note that most of the features relate to the Main Activity, rather than the Revisit Activity or the Teaching Options.

Activity Number and Title Activity 1-7 refers to the 7th activity in Section 1. The Activity title describes the content of the Main Activity.

Organizer Box This feature contains information for doing the Main Activity.
• The **Key Concepts and Skills** describe the key mathematical content of the activity. Each is linked to a Kindergarten Goal.
• The **Terms to Use** list consists of mathematical words that teachers should use informally in the course of conducting the activity.
• The **Materials** list includes materials needed to do the Main Activity. Additional materials may be needed for the Revisit Activity and Teaching Options.

Main Activity This is the first core activity. New content (skills, concepts, games, and so on) is introduced in the Main Activity.

Home Links These describe informal mathematics activities for children to do at home. They can relate to either the Main Activity or the Revisit Activity. Home Link Masters are located in the *Math Masters* book.

Objective This is the teacher's purpose for teaching the Main Activity.

Grouping Suggestions Most activities include more than one grouping suggestion to allow teachers to decide how to implement the Main Activity. Sometimes an activity includes multiple grouping suggestions if the activity can begin with a Whole Group introduction and continue in Small Groups or at a Center. *Small Group* is defined as 3 to 8 children working with adult help. *Center* implies materials at a Center where children work independently.

Planning Tip This includes advance preparation information. These suggestions often pertain to materials acquisition or preparation, or to scheduling or space issues.

Links to the Future These notes indicate how the content in the activity relates to content children will experience later in the Kindergarten year or in future grades. They show how content is developed over time in *Everyday Mathematics*.

58

ACTIVITY 1·7
Sand and Water Play

Objective To introduce volume through sand and water play.

☐ Whole Group
☐ Small Group
☐ Partners
☑ Center

Key Concepts and Skills
• Experiment with and compare volumes and develop awareness of relative size.
[Measurement and Reference Frames Goal 1]

Terms to Use volume, more, less, same

Materials Home Link Master (*Math Masters*, p. 4); water, sand, or dry beans; water table, sand table, or tubs to hold materials; containers of various sizes and shapes including low and wide; tall and thin

Planning Tip Disposable aluminum roasting pans, available in many stores, can hold materials if you do not have a water table or sand table. Plastic dishpans also work well.

A Core Activities

Experimenting with Volume

Allow children to experiment with volume by pouring water, sand, or dry beans from one container to another. This is a natural way for children to begin making comparisons. Vary the materials and containers. After children have had ample time to explore, pose questions about volume, such as: *Which container holds more? Why do you think so? How can you find out which holds more? Can any of the containers fit inside another one?* Prompt children to explain their ideas. Listening to their responses can help you find ways to expand their thinking.

After children have had time to explore on their own, invite them to compare the volume of pairs of containers. Provide three or four pairs of containers that are not too close in capacity. Label the containers set 1A, 1B and set 2A, 2B, for example. Use containers that vary enough in shape to make it difficult to judge visually which holds more.

Links to the Future
This activity is an early exposure to understanding the capacity of containers, such as measuring cups, and the idea that all 3-dimensional objects have volume. Describing and using strategies to find volume is a Grade 4 Goal. (See "Measurement," *Teacher's Reference Manual* Chapter 12.)

Show the pairs of different-size containers to children and introduce the term **volume.** Ask: *Which container holds more material or has the larger volume? How could we find out?* Encourage children to pour the contents from one container into the other to see which holds more. Also provide two containers that hold the same amount of material but have different shapes.

After the pan balance has been introduced in Activity 3–4, use it with beans and a variety of containers to provide new directions for exploration.

NOTE Explain that *volume* is a word that has different meanings. Children may have heard the word used in contexts involving a radio or television. Emphasize that volume is also used in mathematics. To support English language learners, ask children to draw pictures of containers to illustrate *more, less,* and *same.*

Home Link 1·7 (*Math Masters*, p. 4)
Children experiment with volume at home.

▶ **Getting to Know Numbers—Number Three** (Revisit Activity 1•5, p. 54)
Focus on the number 3 as the featured number for Getting to Know Numbers activities.

B Teaching Options

ENRICHMENT
▶ **Estimating Container Capacity**
Put out several 1-cup measuring cups. Show children how to determine the number of cups a container holds. Have children estimate first, then check their estimates by pouring cupfuls of material into their containers. Invite children to use this technique with several containers to figure out which ones hold the most and the least and whether any hold the same amount. Children may wish to record their findings.

Math Masters, p. 4

Revisit Activity This is the second core activity. It repeats a previous Main Activity, often with slight variations to make it more advanced or to encourage children to approach the activity in a new way.

Adjusting the Activity These notes suggest ways to modify an activity to make it accessible and interesting to children with varying needs, learning styles, or levels of proficiency or understanding.

Ongoing Assessment Notes There are two kinds of Ongoing Assessment Notes that relate to either the Main Activity or the Revisit Activity.

- **Recognizing Student Achievement** notes highlight specific assessment opportunities within an activity. These can be used to monitor children's progress toward particular Grade-Level Goals. The Kindergarten Goal is listed as part of the Assessment Note.
- **Informing Instruction** notes point out specific difficulties that children might be experiencing and suggest ways to adapt instruction or provide reinforcement to meet children's needs.

Teaching Options These suggestions are additional ways to explore the content of the Main Activity. Teaching Options often focus on a different curricular area (such as Science or Literature) or another area of the classroom (such as the Block or Dramatic Play Center). Some Teaching Options are labeled Extra Practice, Readiness, Enrichment, or ELL Support, but these labels should not be limiting. Many of the activities are appropriate for all children. Teachers can pick and choose from the Teaching Options to integrate mathematics into all areas of the Kindergarten classroom and curriculum and to help meet the needs of individual children.

***Math Masters* and *My First Math Book* pages** If a Main Activity, Revisit Activity, or Teaching Option requires blackline masters or pages in *My First Math Book,* the necessary pages are listed with the appropriate activity heading. In most cases, minis of the pages are also included in the margin.

68

Give the Next Number Game

ACTIVITY 1·12

Objective To develop number sense and counting skills through an oral counting game.

☑ Whole Group
☐ Small Group
☐ Partners
☐ Center

Key Concepts and Skills
- Count numbers and ordinal numbers in sequence. [Number and Numeration Goal 1]
- Represent numbers with claps or taps. [Number and Numeration Goal 2]

Terms to Use first, second, third, . . .
Materials none

A Core Activities

▶ **Playing *Give the Next Number***

Warm up for the game by quickly counting from 0 to 10 as a class. Then point to children one at a time, prompting each to say the next number in sequence. For example, prompt the first child to say *one*, the next child to say *two*, and so on. If children miss a number or aren't keeping track, quickly say the number for them, have them repeat it, then continue with the next child. When you reach 10, start over so everyone has a turn. You may choose to invite a child to be the pointer. (Some teachers like to use a finger puppet to prompt children during the count.)

After children get the hang of giving the next number, turn the activity into a game. Have children form a circle. Walk around the circle slowly, counting the children (or their feet to generate larger numbers) using a soft voice. Children keep track by counting along, also using soft voices. Every so often, tap a child to stand up and say the next number clearly. Also have the standing child clap or tap the number.

Later in the year, encourage children to count silently or "in their heads" as they play the game.

Adjusting the Activity

This game can be played often and made more challenging as children's oral counting skills advance. When children are ready, vary the game by:
▷ Extending the count to higher numbers
▷ Changing the starting number
▷ Counting backward from different numbers
▷ Skip counting by 2s, 5s, or 10s
To incorporate numeral recognition, hold up a number card to prompt counting rather than saying the number. For children who need it, demonstrate how to use the number line as a reference for figuring out the next number.

AUDITORY • KINESTHETIC • TACTILE • VISUAL

To provide practice identifying and sequencing ordinal numbers, have children take turns saying ordinal numbers in sequence. For example, prompt the first child to say *first*, the next child to say *second*, and so on. You can start over once you reach 10 or continue on through the teens and beyond, depending on children's counting skills. You can also play *Give the Next Number* using ordinal numbers. Children keep track of the ordinal numbers you say softly as you count them and then stand up and say the next ordinal number when you tap them.

▶ **Getting to Know Numbers—Number Eight** (Revisit Activity 1·5, p. 54)
Focus on the number 8 as the featured number for Getting to Know Numbers activities.

B Teaching Options

ENRICHMENT
▶ **Counting On Using Number Cards** (*Math Masters*, pp. 92–102)
Vary the main activity and reinforce numeral recognition by giving individual children a number card or sheet of paper with a number written on it. (You can use *Math Masters*, pages 92–102 to make number cards. Use the numbers in the range that you are practicing.) Have the child with the next number hold up his or her card and say the number out loud. You might also have children work together to line up in order of the numbers on their cards.

TECHNOLOGY
▶ **Counting in Computer Games**
Many computer games for young children provide practice with counting and number sequencing. For example, the dot-to-dot segments in *Piggy in Numberland* (Learning in Motion, 1998) and *Piggy's Birthday Present* (Learning in Motion, 1999) reinforce these skills. See *Resources for the Kindergarten Classroom* for other suggestions.

Ongoing Assessment: Informing Instruction

Monitor children's accuracy and automaticity as they count. Do they say the next number correctly? How much time do they require? Are they able to listen and follow along as the group counts?

Large Number Cards 1 and 2

2

1

Math Masters, p. 93

69 Activity 1·12 *Give the Next Number Game*

Projects

Each section includes an optional project that offers opportunities for extended, in-depth mathematical explorations around a topic that interests children. The projects also incorporate social studies, art, language arts, and science skills. Each project can stretch over several days (or longer), depending on how many of the suggested activities you use and the breadth and depth of children's involvement. Most of the projects can be done at any point in the school year according to your schedule and children's interests.

Assessment

Everyday Mathematics supports a balanced approach to assessment, one that provides information both for guiding instruction and for evaluating student performance. Assessment takes place on an ongoing basis as children complete their everyday work and in special periodic assessment tasks. Information for assessment is gathered both through teacher observations and through children's work products. Refer to the *Assessment Handbook* and the Section Openers for detailed information regarding assessment.

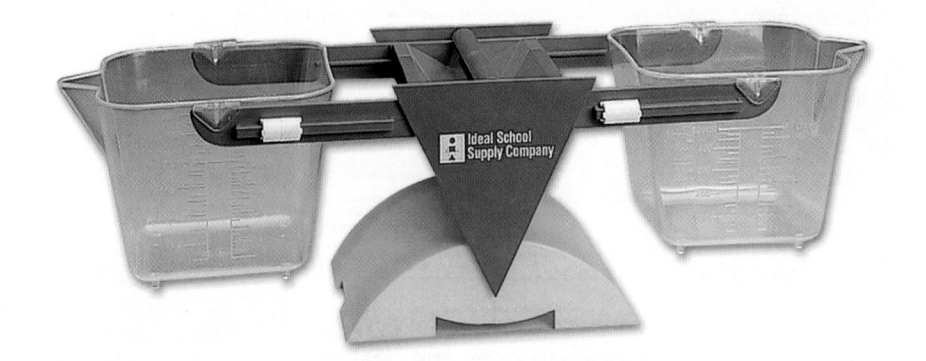

Differentiation

Everyday Mathematics has been designed to accommodate a wide range of student backgrounds and abilities. The program also includes many tools and suggestions to help teachers differentiate instruction to meet children's diverse needs. Refer to the Management Guide in the *Early Childhood Teacher's Reference Manual* and the Section Openers for detailed information about differentiation.

Providing for Home/School Connections

Comprehensive and consistent home/school communication is essential for successful implementation of *Everyday Mathematics*. The *Home Connection Handbook* has many suggestions and tools that can help you introduce parents and primary caregivers to the *Everyday Mathematics* curriculum. In addition, the Family Letters and newsletter ideas in *Resources for the Kindergarten Classroom,* the Home Links, and the *Mathematics at Home* books facilitate ongoing communication and engage parents as partners in their children's learning process.

Ongoing Daily Routines

The Importance of Routines

As every Kindergarten teacher knows, the organization of the classroom and the establishment of daily routines play major roles in determining the quality of learning experiences children will have. In light of this, the Ongoing Daily Routines in *Kindergarten Everyday Mathematics* are a cornerstone of the curriculum. These activities help teachers integrate mathematics into the daily life of the classroom.

As the year progresses, you will become increasingly sensitive to the teaching opportunities offered in the Ongoing Daily Routines. In addition to providing a context for rich mathematical learning experiences, these routines are enjoyable for children. Establishing the Ongoing Daily Routines early in the school year will make teaching easier in the long run. It's like putting a complex machine into operation and watching it become sustained mostly by children's initiative and energy!

Implementation Tips

Read through the eight activities in the Ongoing Daily Routines section before the first day of school so you will be prepared to introduce them as early as your schedule permits. As you introduce and implement the routines, keep in mind the following:

▷ It is best to start the routines early and let children grow into them at their own pace. Don't worry if children need support or don't fully understand the routines from the beginning; they will become increasingly comfortable over time.

▷ Although they are written as separate activities, many of the routines work well together as part of a class meeting at the beginning of the school day.

▷ The needs and interests of the children in your class will help you decide how much time to spend on each routine, as well as which parts of the routines to focus on each day.

▷ Instruction can be differentiated by offering varying levels of support and posing questions suited to individual children's comfort level and understanding.

▷ Many of the routines include suggestions for adding complexity as the school year progresses. You will know best whether these ideas are appropriate for your class and, if so, at what point they should be introduced.

Maintaining Ongoing Daily Routines See the Maintaining Ongoing Routines page in each Section Opener of this book for information about tailoring the routines to children's developing skills and for ideas about using the routines for ongoing assessment. The ideas in the Section Openers are just suggestions. Every class is different, so be sure to follow the needs of your class in determining how to sustain and use the Ongoing Daily Routines throughout the year.

The Ongoing Daily Routines begin on page 8. Math Any Time, pages 4–7, suggests additional ways to incorporate mathematics naturally into everyday classroom life.

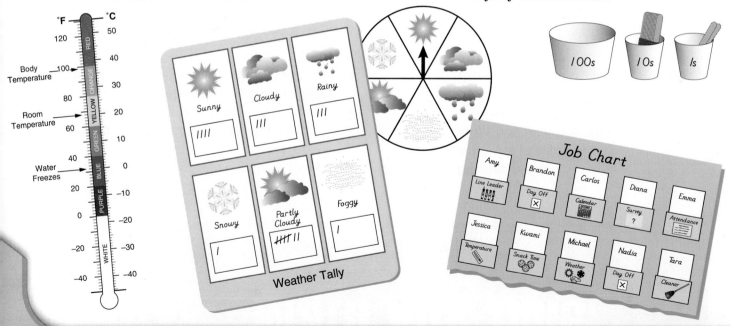

Math Any Time

In addition to the Ongoing Daily Routines, try the following meaningful and interesting ways to integrate mathematics into the school day. If used regularly, these "math any time" ideas will significantly enlarge and enrich children's mathematics experiences in school.

Minute Math The activities in the *Minute Math* book can help you incorporate mathematical problem solving throughout the day. These activities are fun, fast-paced, and can be done anywhere or anytime. Use the activities as springboards for your own (and children's) ideas for problems. Children love to hear their names used in the number stories!

NOTE Many teachers hang their *Minute Math* book in their meeting area or near the classroom door as a reminder to use it during class meeting times and transitions.

Handing Out Supplies When the occasion arises to distribute paper or other supplies to children, have them take turns solving problems such as the following:

- I want you to keep 1 piece of paper and to give away 3 pieces. How many do I need to give to you? (4)

- I'm giving you 4 pieces of paper, how many will you have if you give away 3? (1)

- I want you to have 5 pieces of paper. How many more will you need if I give you only 2? (3)

- I'm giving you 3 pieces of paper. Keep 1 and give the rest away. How many will you give away? (2)

Keep each question at the level of difficulty appropriate for the individual child.

Settling Disputes When trying to settle a disagreement between children, think of a number between 1 and 10. (Use larger numbers as the year progresses.) Write the number on a piece of paper children cannot see, or whisper the number to another child. The disputants try to guess the number; the child who makes the closest guess wins. Ask: *Is this fair? Why or why not?*

Forming Small Groups Have children count up to the number of groups you want to form. For example, if you want to have 4 groups, children count in order from 1 to 4. The fifth child begins counting at 1 again. Then, all the 1s form a group, all the 2s form another, and so on. Children will catch on to this procedure, although they may be confused at first.

Voting When the class has a decision to make, let children decide by a vote. Keep track of the votes with tally marks. Count and compare the tally marks and discuss the results.

Quantifying Directions Try to include numbers when giving directions. For example, say: *Six children may use clay today, five may play in the Dramatic Play Center, and two may use the water table. Only three at the workbench, please.*

Lining Up Have children line up by categories. For example, say: *Everyone wearing something red, line up now. Everyone wearing a belt, line up now. Everyone wearing brown shoes, line up now.* Later in the year, play *"What's My Rule?"* as you line up children by categories. Decide on a category, and call the names of children who fit in the category without revealing what the category is. Ask: *Why have I chosen this group? What's my rule?* Don't insist on your own rule if children see one that's equally valid. Say: *What I had in mind was _____, but your rule works too.*

When children are waiting in line, identify them by ordinal numbers and words. Ask: *Who is first? Second? Last?* Every so often, have children turn around and face the other direction, so that the person at the end of the line becomes the leader. Ask again: *Who is first (second, last)?* Extend to higher ordinal numbers (10th, 12th, 20th, and so on). Children can count by ordinal numbers to determine their place in line.

Cleaning Up and Transitioning When the class is cleaning up or transitioning to another activity or place, slowly count how long it takes for children to complete the activity or movement. Invite children to count aloud with you. Determine how many counts it takes to walk from one place to another. Occasionally, you might want to set a target number for finishing a task or getting to a destination and then count to, or back from, your goal number.

Distributing Snacks or Treats If your program includes a snack, meal, or special treat time, invite children to count and distribute cups, napkins, crackers, and other treats. The Snack Helpers make a social contribution to the group and have a real situation in which to carry out one-to-one correspondence. They can determine how many of their classmates are present by counting or looking at the Attendance Chart and then count out the number of treats needed. When children are ready, show them how to lay out items by 2s or 5s or arrange them in arrays for easy counting. (This also provides an early introduction to multiplication.)

3 crackers for each child.

Cooking If you are able to cook in your classroom, do so frequently with small groups of children. Cooking provides wonderful opportunities to practice measuring and counting.

Helping Classmates Encourage children to ask one another for help when they are having difficulty understanding something or solving a problem. A good rule for helpers is: *Give a hint, not an answer.* This enables children who need help to think through a problem, rather than receive an answer they may not understand. It also requires the helpers to examine their answers in order to give hints. The whole class can become involved in the solution. As a result, the child having difficulty becomes part of a solution process instead of being stigmatized for not knowing how to do something.

CCSS **Mathematical Practices**
SMP2, SMP4, SMP5, SMP6, SMP7

Content Standards
K.CC.1, K.CC.2, K.CC.3, K.CC.4a, K.CC.4b, K.CC.4c

Bold SMP = Guiding Questions
at everydaymathonline.com

Bold = Focus of routine

ROUTINE 1

Number of the Day Routine

Introduction

▶ Purpose

Children track the number of days in school on a Growing Number Line and represent the number of the day with objects. They become familiar with the numbers 1–100 and beyond and make sense of written numbers and place value.

Supporting Kindergarten Goals

- Count by 10s and 1s. [Number and Numeration Goal 1]
- Count objects. [Number and Numeration Goal 2]
- Connect the number sequence with number quantities and explore the "one more" relationship of successive numbers. [Number and Numeration Goal 2]
- Read and write numbers. [Number and Numeration Goal 3]
- Represent numbers with manipulatives and exchange 1s for 10s and 10s for 100. [Number and Numeration Goal 3]

Terms to Use

ones • tens • hundreds • number of the day

Materials

Growing Number Line	Concrete Number Count
☐ small index cards or long strips of paper	☐ craft sticks or straws
☐ markers	☐ rubber bands
	☐ 3 boxes, cups, or clear plastic bags

▶ Advance Preparation

Plan to begin both parts of this routine on the first day of school, and continue them every day.

Growing Number Line Choose cards or long strips of paper to construct the Growing Number Line. Gather the materials and consider where you will start it. There should be room to extend the number line well beyond 100. It may extend along more than one wall by the end of a 180-day school year. Post a 0 to begin your number line.

Concrete Number Count Collect straws or craft sticks (and rubber bands to bundle them). Some teachers also use a 100-bead frame. Label three containers: "1s," "10s," and "100s" and display them where children can reach them. Use cups, small boxes, or clear plastic bags as containers.

Overview Every day... Add a number to the Growing Number Line and an object to the Concrete Number Count collection. **Any time...** Use both parts of the routine to reinforce numeration skills.

Getting Started

▶ Building the Growing Number Line

Every day On the first day of school, write the number 1 on an index card to add to the Growing Number Line. Or write 1 after the 0 on a long strip of paper. Each day thereafter, enlist the children's help in writing the next number on a card (or strip of paper). Place it sequentially to create the number line. The Number of the Day job helper can tell you what the number of the day should be, as well as how to write the day's number (which digits to use and in what order).

0	1	2	3	4	5	6	7	8	9	10	11	12

You might use color, shapes, or stickers to highlight number patterns, such as every 5th number (5, 10, 15, 20) or every 10th number (10, 20, 30).

> **NOTE** As you write the number 1 for the first day, you may want to discuss the fact that, since there was no school yesterday, 0 represents the day before school began.

▶ Making a Concrete Number Count Collection

Every day On the first day of school, ask the Number of the Day job helper to count one straw or stick and place it in the 1s container to represent

the number of the day. Each subsequent day, a child adds one straw or stick, counts the collection, and announces the new total. When you reach 10, bundle the objects in the 1s container and move the bundle to the 10s container, leaving the 1s container empty. (On the next day, be sure the child adds a new object to the 1s container.) When you reach 100, bundle the 10 groups of 10s together and place it in the 100s container. Each day, have the class note how many 100s, 10s, and 1s are in the containers and use the collection to help them count to the number of the day by 10s and 1s.

Reinforce that the number they add to the Growing Number Line each day matches the number of items in the Concrete Number Count collection on that day. Discuss how each successive number on the number line corresponds to one more item in the collection.

> **NOTE** Through daily repetition and practice, the Growing Number Line and Concrete Number Count help children solidify their understanding of important numeration concepts, such as one-to-one correspondence, cardinality, and early place value.

Moving Forward

▶ Using the Growing Number Line

Any time Use the Growing Number Line throughout the year for counting, number recognition, and number games. For example, ask children to find or read a number, count to or on from a given number, count from one number to another, read the biggest number they can, tell what comes before or after a given number, or skip count to or from a given number. The Growing Number Line can be used in games, such as *Monster Squeeze* (see Activity 3-6, page 150), and used as a tool for figuring out number stories and *Minute Math* problems.

▶ Thinking about Place Value

Any time Over time, help children see the correspondence between the written number on the number line and the number of 100s, 10s, and 1s in the objects collection. Children will use bundles of 10 craft sticks and single craft sticks in later Kindergarten activities aimed at developing their understanding of place value.

Later in the year, some teachers begin to use base-10 blocks to represent the 10s and 1s for their Concrete Number Count to familiarize children with these materials.

After coins have been introduced, some teachers make a connection to money by adding 1 penny each day to the Concrete Number Count, then exchanging 10 pennies for a dime and 10 dimes for a dollar.

NOTE As the 100th day of school approaches, plan a special celebration. (See Project 5, page 268 for ideas and suggestions.)

NOTE For more information about the development of numeration concepts such as number sequencing and place value, see "Number and Counting" in the *Teacher's Reference Manual,* Chapter 8.

Ongoing Assessment:
Observing Children

Over time, you can use the Number of the Day Routine to assess children's development of the following concepts and skills:

- **Oral counting:** Can they count to the number on the Growing Number Line? By 1s? By 2s? By 5s? By 10s? [Number and Numeration Goal 1]

- **Rational counting (counting objects):** Can they count the objects as part of the Concrete Number Count? Do they understand that the last number they say tells the number of objects in the collection? [Number and Numeration Goal 2]

- **Connecting number words and quantities:** Do they understand that each successive number on the Growing Number Line represents one more day of school? Do they connect the number on the Growing Number Line to the number of objects in the Concrete Number Count collection? [Number and Numeration Goals 2 and 3]

- **Reading and writing 2- and 3-digit numbers:** Can children read numbers on the Growing Number Line? Can they tell you how to write the next number on the Growing Number Line? [Number and Numeration Goal 3]

- **Representing numbers with manipulatives:** Can they represent the number of the day with sticks, straws, or other manipulatives? [Number and Numeration Goal 3]

- **Exchanging 1s for 10s and 10s for 100:** Do children know when to bundle sticks or straws during the Concrete Number Count? Do they understand why these exchanges can be made? [Number and Numeration Goal 3]

Attendance Routine

CCSS
Mathematical Practices
SMP1, SMP2, SMP4, SMP6
Content Standards
K.CC.4a, K.CC.4b, K.CC.5
Bold SMP = Guiding Questions
at **everydaymathonline.com**
Bold = Focus of routine

Introduction

▶Purpose

Children assist in recording and charting daily attendance to practice counting, number writing, data collection, and problem-solving skills.

Supporting Kindergarten Goals

• Count the number of children who are absent and/or present.
[Number and Numeration Goal 2]

• Solve number stories based on attendance data.
[Operations and Computation Goal 1]

• Create a daily record of children who are absent and children who are present. [Data and Chance Goal 1]

• Answer questions based on an attendance chart.
[Data and Chance Goal 2]

Terms to Use

more • less • same • some • none • all • all together • present • absent • chart • record

Materials

Pocket Chart
☐ posterboard
☐ paper pockets
☐ small index cards

T Chart
☐ posterboard (laminated)
☐ index cards (cut in half)
☐ self-stick fabric or magnets

Sign-in Grid
☐ Routine Master (*Math Masters,* p. 83) or other sign-in grid; pencil

▶Advance Preparation

Three possible sign-in systems are described and pictured below:

• **Pocket Chart** Glue paper pockets (such as library book pockets) onto posterboard in rows. Prepare a name card for each child to place in the pockets. (If you have two classes, use a double-sided laminated chart—one side for each class.)

• **T Chart** Prepare a T chart on laminated posterboard. Label one column "Present" and one column "Absent." Cut index cards in half and write each child's name on a card. Prepare a system for attaching the cards to the chart.

> **NOTE** Children can decorate their name cards. You might want to include a small picture of each child on his or her name card.

• **Sign-in Grid** Photocopy *Math Masters,* page 83 and write each child's name on the grid, or create your own sign-in grid.

> **Overview Every day...** Record attendance and discuss observations. **Any time...** Use attendance data to create number stories.

▶ Recording and Discussing Attendance Data

Every day On the first day of school, demonstrate the attendance sign-in system to the class. Continue to assist children until they can do it independently. This may take anywhere from a few days to a couple of weeks.

After everyone has signed in (perhaps at a class meeting), have children use the attendance chart or grid to figure out how many are present.

Name	MONDAY	TUESDAY	WEDNESDAY	THURSDAY	FRIDAY
Abra	X	X	X		
Andrew	X	X			
Colin		X	X		
Dana	X	X	X		
Elena	X	X	X		

Sign-in Grid Children draw an X or write their initials in the appropriate space on the grid. Help children find the correct place to sign in. At first, highlight the column for the day and show children how to move their fingers from their names to the correct column.

Attendance Chart

Avis		Clarence	Danusia	Edwin
Avis	Brita	Clarence	Danusia	Edwin
Jaden	Ione	Laetitia	Helen	Jonas
Jaden	Ione	Laetitia	Helen	Jonas

Pocket Chart Children place cards with their names and/or pictures into pockets labeled with their names.

Present | Absent

Present	Absent
Carla	Rebecca
Aimee	Sybill
John	
David	
Erik	

T Chart Children place small cards with their names in the "Present" column.

NOTE Some teachers begin the year with a relatively simple attendance routine and then move to a more challenging routine as the year progresses and children seem ready. Others like to stick with a single system throughout the year.

Have children verify the attendance record by
"counting off" one by one, or have the Attendance
job helper count each child. After counting all the
children present, encourage children to share
various strategies to figure out the number of
children who are absent. If desired, the Attendance
job helper can record a summary of the daily
attendance data on an Attendance Record Slip
(*Math Masters,* page 82), or on the board.

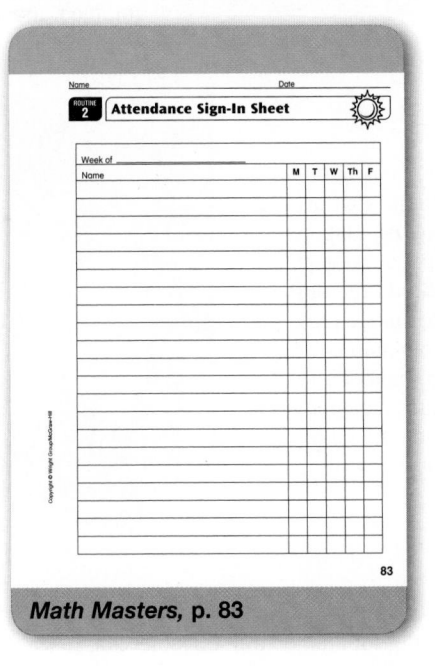

Math Masters, **p. 83**

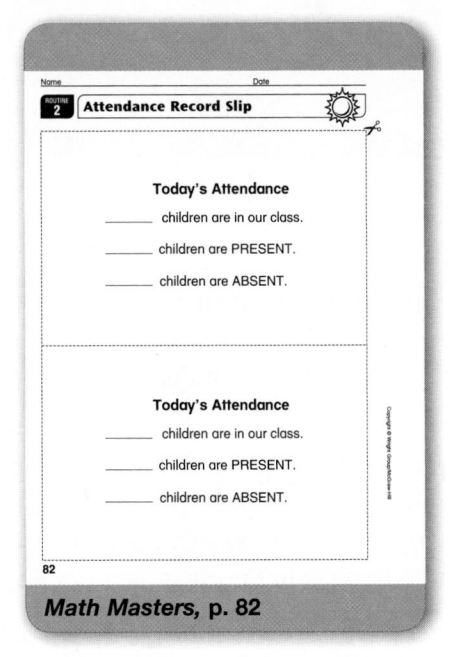

Math Masters, **p. 82**

▶Using Attendance Data in Context

Any time Use the attendance data as a source for number stories and problem solving. Encourage children to use your chart or sign-in sheet to help them figure out the answers, and have them share their strategies with one another. For example, you might ask them:

- Are there more boys or girls at school today? Can you figure out how many more? How did you figure it out?

- If two children leave early, how many will be present?

- Everyone should get two crackers. How many crackers will we need for our snack?

Later in the year, the class might try writing number sentences to model the attendance number stories.

If you complete Attendance Record Slips each day and save them, you might ask children questions that compare one day's attendance to another's. For example, you could post all of the record slips from one week and ask children which day had the highest attendance or which two days had the same attendance.

Children will enjoy using calculators to add and subtract large numbers (the total of all the PRESENT numbers for a given week, for example).

Ongoing Assessment:
Observing Children

Over time, you can use the Attendance Routine to assess children's development of the following concepts and skills:

- **Oral counting:** Do they say the correct number in sequence as they "count off" to verify the attendance record? [Number and Numeration Goal 1]

- **Rational counting (counting things):** Can they figure out how many children are present (or absent) by counting cards on the attendance chart, counting marks (or empty spaces) on the attendance grid, and/or counting actual children at a group time? Do they understand that the last number they say tells the number of children present (or absent)? Do they understand that the number is the same regardless of the order in which they count the objects (e.g., cards, marks, spaces, or children)? [Number and Numeration Goal 2]

- **Solving problems:** Can they figure out the number of children who are absent using the total number of children in the class and the number who are present? Can they solve number stories based on the attendance data? [Operations and Computation Goal 1]

- **Interpreting data:** Can they answer questions based on the attendance chart? [Data and Chance Goal 2]

You can also use the Attendance Routine to assess whether children can read their own and other children's names.

Job Chart Routine

Introduction

▶ Purpose

Children carry out daily mathematics routines such as adding the date to the calendar and keeping track of attendance. Children also begin to recognize the pattern of job rotation.

Supporting Kindergarten Goals

- Recognize the pattern of job rotation.
  [Patterns, Functions, and Algebra Goal 1]

- Develop mathematics skills by carrying out other Ongoing Daily Routines. [Multiple Goals]

Terms to Use

rotate • before • after • next • pattern

Materials

☐ Routine Masters (*Math Masters,* pp. 84–86) (optional)

☐ posterboard

☐ paper pockets (such as library book pockets)

☐ small index cards

▶ Advance Preparation

Staple or glue a card pocket for each job to a piece of posterboard. On each pocket, write a job title and add a picture to illustrate these jobs: Attendance, Number of the Day, Calendar, Daily Schedule, Temperature, Weather, and Survey. Include other jobs that fit the needs of your classroom, such as Line Leader, Door Holder, or Snack Helper. There can be as many jobs as there are children or fewer jobs than children (to give children some days off). Some teachers have two children work together to do some jobs. (In this case, make two pockets for a job.)

Make a name card for each child to place in the pockets. If you have two classes, create two sets of name cards using a different color card for each class. Move the correct set of cards to the front of the pockets at the start of each class.

NOTE You may wish to use the pictures on *Math Masters,* pages 84–86, for your job chart.

Overview **Every day or once a week...** Rotate and read the jobs on the chart.

Getting Started

▶ Using the Job Chart

Every day or once a week Decide whether you will change job assignments daily or weekly. At the beginning of each day or week, rotate the name cards on the chart. It is best to move the cards through the rows from left to right and then top to bottom, to reinforce the tracking of text in reading. To help children understand how the pattern of job rotation works and begin to make predictions about upcoming jobs, move the cards while children are watching, at least at the beginning of the year. (You might enlist a child's help by creating a job for moving the cards.) After the cards have been moved, go over children's job assignments with them until they can recognize their jobs independently and recall what each job entails. By mid-year, this routine runs itself and requires little or no group time.

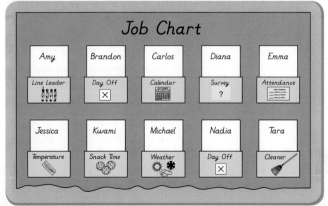

Ongoing Assessment:
Observing Children

Over time, you can use the Job Chart Routine to assess children's development of the following concepts and skills:

- **Recognizing the system or pattern of movement of the job cards:** Can children predict when they (or someone else) will have a particular job?
  [Patterns, Functions, and Algebra Goal 1]

You can also use the Job Chart Routine to assess whether children can read their own and each other's names and whether they can track from left to right and top to bottom.

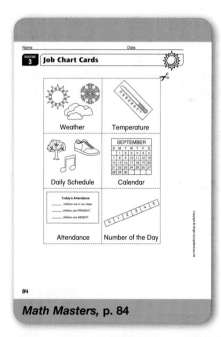

Math Masters, p. 84

Monthly Calendar Routine

Introduction

▶Purpose

Children learn the days of the week and the months of the year and understand the number and grid system of the calendar. They learn and use vocabulary related to periods of time.

Supporting Kindergarten Goals

• Read numbers 1–31. [Number and Numeration Goal 3]
• Order numbers 1–31. [Number and Numeration Goal 6]
• Use vocabulary related to periods of time.
 [Measurement and Reference Frames Goal 4]
• Recognize patterns on a calendar.
 [Patterns, Functions, and Algebra Goal 1]

Terms to Use

month • day • date • week • year • calendar • today • yesterday •
tomorrow • days of the week • weekend

Materials

Calendar
☐ reusable calendar or laminated posterboard
☐ wipe-off marker or stick-on notes, cards, or shapes
☐ material to attach numbers to calendar (optional)

Days Board
☐ sturdy paper or posterboard
☐ cards with the days of the week written on them

▶Advance Preparation

Calendar Purchase a large reusable calendar or construct and laminate a large grid with 7 columns and 5 rows on posterboard. Write the days of the week across the top of the grid, and leave a space at the top for the month and year.

Add dates to the calendar with a wipe-off marker or attach cards, stick-on notes, or shapes with the date numbers to the grid. The Calendar job helper can write the appropriate number on one of the shapes each day. If you plan to add weather cards to your calendar, size the shapes accordingly. (See the Weather Observation Routine, page 24.)

Days Board Write the following on sturdy paper:
Yesterday was_____ .
Today is_____.
Tomorrow will be_____ .
Write the days of the week on cards and laminate the board and the cards.

Overview **Every day...** Read the date on the calendar and complete the Days Board. **Once a month...** Dismantle the calendar. **Any time...** Use the calendar to keep track of events and note the passage of time.

Getting Started

▶ Reading and Building the Calendar

Every day Find the current day on the calendar and read the day of the week, the month, the date number, and the year with children. (Have the Calendar job helper take the lead; provide help as needed.) Some teachers post the calendar with the numbers already in place. Others have the Calendar job helper write and/or place a new number on the grid each school day. After a weekend or holiday, the Calendar job helper can add the missing days to the calendar.

Indicate significant days such as children's birthdays, holidays, and no-school days on the class calendar. The days can be noted with a dot, or children can develop symbols to represent these days on the calendar (for example, a candle might represent a birthday).

▶ Completing the Days Board

Every day As children become familiar with the calendar and names of the days of the week, add the Days Board to the Calendar routine. The Calendar job helper places the correct days of the week on the chart to complete the sentences.

OCTOBER 20_ _

SUNDAY	MONDAY	TUESDAY	WEDNESDAY	THURSDAY	FRIDAY	SATURDAY
	1	2	3	4	5	6
7	8	9	10	11	12	13
14	15	16	17	18	19	20
21	22	23	24	25	26	27
28	29	30	31			

Some teachers use a different shape each month for the numbers on their calendars. Others add shapes in a pattern.

Days Board

Yesterday was [Tuesday].

Today is [Wednesday].

Tomorrow will be [Thursday].

▶Dismantling the Monthly Calendar

Once a month In preparation for the new month, enlist children's help in taking down the calendar. Dismantling the calendar provides an opportunity to enhance number skills and awareness of calendar patterns. This can be a rich whole-class activity. Give many, if not all, children a chance to clear the dates, using clues that you provide. Change the clues as the year progresses and children become more experienced with the calendar. Here are some suggested clues:

Remove or erase ...

- a number you can read.
- the first Monday.
- all the Sundays.
- the third day of the month.
- Tim's birthday.
- all the teens.
- the highest numbered day.
- two days whose sum is 8.

- the day in the third row, second column.
- all days with 4 in the ones place.
- a number that is 1 ten and 4 ones.

As children become familiar with this routine they can suggest clues for taking off dates.

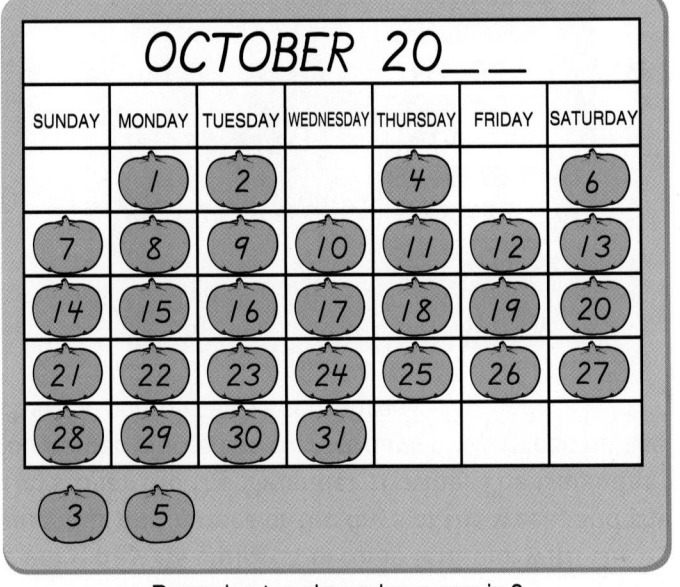

Removing two days whose sum is 8

NOTE Occasionally, dismantling the calendar can be the mathematics activity for the day.

▶ Using the Calendar

Any time Look for real-life reasons to refer to the calendar, and use the names of the days and other calendar-related vocabulary. For example, you might count how many days until the weekend, or you might note that the field trip is on Wednesday. Ask questions to help build children's familiarity with the calendar. *For example:*

● How many Wednesdays are in this month?

● Which day did the month start on?

● Point to the second Monday of this month. What is the date for this day of the month?

> **NOTE** For more information about calendars, see "Reference Frames" in the *Teacher's Reference Manual*, Chapter 13.

Ongoing Assessment:
Observing Children

Over time, you can use the Calendar Routine to assess children's development of the following concepts and skills:

● **Reading numbers:** Can they read the numbers on the calendar? [Number and Numeration Goal 3]

● **Understanding how digits are combined to make numbers:** Can they use place-value clues (a day that is 1 ten and 4 ones, or all days with the number 4 in the ones place) to find a given date or dates on the calendar?
[Number and Numeration Goal 3]

● **Sequencing numbers:** Can they put the numbers on the calendar in order? [Number and Numeration Goal 6]

● **Performing simple addition and subtraction problems:** Can they use addition and subtraction clues (2 days whose sum is 8, for example) to find a given date or dates on the calendar? [Operations and Computation Goal 1]

● **Knowing the days of the week and understanding the organization of the calendar:** Can they name the correct day? Can they find a given date on the calendar using day of the week or similar clues (the first Monday of the month, or the day in the third row, second column)?
[Measurement and Reference Frames Goal 4]

Daily Schedule Routine

Introduction

▶ Purpose

Children develop their understanding of the language and concepts of time by ordering classroom activities and special classes. They also gain experience with sequencing events.

Supporting Kindergarten Goals

- Describe time period relationships.
  [Measurement and Reference Frames Goal 4]
- Increase awareness of the time of day and the sequence of daily events. [Measurement and Reference Frames Goal 4]

Terms to Use

morning • afternoon • noon • before • after • following • next • early • late

Materials

- ☐ posterboard, bulletin board, or pocket chart
- ☐ cardstock or index cards to make activity and day-of-the-week cards
- ☐ paper pockets (such as library book pockets) or adhesive material
- ☐ clothespin or pointer

▶ Advance Preparation

Create cards that depict and name activities and special classes that occur on a daily or regular basis. Cards might include Gym, Music, Story, and Sharing Time. You may also wish to make cards for special events such as birthdays or field trips. Write the days of the week on cards to place at the top of the schedule each day.

Designate an area on a bulletin board or prepare a board with a means of attaching the cards. Some teachers use pockets or a pocket chart for the cards. Others attach the cards with self-stick fabric, tape, or tacks. Add a pointer (a clothespin or an arrow cut from cardboard) that can be moved to each activity on the schedule over the course of the day.

Overview **Every day...** Order and track daily activities.
Late in the year... Add clock pictures to the schedule if desired.

▶ Ordering Daily Activities

Every day At the beginning of each school day, the Daily Schedule job helper places the correct day-of-the-week card on the bulletin or display board. With your help, the child also adds activity cards for that day in the correct sequence. During a class meeting, the child reports on the daily schedule to the class; he or she also moves the pointer to the correct activity on the schedule as the day progresses.

> **NOTE** At the beginning of the year, children may need considerable help setting up the daily schedule. Over the course of the year, children will be able to do more and more of the job on their own.

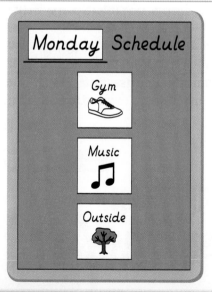

▶ Using Clocks with the Daily Schedule

> **NOTE** Clocks are introduced in Section 8, with a focus on estimating time using the hour hand.

Late in the year You might want to add clocks to your daily schedule to show the approximate starting time of each event on the schedule. You can use the blank clock on *Math Masters,* page 56, to make clocks for the schedule. If you add clocks, decide whether you want to draw the hour and minute hands or only the hour hand on the clocks.

> ### ✓ Ongoing Assessment:
> **Observing Children**
>
> Over time, you can use the Daily Schedule Routine to assess children's development of the following concepts and skills:
>
> - **Describing and using measures of time periods:** Do they correctly use day-of-the-week and time-of-day terminology as they set up and read the daily schedule? Do they use the daily schedule to get information about their day? [Measurement and Reference Frames Goal 4]
> - **Sequencing events:** Can they correctly order the events of the day? [Measurement and Reference Frames Goal 4]

ROUTINE

6

Weather Observation Routine

CCSS Mathematical Practices
SMP1, SMP2, SMP3,
SMP4, SMP6, SMP7
Content Standards
K.CC.5, K.CC.6, K.MD.3

Introduction

▶Purpose

Children collect, organize, display, and interpret real, familiar, and interesting data and look for recognizable patterns or trends in the data. They also think and talk about probability and chance.

Supporting Kindergarten Goals

- Count and compare data from different categories.
  [Number and Numeration Goal 6]

- Collect, organize, and display weather data.
  [Data and Chance Goal 1]

- Discuss and answer questions about weather tally charts and/or bar graphs. [Data and Chance Goal 2]

- Describe the likelihood of weather events or patterns.
  [Data and Chance Goal 3]

Terms to Use

some • none • all • more • fewer • same • most • least • likely • more likely • least likely • definite • certain • sure • maybe • impossible

Materials

- ☐ Routine Master
  (*Math Masters*, p. 87)

- ☐ cardstock for a weather circle; black paper and a brad for a movable pointer

- ☐ index cards for tally charts and all weather cards

- ☐ large paper for a bar graph

▶Advance Preparation

Make a large Weather Circle by cutting a circle out of cardstock. Divide the circle into six equal sections. Add pictures from *Math Masters*, page 87, (and labels, if desired) to represent the following weather conditions: sunny, cloudy, rainy, snowy, partly cloudy, and foggy. Cut an arrow from sturdy black paper and attach it to the center of the circle with a brad fastener.

Display the Weather Circle and recording system where children can see and reach them.

Create a graph, set of tally charts, or other weather recording system to use with your Weather Circle. (See page 25.) You will need to create a new graph or set of tally charts each month.

Overview **Every day...** Record and discuss observations. **Once a month...** Compile data and describe the month's weather. **Every few months...** Compare data from different months and look for patterns. **Any time...** Use data to investigate and discuss probability and chance.

Getting Started

▶ Observing and Recording Data

Every day As the year begins, encourage children to observe weather conditions at about the same time every day. Then have the Weather job helper move the pointer to the appropriate section on the Weather Circle.

When they are ready, children can begin recording weather observations using any of the recording systems shown here. The Weather job helper can record the daily weather observation. Help children make sense of the accumulating data by discussing it as it is collected.

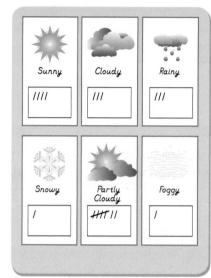

Weather Tally Chart
Add tally marks to the appropriate card.

NOTE Many teachers find it convenient to combine the Weather Observation Routine with the Temperature Recording Routine. Both routines provide rich opportunities for integrating mathematics and science. Some teachers embellish their weather recording system as the year progresses.

Weather Calendar Draw the weather conditions for the day on a card and add the card to the calendar. At the end of the month, compile the cards into a bar graph showing the number of days that were sunny, rainy, cloudy, and so on.

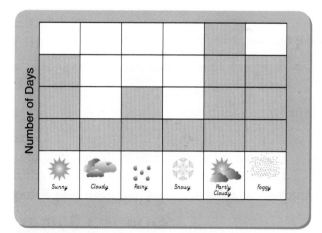

Weather Graph Color in the appropriate column in an ongoing bar graph.

Moving Forward

▶ Compiling and Describing Data

Once a month At the end of the month, discuss the compiled record of the month's weather. For instance, have children count and compare the number of days of each type of weather. *Ask:*

- How many sunny days were in October?

- Were there more sunny days than cloudy days this month? How many more?

Help children develop and use strategies for comparing the number of days in each category. For example, if you use weather cards, children can line up the cards that depict each type of weather and use matching to determine which line has more (or fewer) cards and how many more (or fewer). Children can use a similar strategy to compare the number of days that make up each "bar" on a weather bar graph.

Encourage children to refer to the monthly graph or chart to describe the month's weather. Initially, you may need to model this with statements such as: *February was a very snowy month. There were many more sunny days than cloudy days in October. It didn't rain very much in April.*

▶ Comparing Data and Finding Patterns

Every few months After you have more than one graph or tally chart, have children compare data from different months and look for weather patterns. Pose questions such as:

- Did we have more or fewer cloudy days this month compared to last month?

- Which month had more snowy days?

- How do our graphs show that the season has changed?

At the end of each season, discuss the season's name and look at the weather data for the corresponding months. Use the data to discuss the weather that characterizes that season in your area.

> **NOTE** For more information about organizing and displaying data, see "Data and Chance" in the *Teacher's Reference Manual*, Chapter 10.

▶ Exploring Probability and Chance

Any time Use the Weather Observation Routine to introduce and explore basic concepts and language related to probability and chance. For example, you might discuss questions such as:

- Is it likely to snow? Is it more likely to rain or snow tomorrow?

- Are you sure it rained yesterday? Can we be certain that it will rain tomorrow?

- Which type of weather are we least (or most) likely to have this afternoon?

As you talk with children, use a mix of informal and formal language related to probability. Use terms such as *definite, for sure, maybe, likely, impossible,* and *no way*. Help children think about the difference between using the weather data to *know* what happened and using the data and other information to think about the *chance*, or *probability*, of something happening in the future.

Ongoing Assessment:
Observing Children

Over time, you can use the Weather Routine to assess children's development of the following concepts and skills:

- **Counting and comparing:** Can children correctly count the number of days of each type of weather from your weather chart or graph? Can they compare the numbers to say whether one category had more, fewer, or the same number of days as another category? Can they figure out how many more or fewer? [Number and Numeration Goals 2 and 6]

- **Adding data to graphs or tally charts:** Can they correctly add daily data to the weather recording system? [Data and Chance Goal 1]

- **Interpreting data:** Can they interpret and compare the weather data? [Data and Chance Goal 2]

- **Using probability language:** Do children use probability language as they make or check predictions and describe weather patterns or trends? [Data and Chance Goal 3]

> **NOTE** For more information about probability and chance, see "Data and Chance" in the *Teacher's Reference Manual,* Chapter 10.

Recording Daily Temperature Routine

CCSS Mathematical Practices
SMP1, SMP2, SMP3, SMP4, SMP5, SMP6, SMP7
Content Standards
K.MD.3

Introduction

▶Purpose

Children collect daily temperature data and create a growing data display which they use to discuss findings and trends and relate them to probability and chance.

Supporting Kindergarten Goals

• Collect and record data about temperature. [Data and Chance Goal 1]

• Interpret and discuss temperature data. [Data and Chance Goal 2]

• Use temperature trends to discuss probability. [Data and Chance Goal 3]

• Describe temperature using appropriate vocabulary and use a thermometer to measure temperature. [Measurement and Reference Frames Goal 3]

Terms to Use

thermometer • temperature • hot • cold • warm • cool • higher • lower • more • fewer • some • all • none • definite • sure • maybe • likely • unlikely • impossible • certain

Materials

☐ Routine Master (*Math Masters*, p. 88)

☐ thermometer

☐ sticky dots (white or colored)

☐ markers to color white dots

☐ adding machine tape or long strips of construction paper (about $1\frac{1}{2}$ inches wide)

☐ permanent markers, crayons, or colored strips of paper

▶Advance Preparation

Color-code a large outdoor thermometer using permanent markers, crayons, or colored strips of paper as shown on page 29. Place the thermometer outside where children can see it from the classroom. (Alternatively, get the temperature from the Internet, radio, television, newspapers, or some other source.)

Collect white dot stickers or dot stickers that match the colors on the thermometer, and post a long strip of paper or adding machine tape on a wall. The class will add dot stickers to the strip to record the color of the day's temperature zone. Some teachers prefer to add the colored dot to their monthly calendar or to place it on their Growing Number Line.

Overview **Every day...** Read the thermometer and record the colored temperature zone. **Once a month...** Compile data and describe temperature trends. **Any time...** Use temperature data to discuss probability and chance.

Getting Started

► Collecting and Recording
Temperature Data (*Math Masters*, p. 88)

Every day At the beginning of the year, introduce
the thermometer as a tool for measuring
temperature. Discuss temperature as a way to
describe how hot or cold the air feels, and introduce
the color zones on the thermometer. You can use
the clothing pictures from *Math Masters,* page 88,
to help children relate to the color zones. For
instance, use the bathing suits to illustrate the
red zone.

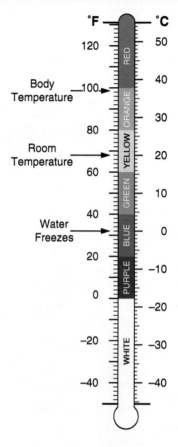

Math Masters, p. 88

Each day at about the same
time, the Temperature job
helper checks the color
zone corresponding to the
temperature on the
thermometer. The child
reports to the class and
places a matching colored
sticky dot on the long strip
of paper (or calendar or
Growing Number Line). If
you use white sticky dots,
the Temperature job helper
should color the dot the
appropriate color before
posting it. As the recording
strip grows, a meaningful
display is created. As the
year goes on, use the color
codes to discuss temperature
trends and encourage the
use of descriptive language
such as *cool, warm,* or
very cold.

NOTE For more information about temperature and thermometers, see "Reference Frames" in the *Teacher's Reference Manual*, Chapter 13.

Moving Forward

▶ Compiling and Discussing Monthly Data

Once a month At the end of each month, you might have the class count the number of dots of each color and create a graph. Engage children in discussing the graph, comparing it to previous months, and predicting what the graph will look like the next month. You might pose questions such as:

- Did we have more cold days this month or last month?

- Which month had more cool days?

- Do you think next month's graph will have more or fewer cold days?

- How do our graphs show us that the season has changed?

Display the graphs together, or save them in a class book to use in future discussions.

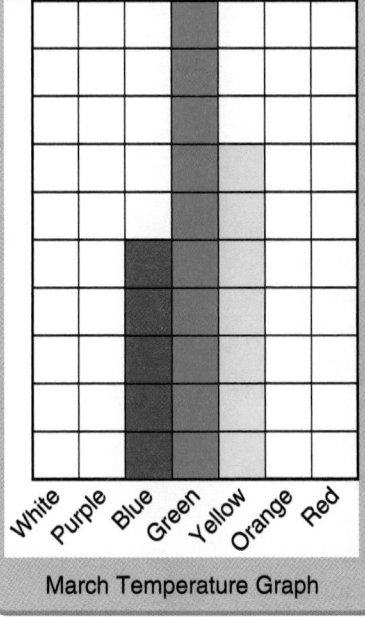

March Temperature Graph

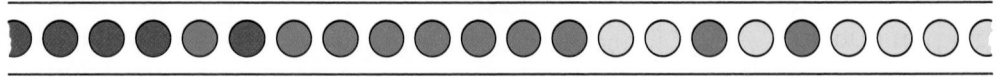

March Temperature

▶ Exploring Probability and Chance

Any time Use the Temperature Routine to explore basic concepts and language related to probability and chance. For example, you might discuss answers to questions such as:

- Is it likely to be warm or cold today?

- Are you sure about today's temperature? Do you know what the temperature will be tomorrow?

As you talk with children, use a mix of informal and formal language related to probability. For example, use terms such as *definite, for sure, maybe, likely, impossible,* and *no way*. Encourage children to think about the difference between using the temperature data to *know* what happened and using the data and other information to think about the *chance,* or *probability,* of something happening in the future.

Ongoing Assessment:
Observing Children

Over time, you can use the Recording Daily Temperature Routine to assess children's development of the following concepts and skills:

- **Collecting and interpreting data:** Can children add data to the growing temperature record? Can they interpret the temperature data? [Data and Chance Goals 1 and 2]

- **Using probability language:** Do they correctly use probability language as they predict and describe temperature trends? [Data and Chance Goal 3]

- **Using a thermometer:** Do children understand that a thermometer is a tool used for measuring temperature? Are they becoming proficient at using the color zones to read the thermometer? [Measurement and Reference Frames Goal 3]

- **Describing temperature:** Do they use appropriate vocabulary (*hot, warm, cold,* and so on) to describe the temperature? [Measurement and Reference Frames Goal 3]

Survey Routine

Introduction

▶ Purpose

Children collect, record, display, and discuss data that interest them by surveying their classmates. As they conduct class surveys, they also practice reading and writing skills and make connections to other curriculum areas.

Supporting Kindergarten Goals

• Count and compare numbers of different responses.
[Number and Numeration Goal 6]

• Create and solve number stories using survey data.
[Operations and Computation Goal 1]

• Collect and record data on a chart or graph. [Data and Chance Goal 1]

• Answer questions based on survey data.
[Data and Chance Goal 2]

Terms to Use

tally • record • graph • count • compare • more • less • same as • some • all • none

Materials

☐ Routine Master
(*Math Masters*, p. 89)

☐ pictures from magazines or other sources

☐ magnets and a cookie sheet or chart paper and a marker

☐ class lists, pencils and a clipboard

☐ connecting cubes (optional)

▶ Advance Preparation

Establish a place in the classroom to post the survey question and decide how children will record their responses. *Suggestions:*

• Have children place magnets on a cookie sheet in the appropriate column.

• Have children write their initials or an X in the appropriate column on chart paper. Once children know how to use tally marks, they can record a tally mark in the appropriate column on the chart paper.

Collect old magazines with a variety of pictures that can be used to illustrate the survey question.

Overview **Every day or once a week...** Conduct a class survey. Display and discuss results. **Any time...** Have children collect and compile survey information from family members, or invite them to conduct their own class surveys. Have children create and solve number stories based on survey data.

Getting Started

▶ Conducting Surveys and Recording Data

Every day or once a week Pose a survey question for children to answer. Add a picture to help children read or remember the question. At the beginning of the year, choose *yes* or *no* questions such as: *Did you play outside over the weekend?* Children record their responses on a T chart that has one column labeled "Yes" and the other labeled "No." Once children are comfortable with the survey procedures, ask questions with multiple possible responses and add columns to the response charts; for example, *What is your favorite color?* or *How many people live in your house?*

After all children have recorded their responses on the chart, ask the class to help you count and record the number of responses in each column. Discuss the results with the class.

Save responses that have been recorded on chart paper. Children will enjoy referring back to them over the course of the year, and you can use them for creating number stories.

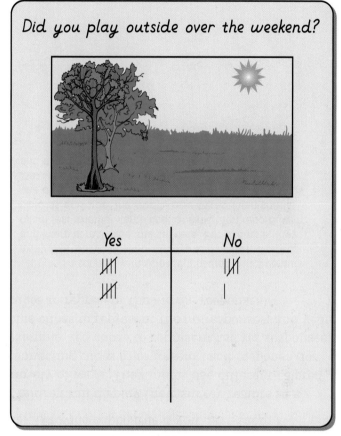

Did you play outside over the weekend?

T Chart

▶Conducting Surveys with Families

(*Math Masters*, p. 89)

Any time Occasionally, children can take the survey question home and record family responses on a Yes/No T Chart. Children can use *Math Masters*, page 89 to gather responses from home. The class can display and discuss the compiled results. You might also use this master to compile class results.

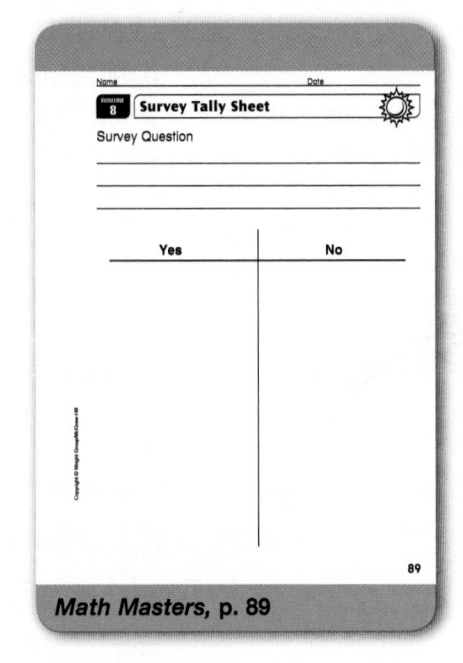

Math Masters, p. 89

▶Conducting Surveys Independently

Any time As the year progresses, children can formulate their own survey questions and conduct independent surveys. Children write their questions at the top of an easy-to-read class list. Then they circulate around the room and record their classmates' responses next to their names on the list. (Provide clipboards if you have them.)

Children can display their survey results in a variety of ways. They might use different-colored connecting cubes to represent each response (for example: red cubes to represent the *yes* responses; blue cubes to represent the *no* responses; and yellow cubes to represent the *maybe* responses).

> **NOTE** To connect with science, children might venture away from opinion-based surveys and collect, display, and interpret real experimental data. For example, they might test whether items float or sink, then record (with pictures or words) the results on a two-column chart: one column for things that float and the other for things that sink. Children can count and compare the results and discuss their theories about the results.

Alternatively, children might construct bar graphs on paper. (See Activity 6-5, page 292, for one procedure for a child-constructed bar graph.) Allow children to share the results of their surveys with the class and to use their data as the basis for number stories.

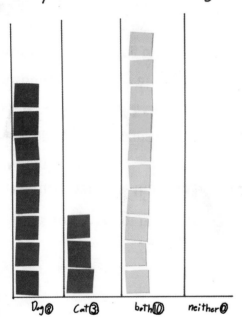

Do you like cats or dogs?

Dog⑧   Cat③   both⑩   neither⓪

Ongoing Assessment:
Observing Children

Over time, you can use the Survey Routine to assess children's development of the following concepts and skills:

- **Counting and comparing:** Can children correctly count the number of each type of response on their surveys? Can they compare these numbers?
  [Number and Numeration Goals 2 and 6]

- **Solving number stories:** Can they solve addition and subtraction number stories based on their survey data?
  [Operations and Computation Goal 1]

- **Collecting, organizing, and displaying data:** Can children collect and organize survey data? Can they display their data on a chart and/or graph? [Data and Chance Goal 1]

- **Interpreting data:** Can they answer questions based on survey graphs? [Data and Chance Goal 2]

NOTE For more information about collecting, organizing, and displaying data, see "Data and Chance" in the *Teacher's Reference Manual*, Chapter 10.

Section 1

Overview

Section 1 has a number of main areas of focus:

- To introduce materials that will be used throughout the year, such as pattern blocks, coins, and other manipulatives,
- To develop counting skills through multisensory activities and games,
- To build familiarity with the numbers 0–10,
- To introduce sorting by attributes,
- To introduce patterning through multisensory activities,
- To introduce graphing by creating age and birthday graphs,
- To explore measurement by comparing lengths,
- To explore shapes and shape combinations,
- To introduce volume through sand and water play, and
- To establish Ongoing Daily Routines.

Maintaining Ongoing Daily Routines

Doing the Routines

Plan to spend extra time establishing the following Ongoing Daily Routines during the first few weeks of school.

- Number of the Day
- Daily Schedule
- Attendance
- Weather Observation
- Job Chart
- Recording Daily Temperature
- Monthly Calendar
- Survey

These activities are a cornerstone of the curriculum, so the time you devote at the beginning of the school year will pay off in the long run. The Revisit Activities in Activities 1-1 through 1-5 serve as reminders to spend enough time setting up and implementing these routines.

Adjusting the Routines

During Section 1, plan to do the Ongoing Daily Routines the same way each day to help children learn the routines and build independence in doing each routine. In later sections, you might adjust the routines periodically according to children's progress and interests. You can also use the Ongoing Daily Routines as powerful tools for practicing and reinforcing the skills that are introduced in the activities throughout the year.

Using Routines for Ongoing Assessment

All of the Ongoing Daily Routines offer opportunities for ongoing assessment of a variety of skills and concepts. You might want to use the following routines for ongoing assessment during Section 1:

- **Number of the Day** Do children know what number comes next on the Growing Number Line? Can they read the numbers on the Growing Number Line? Can they tell you how to write the next number? Do they understand that each successive number on the Growing Number Line represents one more day of school? Do they connect the number on the Growing Number Line to the number of objects in the Concrete Number Count collection?

- **Job Chart** Can children find and read their own names on the job chart?

Learning in Perspective

Core Activities

Activity	Objective	Revisit Activity	Page
1·1	**Partner Match** To introduce measurement comparisons through a partner activity. **Links to the Future** Beginning in Activity 3-7, children will measure with nonstandard units. In Section 5, children will be introduced to standard measurement tools and units.	**Establishing Daily Routines** (Routines 1–8, pp. 8–35) **Links to the Past** Children should have begun the Ongoing Daily Routines on the first day of school.	46
1·2	**Introduction to Pattern Blocks** To introduce pattern blocks.	**Establishing Daily Routines** (Routines 1–8, pp. 8–35)	48
1·3	**Multisensory Counts** To reinforce counting principles through multisensory activities.	**Establishing Daily Routines** (Routines 1–8, pp. 8–35)	50
1·4	**Countdown to Zero** To introduce the concept of zero, the word *zero*, and the numeral "0."	**Establishing Daily Routines** (Routines 1–8, pp. 8–35)	52
1·5	**Getting to Know Numbers (1–9)** To introduce the numbers 1–9 in a variety of activities and to reinforce early counting and numeration skills and principles.	**Establishing Daily Routines** (Routines 1–8, pp. 8–35)	54
1·6	**Introduction to Sorting** To introduce attributes and sorting. **Links to the Future** Children apply rules to numbers when they work with function machines in Section 8, and in later grades.	**Getting to Know Numbers—Number 2** (Activity 1-5, p. 54) **Links to the Past** In Activity 1-5, children participated in Getting to Know Numbers activities for Number 1. (They will do Getting to Know Numbers activities for numbers 3–9 in Activities 1-7 through 1-13.)	56
1·7	**Sand and Water Play** To introduce volume through sand and water play. **Links to the Future** In Grade 4, children will describe and use strategies to find volume.	**Getting to Know Numbers—Number 3** (Activity 1-5, p. 54)	58

Core Activities, *continued*

Activity	Objective	Revisit Activity	Page
1·8	**Birthday Graphs** To introduce bar graphs using age and birthday information.	**Getting to Know Numbers—Number 4** (Activity 1-5, p. 54)	60
1·9	**Sound and Motion Patterns** To introduce patterns through multisensory, experiential activities. **Links to the Future** Children will work with visual and numeric patterns in Kindergarten and in later grades.	**Getting to Know Numbers—Number 5** (Activity 1-5, p. 54)	62
1·10	**Patterns with Color** To introduce simple color patterns.	**Getting to Know Numbers—Number 6** (Activity 1-5, p. 54)	64
1·11	**Coin Comparisons** To provide practice with sorting and to lay groundwork for coin recognition. **Links to the Future** In Section 6, children will begin to learn coin names and values.	**Getting to Know Numbers—Number 7** (Activity 1-5, p. 54)	66
1·12	***Give the Next Number* Game** To develop number sense and counting skills through an oral counting game.	**Getting to Know Numbers—Number 8** (Activity 1-5, p. 54)	68
1·13	**Body Height Comparisons** To provide practice with comparing lengths.	**Getting to Know Numbers—Number 9** (Activity 1-5, p. 54)	70
1·14	**Finger Count Fun** To reinforce counting and recognizing numerals 1–10.	**Getting to Know Numbers—Counting Book** (Activity 1-5, p. 54)	72
1·15	**Shape Puzzles** To provide experiences with manipulating and combining shapes.	**Comparing Numbers** (Activity 1-5, p. 54)	73A
1·16	**Ten Frames** To use ten frames to explore numbers and number relationships through 10.	**Exploring Shape Combinations** (Activity 1-15, p. 73A; *Math Masters*, pp. 5A–5H)	73C

Ongoing Learning and Practice

Practice through Games

Games are an essential component of practice in the *Everyday Mathematics* program. Games offer skills practice and promote strategic thinking. The following game is introduced in this section:

Activity	Game	Skill Practiced
1◆5	*Match Up*	Matching numerals and sets [Number and Numeration Goal 3]
1◆12	*Give the Next Number*	Counting numbers in sequence [Number and Numeration Goal 1]

Home-School Connection 🏠

Home Links provide homework and home communication. The following activities contain Home Links: 1-3, 1-5, 1-7, 1-11.

Home Connection Handbook provides more ideas to communicate effectively with parents. ▶

◀ *Mathematics at Home* Books **1–4** provide additional ideas for enjoyable mathematics activities that families can do together, as well as lists of children's books related to topics in each strand area. Families can do activities from *Mathematics at Home* Book **1** during Section 1.

Balanced Assessment

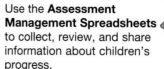

Use the **Assessment Management Spreadsheets** to collect, review, and share information about children's progress.

Ongoing Assessment

Recognizing Student Achievement

Opportunities to assess children's progress toward Kindergarten Goals:

Activity	Content Assessed
1◆13	Compare lengths of two objects. [Measurement and Reference Frames Goal 1]
1◆14	Read numbers 0–10. [Number and Numeration Goal 3] Count using one-to-one correspondence. [Number and Numeration Goal 2]

Informing Instruction

To anticipate common trouble spots and to highlight problem-solving strategies:

Activity 1◆1
Use correct measurement technique

Activity 1◆3
Use understanding of one-to-one correspondence and cardinality

Activity 1◆5
Count and create sets for numbers 1–9; identify and represent numbers 1–9

Activity 1◆10
Make and extend patterns

Activity 1◆12
Count by rote accurately

Periodic Assessment

Baseline assessment tasks should be completed during Section 1 in the first few weeks of the school year. Mid-Year assessment tasks will be completed in Sections 4 and 5.

Portfolio Opportunities

Portfolio Ideas

◆ Paper quilts, **Activity 1-2,** Teaching Option

Assessment Handbook

◆ Kindergarten Goals, pp. 27–33
◆ Section 1 Assessment Overview, pp. 50–51
◆ Assessment Overviews by Strand, pp. 66–75
◆ Baseline Periodic Assessment Tasks, pp. 40–41
◆ Individual Profile of Progress and Class Checklist (Baseline), pp. 85–86
◆ Individual Profile of Progress and Class Checklist (Sections 1–2), pp. 77–78
◆ Cumulative Individual Profile of Progress (Sections 1–4), pp. 97–98

Differentiated Instruction

Teaching Options

Use optional Part B activities as time permits to meet individual and class needs and to integrate mathematics throughout the Kindergarten classroom and schedule.

ELL SUPPORT

1•2	Discussing a story about patterns
1•13	Discussing the terms *long* and *short*

READINESS

1•4	Counting down with snacks
1•6	Singing about attributes
1•14	Counting beans

CONNECTIONS

Literacy

1•2	Reading books about patterns and quilts
1•4	Reading a counting story
1•5	Reading counting books
1•6	Reading about attributes
1•8	Reading birthday stories
1•9	Reading books with patterns
1•13	Reading a book and comparing heights

Science

1•6	Sorting nature collections
1•8	Representing Earth's revolution
1•10	Creating patterns with natural objects

Art

1•10	Exploring patterns through art projects
1•15	Making shape pictures and puzzles

Music

1•3	Singing "one more" songs
1•9	Singing a patterned song

ENRICHMENT

1•4	Counting down from higher numbers	1•7	Estimating container capacity
1•5	Taking apart featured numbers	1•12	Counting on using number cards

EXTRA PRACTICE

1•1	Comparing hand and foot sizes	1•11	Using coins in a Feely Box or Feely Bag
1•3	Making a Feely Box or Feely Bag	1•14	Using ten frames
1•3	Playing Simon Says	1•15	Doing Pattern-Block Puzzles
1•5	Playing *Match Up*	1•16	Exploring ten pennies with two hands

CENTERS

Block Center

1•1	Comparing block structures

Dramatic Play Center

1•11	Playing with money and banks

TECHNOLOGY

1•12	Counting in computer games

Language Support

Everyday Mathematics provides activity-specific suggestions to help *all* young children develop the language necessary to acquire, process, and express mathematical ideas. Activities that provide additional support for non-native English speakers are marked by **ELL SUPPORT** and **ELL**.

Connecting Math and Literacy

Activity 1◆4 *Five Little Monkeys Jumping on the Bed* by Eileen Christelow (Clarion Books, 1989)

Activity 1◆5 *Emily's First 100 Days of School* by Rosemary Wells (Hyperion, 2005)

Activity 1◆6 *The Button Box* by Margarette S. Reid (Dutton, 1990)

Activity 1◆8 *Flower Garden* by Eve Bunting (Harcourt, 1994)

Activity 1◆13 *Where's My Teddy?* by Jez Alborough (Candlewick Press, 1994)

See pages 49, 61, and 63 for more literature suggestions.

Using the Projects

Use Numbers in Our World (Project 1, page 74) during or after Section 1 to reinforce skills and concepts related to number uses, numeral identification, and counting.

Adjusting the Activity

AUDITORY   ◆   **KINESTHETIC**   ◆   **TACTILE**   ◆   **VISUAL**

Activity 1◆4   Acting out a counting down to zero song   **ELL**

Activity 1◆10 Making more complicated patterns

Activity 1◆12 Incorporating numeral recognition and/or varying starting or ending numbers in an oral counting game

Planning Tips

Pacing
Pacing depends on a number of factors, such as children's individual needs and how long your school has been using *Everyday Mathematics*. Use the optional Part B activities throughout Section 1 if you have extended mathematics instructional time. See page 42 for a list of these activities.

AUGUST	←— MOST CLASSROOMS —→ SEPTEMBER	OCTOBER

Teaching Resources

Resources for the Kindergarten Classroom provides additional teaching ideas, including suggestions for bringing mathematics into thematic instruction, as well as using games, literature, technology, songs and rhymes to support mathematics learning. ▶

Minute Math provides brief activities for transition times and for spare moments throughout the day. During Section 1, use activities in Part 1, pages 5–66.

NCTM Standards

Content Standards: 1 Number and Operations, **2** Algebra, **3** Geometry, **4** Measurement, **5** Data Analysis and Probability
Process Standards: 6 Problem Solving, **7** Reasoning and Proof, **8** Communication, **9** Connection, **10** Representation

Section 1 Activities	1•1	1•2	1•3	1•4	1•5	1•6	1•7	1•8	1•9	1•10	1•11	1•12	1•13	1•14
NCTM Standards	4, 6, 8	2, 3, 8	1	1, 8	1, 10	2, 6, 7, 8	4, 6, 7, 8	5, 10	2, 6	2, 6	2, 4, 7, 8	1, 10	4, 5 6, 10	1, 10

Professional Development

Teacher's Reference Manual Links

Activity	Topic	Section	Activity	Topic	Section
1•1	Measurement Tools and Techniques	12.10	1•6	Patterns, Sequences, and Functions	15.1
1•3	Plain and Fancy Counting	8.2.2	1•9	Organizing and Displaying Data	10.2.3

Materials

Activity	Masters	Materials	
1·1		• strips of heavy paper or cardstock	
1·2		• class set of pattern blocks*	
1·3	Home Link Master, p. 2	• coins, screws, or bottle lids	• empty coffee can
1·4		• small food items or counters*	• plastic animals
1·5	Home Link Master, p. 3	• various manipulatives such as craft sticks*, connecting cubes* or links, inch	cubes*, and beads • markers • chart paper or posterboard • plastic bags
1·6		• collection of small objects with a common characteristic and several different attributes, such as buttons, beads, pasta shapes, play food, magnetic	letters and numbers, or screws, nuts, and bolts • sorting containers such as deli trays, muffin tins, egg cartons, or compartmentalized boxes
1·7	Home Link Master, p. 4	• water, sand, or dry beans • water table, sand table, or tubs to hold materials	• containers of various sizes and shapes including low and wide, tall and thin
1·8		• index cards cut into 3-inch squares • posterboard	• material to attach cards to posterboard • markers
1·9			

Activity	Masters	Materials	
1·10		• one set of objects of different colors (cubes, crayons, beads, counters*, and so on)	
1·11	Home Link Master, p. 5	• pennies, nickels, dimes, and quarters • muffin tins, egg cartons, or sorting trays	• pencils and small strips of paper (optional)
1·12			
1·13		• classroom objects • sheet of chart paper about a foot taller than a typical kindergartner • stick-on notes • crayons or markers	• four strips of paper (one long, one short, and two medium that are exactly the same length)
1·14	Teaching Aid Masters, pp. 92–97		
1·15	Teaching Masters, pp. 5A–5D		
1·16	Teaching Aid Masters, pp. 103–103B	• counters*	
Baseline Assessment	*Assessment Handbook,* pp. 40–41	• objects for counting, sorting, and comparing • plastic bags • number cards 0–5*	• shape cutouts or attribute blocks* • connecting cubes* • drawing of something symmetrical

* Indicates items in the Kindergarten manipulative kit.

Partner Match

Objective To introduce measurement comparisons through a partner activity.

CCSS

Mathematical Practices
SMP3, SMP6
Content Standards
K.MD.2
Bold SMP = Guiding Questions
at **everydaymathonline.com**
Bold = Focus of activity

☑ Whole Group
☐ Small Group
☑ Partners
☐ Center

Key Concepts and Skills
• Explore measurement by comparing lengths. [Measurement and Reference Frames Goal 1]
• Use measurement comparison words. [Measurement and Reference Frames Goal 1]

Terms to Use length, match, compare, bigger, smaller, longer, shorter, same length

Materials strips of heavy paper or cardstock

NOTE Partner Match provides a social activity with a mathematical purpose early in the school year!

A Core Activities

▶ Matching Strips

Cut enough matching-length pairs of paper strips so that each child will have one strip. All strips should be the same color, but each pair should be a noticeably different length from the other pairs (a difference of at least an inch). You may want to laminate the strips for future use.

Take a pair of matching strips and show children how to compare lengths by lining up the ends. Discuss how to tell if they are the same length. To support English language learners, display two strips that are the same length and label them **same length.** (Later, display two strips that differ in length and label the strips **shorter** and **longer.**)

Give each child a strip and have him or her find the person who has the strip that is exactly the same length. When they find their partner match, they sit next to that person. (If there are an odd number of children, you should take a strip and partner with a child.)

Encourage children to talk to their partners to find out something about each other. You may want to suggest some questions such as: *What is your favorite game? Do you have a brother or a sister?*

Redistribute the strips and repeat the game as time and interest allow. After a couple of rounds, have partners take their strips and find something in the room that is longer or shorter than their strips and report their findings to the group. Informally introduce and use measurement comparison words, such as *bigger/smaller* and *longer/shorter*. If time permits, have them find something that is about the same length as their strips.

▶ Establishing Daily Routines (Revisit Routines 1–8, pp. 8–35)

Be sure to spend enough time to establish your Ongoing Daily Routines.

B Teaching Options

EXTRA PRACTICE

▶ Comparing Hand and Foot Sizes

Repeat the Matching Strips activity described above. When children have found their partners, ask them to compare their hand sizes and foot sizes and report to the group.

MATHEMATICS IN THE BLOCK CENTER

▶ Comparing Block Structures

Encourage children to cut strips of cardstock or heavy paper to match the heights or lengths of their block structures. Save and date the strips so children can use them to compare the sizes of different structures.

Links to the Future

Comparison is an essential part of measurement, whether children compare strips of paper or compare objects to standardized measuring tools such as rulers. Children will measure with nonstandard units beginning with Activity 3-7 and will be introduced to standard measurement tools and units in Section 5. (See "Measurement," *Teacher's Reference Manual* Chapter 12.)

Ongoing Assessment:
Informing Instruction

Watch for children who are not able to find their partners by lining up the lengths of paper properly. Remind them to line up the ends of the strips.

ACTIVITY 1·2

Introduction to Pattern Blocks

 Objective To introduce pattern blocks.

CCSS

Mathematical Practices
SMP3, **SMP6,** SMP7
Content Standards
K.G.2, K.G.4, K.G.6
Bold SMP = Guiding Questions
at **everydaymathonline.com**
Bold = Focus of activity

Key Concepts and Skills
• Identify and describe shapes. [Geometry Goal 1]
• Explore pattern blocks. [Patterns, Functions, and Algebra Goal 1]

Terms to Use shape, triangle, square, rhombus, trapezoid, hexagon, pattern

Materials class set of pattern blocks

☑ Whole Group
☑ Small Group
☐ Partners
☑ Center

A **Core Activities**

▶ Exploring Pattern Blocks

Give each child a small handful of pattern blocks. (It is not important for all to have the same number or shapes.) Introduce each of the six pattern-block shapes: green triangle, orange square, blue rhombus, tan rhombus, red trapezoid, and yellow hexagon. Have children look at their blocks and find blocks that match the ones you hold up. Use the correct shape names during the activity. For example, as you show the triangle, say: *If you have a green triangle, hold it up.* Then hold up the trapezoid and ask: *Who has a red trapezoid?* Model as needed, and repeat until all shapes have been found.

NOTE Children like hearing, and occasionally even using, the pattern-block names, but do not expect them to remember all of the names all of the time.

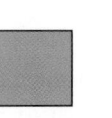  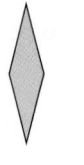 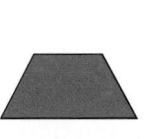 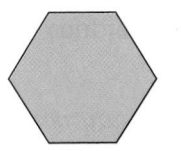

green triangle   orange square   blue rhombus   red trapezoid   tan rhombus   yellow hexagon

Have children choose one of their blocks. Help them focus on the shape by posing and discussing questions such as: *How many sides does it have? Can you find a shape with a different number of sides? Do all the shapes with four sides look the same?*

You might ask children whether they can put shapes together to make other shapes. Give children time to experiment and share their discoveries.

Invite children to think of other uses for the pattern blocks. Children might use the blocks to create pictures, designs, or patterns, or they might continue to combine them to make new shapes. Some children may sort the pattern blocks. Show the class where the blocks will be kept in the Math Center and invite children to use them for individual or group play. As the year progresses, children will use pattern blocks for various activities related to shapes, attributes, and patterns.

▶ **Establishing Daily Routines** (Revisit Routines 1–8, pp. 8–35)

Be sure to spend enough time to establish your Ongoing Daily Routines.

B **Teaching Options**

ELL SUPPORT

▶ **Discussing a Story about Patterns**

Children can look at and discuss *Changes, Changes* (Aladdin, 1987) a book by Pat Hutchins in which clowns use blocks to make different structures.

LITERACY CONNECTION

▶ **Reading Books about Patterns and Quilts**

Read *The Quilt* by Ann Jonas (Puffin Books, 1994) or *Selina and the Bear Paw Quilt* by Barbara Smucker (Stoddart Kids, 2002). Discuss the similarity between the quilt designs and children's pattern-block designs. Children might enjoy creating their own "quilts" by cutting shapes to arrange and glue on paper.

Multisensory Counts

CCSS **Mathematical Practices**
SMP2, SMP6
Content Standards
**K.CC.1, K.CC.4a, K.CC.4b,
K.CC.4c**
Bold SMP = Guiding Questions
at everydaymathonline.com
Bold = Focus of activity

Objective To reinforce counting principles through multisensory activities.

ACTIVITY **1·3**

✔ Whole Group
✔ Small Group
✔ Partners
☐ Center

Key Concepts and Skills

• Use understanding of one-to-one correspondence and cardinality to count objects, sounds, and taps. [Number and Numeration Goal 2]

• Connect the number sequence with number quantities and explore the "one more" relationship of successive numbers. [Number and Numeration Goal 2]

Terms to Use count, number, set

Materials Home Link Master (*Math Masters*, p. 2); coins, screws, or bottle lids; empty coffee can

---

 **A** **Core Activities**

▶ Counting by Touch and Sound

Show a few objects and ask children to tell how many there are. Confirm by lining up the objects and pointing to each as children count aloud. Reinforce that the last number tells how many are in the set by gathering the set together and repeating the last (cardinal) number at the end of the count. Rearrange the objects and ask how many there are. Count the set again to confirm that the total is the same. Ask: *How many objects will there be if I add one more to the set? How do you know?* Add one object and count the set together again. Discuss how the next number refers to a quantity that is one larger.

Focus on the sense of touch. Have children work with a partner. One child taps slowly with one finger on his or her partner's back. The partner counts and reports the number of taps. Encourage children to increase the number of taps by one tap each turn.

Next, focus on listening. One at a time, drop small objects into an empty coffee can. Have children shut their eyes and count silently as they hear each object drop. Ask several children to report the number of sounds they heard.

 **Ongoing Assessment:**
Informing Instruction

Watch for children who do not use one-to-one correspondence to match a single count with a sound or a tap or who do not comprehend that the last number name they say tells the number of objects counted. Some may have an easier time using one sense than another for counting activities.

Home Link 1·3 (*Math Masters*, p. 2)

Families count together and become acquainted with Home Links.

▶ Establishing Daily Routines (Revisit Routines 1–8, pp. 8–35)

Be sure to spend enough time to establish your Ongoing Daily Routines.

B Teaching Options

EXTRA PRACTICE

▶ Playing Simon Says

Have children perform various actions a specific number of times. For example, *Simon says ... Jump 4 times; Turn around 3 times; Tap your head 5 times.*

EXTRA PRACTICE

▶ Making a "Feely Box" or "Feely Bag"

Put a small number of objects into a box. Have a child reach in and count the objects without looking. Then have the child pull out the objects and count to check the number. Place the Feely Box in the Math Center and encourage children to take turns counting and checking with a partner. Keep the game fresh by allowing children to find different objects to place in the Feely Box. Encourage them to place larger numbers of objects in the box as they become more proficient with counting.

MUSIC CONNECTION

▶ Singing "One More" Songs

Sing "one more" songs, such as "One Elephant Went Out to Play." Use the songs to reinforce the "one more" pattern of successive numbers. Children can draw pictures to illustrate each verse.

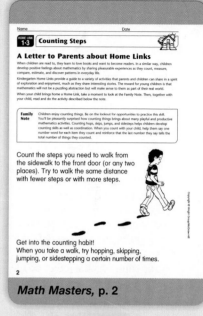

Math Masters, p. 2

Decorate a special box for activities throughout the year. It should have an opening large enough for children to reach in, but the objects inside should not be visible.

Countdown to Zero

 Objective To introduce the concept of zero, the word *zero*, and the numeral "0."

CCSS

Mathematical Practices
SMP2, SMP4

Bold SMP = Guiding Questions at everydaymathonline.com

Bold = Focus of activity

Key Concepts and Skills
- Count backward by ones. [Number and Numeration Goal 1]
- Recognize and understand zero as a number for "none." [Number and Numeration Goal 2]
- Represent numbers with concrete objects. [Number and Numeration Goal 3]

Terms to Use none, zero

Materials plastic animals; small food items or counters

☑ Whole Group
☑ Small Group
☐ Partners
☐ Center

 **Adjusting the Activity** ELL

You might want to have five children act out the story as you sing it. Give each "actor" a numeral card (1–5) to hold so they can "fall off" the bed in the correct order (beginning with 5). At the end of the song, hold up the 0 card.

AUDITORY ♦ KINESTHETIC ♦ TACTILE ♦ VISUAL

A Core Activities

▶ Singing and Eating Down to Zero

To introduce the concept of zero, use plastic animals and fingers to act out the song "Five Little Monkeys." (See *Resources for the Kindergarten Classroom* for words to the song.) You can substitute the name of any animal for monkeys. As children sing, have them hold up their fingers to show the number of monkeys that are left on the bed. At the end of each verse, remove one animal and have children put down one finger. At the end of the song, ask children how many animals are left on the bed. Ask them if they know the number for "none." Write the numeral "0" on the board.

Do an eat-and-countdown exercise ending with zero. Give each child the same number of small food items, such as 5 raisins or 6 pieces of popcorn. Tell children to eat one item, then ask: *How many are left?* (To support English language learners, discuss the meaning of *left* in this mathematical context.) After children have counted their remaining items,

NOTE If any children in your classroom have food allergies, you may want to substitute something nonedible such as counters, chips, or buttons for children to use during an alternative countdown exercise.

write the number on the board. Continue until all the items are gone. After the activity, leave the numeral 0 and the word *zero* on the board where they can remain in view. Find occasions over several days to reinforce the concept and symbols for zero as a number for "none." Children will enjoy a bit of humor. For example, ask: *How many live dinosaurs (or pink elephants) are in the room today? How many marbles are in an empty jar?*

▶ Establishing Daily Routines (Revisit Routines 1–8, pp. 8–35)

Be sure to spend enough time to establish your Ongoing Daily Routines. If you haven't started the Survey Routine yet, you might begin by posing questions about school activities such as: *Do you like outside time at school? Do you like story time?*

B Teaching Options

READINESS

▶ Counting Down with Snacks

As they eat, have children identify how many food items or bites they have left, and then count backward until the food is gone.

ENRICHMENT

▶ Counting Down from Higher Numbers

Children can count backward by ones from increasingly higher numbers. Point to starting numbers on the number line. Children can pretend to be a rocket and blast off when they get to 0. Count down when transitioning between activities or waiting in line.

LITERACY CONNECTION

▶ Reading a Counting Story

Read and sing *Five Little Monkeys Jumping on the Bed* by Eileen Christelow (Clarion Books, 1989). You might have children collaborate to illustrate a class book version of the song with the correct number of monkeys on each page.

> **NOTE** Readiness activities help children gain prerequisite skills so that they can be successful in the activity.

Getting to Know Numbers (1–9)

CCSS

Mathematical Practices
SMP1, SMP2, SMP4, SMP6, SMP7

Content Standards
K.CC.3, K.CC.4a, K.CC.4b, K.CC.4c, K.CC.5, K.OA.3

Bold SMP = Guiding Questions at everydaymathonline.com

Bold = Focus of activity

 Objective To introduce the numbers 1–9 in a variety of activities and to reinforce early counting and numeration skills and principles.

☑ Whole Group
☑ Small Group
☐ Partners
☑ Center

Key Concepts and Skills

- Use understanding of one-to-one correspondence and cardinality to count and create sets of objects. [Number and Numeration Goal 2]

- Recognize that the number of objects in a set is the same regardless of the arrangement or type of object. [Number and Numeration Goal 2]

- Represent numbers in various ways. [Number and Numeration Goal 3]

- Associate number names, quantities, and written numerals. [Number and Numeration Goal 3]

Terms to Use number, count, set

Materials Home Link Master (*Math Masters,* p. 3); various manipulatives such as craft sticks, connecting cubes or links, inch cubes, and beads; markers; chart paper or posterboard; clear, resealable plastic bags

Planning Tip Repeat this activity, focusing on one number per day, beginning with the number 1. You may wish to spend more than one day on some numbers.

 **A** **Core Activities**

▶ Exploring Featured Numbers

You may wish to read *Emily's First 100 Days of School* by Rosemary Wells (Hyperion, 2005) or a similar book to initiate this activity. Tell children that the class is going to explore a different number from 1 to 9 each day. Have the class locate the featured number on your Growing Number Line. Explain that the class will explore the featured number in many different ways during the day—using objects, pictures, games, songs, and other activities. Conduct all of the following activities about each day's featured number. The activities can be done in any order and may be broken up throughout the day.

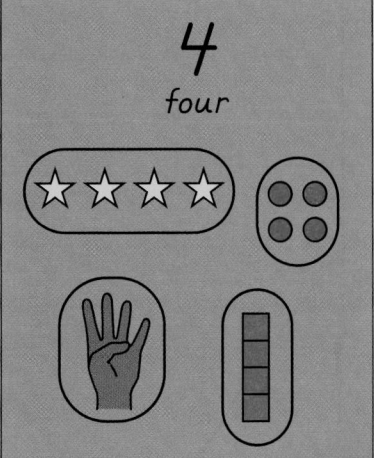

Number Poster

Number Stations Set up several stations where children will count and arrange manipulatives to represent the featured number. Each station should include one type of manipulative. (Craft sticks, inch cubes, connecting cubes and links, and beads are particularly good for number stations.) Children may choose a station or rotate among them. Direct children to use the materials at the stations to show the featured number in a variety of ways. Encourage them to describe their designs and combinations, and to check one another's arrangements for the correct number. After children have had time to generate a variety of representations of the number, bring them together to discuss the representations. You might begin discussion by asking, *How can these all be* 4 (or whatever your featured number is)? *They look so different!* Be sure to highlight the important idea that numbers can be represented with different objects and in different ways. For example, 4 cubes stacked vertically is the same amount as 4 cubes laying side by side, and both of these are the same amount as 4 craft sticks or 4 beads. You may wish to photograph the stations before cleaning them up. These photographs can be added to the class Number Poster (see below) or compiled into a class number book.

Number Collections Give pairs or small groups of children a clear, resealable plastic bag. Label (or have the children label) the bag with the featured number. Invite children to choose a type of object (coins, cubes, counters, raisins, buttons, and so on) and put the featured number of objects in their bags. You can either set out an assortment of possible objects or allow children to choose more freely from around the classroom. Check children's counting and provide assistance as needed. Save the bags for use in a comparison activity in 1-15 and a ten-frame activity in 1-16.

Number Poster Begin a poster about the featured number by writing the number on chart paper or posterboard. Then draw several groups of objects in different arrangements to match the featured number on the poster. Invite children to add their own representations to the poster. Relate each number poster to the poster for the previous number and emphasize that each successive number name refers to a quantity that is one larger. To model this concept, you may wish to line up and compare the objects in the number collection bags for each number. Compile the number posters into a class *Big Book of Numbers* or display them in the Math Center.

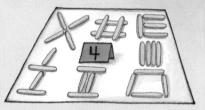

A craft-stick station for the number four

An inch-cube station for the number four

NOTE By making numbers in a variety of ways using many different materials, children discover and gradually internalize the unique patterns and combinations each number forms (for example, even numbers can always be arranged in pairs). They also develop their understanding that numbers can be represented in different ways.

In addition to the previous activities, find various other ways to focus on the featured number during the day. Work in as many of the following activities (and others that you or the children devise) as your schedule allows. Keep them brief and playful.

▷ Play movement games such as Mother, May I? or Simon Says. Have children jump, clap, or turn around as many times as the featured number. (You might do this during outside time.)

▷ Look for the featured number around the classroom or school (on clocks, room numbers, notes from home or the office, and so on).

▷ Use the number in counting songs. For example, change "Five Little Monkeys" to "Three Little Monkeys" on "3 Day."

▷ Have children sit and/or line up in groups of the featured number.

▷ At snack time, eat the featured number of snacks (for example 3 crackers or 5 grapes).

▷ Read or tell the featured number of stories, nursery rhymes, or jokes.

▷ Identify and list children who have the featured number of letters in their names, people in their families, siblings, pets, and so on.

Home Link 1·5 (Math Masters, p. 3)
Children look for numbers at home.

▶ Establishing Daily Routines (Revisit Routines 1–8, pp. 8–35)

Be sure to spend enough time to establish your Ongoing Daily Routines. Also remember to use *Minute Math* during spare moments in the day.

✓ Ongoing Assessment:
Informing Instruction

Watch for children who cannot count or create a set of objects or make representations of the featured number. Spend extra time on Number Stations for these children. Children who are still learning to identify numerals 1–9 may benefit from *Match Up* (see page 55B) and from kinesthetic and tactile experiences to associate number names and symbols.

Name   Date

HOME LINK 1·5   **Numbers All Around**

Family Note   In this activity, children become more aware of numerals all around them, as well as the varied uses of numbers. Look around and encourage your child to notice numbers in your home. Talk with them about what the numbers represent and how they are used.

Look for numbers around your house.

Where did you find the most? In your bedroom? In the kitchen?

Where else did you find numbers?

Draw a picture of some of the things with numbers that you found.

You can use the back of this page or a separate sheet of paper if you need more room.

3

Math Masters, p. 3

Examples of "taking apart" 4

ENRICHMENT

▶ Taking Apart Featured Numbers

Some children may enjoy finding and representing different ways to "take apart" the featured number. They might begin by counting out the featured number of connecting cubes (preferably of the same color) and creating a stack. Then, invite them to separate the stack into two (or more) smaller parts. Ask whether there are still the same numbers of cubes all together. Encourage children to record the combinations they discover with pictures and/or numbers. These may be added to the class Number Poster for each featured number.

EXTRA PRACTICE

▶ Playing *Match Up* (Math Masters, pp. 124A–124D)

Place the numeral cards face down in one row and the dot cards face down in another row. Have children turn over one card in each row. If the number of dots matches the numeral, the child keeps the card. If the cards do not match, they are turned facedown again. Players take turns until all the matching pairs are found.

Invite children to use the blank cards on *Math Masters,* page 124D to create new cards with different representations of the numerals. Vary the game either by having children look for matches between the numerals and the alternate representations they made or between their alternate representations and the dot cards.

LITERACY CONNECTION

▶ Reading Counting Books

Use counting books to reinforce the concept that each successive number name refers to a quantity that is one larger. See *Resources for the Kindergarten Classroom* for suggestions.

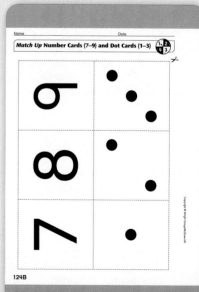

Math Masters, p. 124B

Introduction to Sorting

Objective To introduce attributes and sorting.

CCSS Mathematical Practices
SMP2, **SMP7**

Content Standards
K.CC.3, K.CC.4a, K.CC.4b, K.CC.4c, K.CC.5, K.CC.6, K.OA.3, K.MD.1, **K.MD.3**

☑ Whole Group ☐ Partners
☐ Small Group ☑ Center

Key Concepts and Skills

• Count objects in each sorted category. [Number and Numeration Goal 2]

• Compare the number of objects in each category. [Number and Numeration Goal 6]

• Find ways to sort objects using a variety of attributes. [Patterns, Functions, and Algebra Goal 1]

• Identify attributes. [Patterns, Functions, and Algebra Goal 1]

Terms to Use sort

Materials a collection of small objects with a common characteristic and several different attributes, such as buttons, beads, pasta shapes, play food, magnetic letters and numbers, or screws, nuts and bolts; sorting containers such as trays, muffin tins, egg cartons, or compartmentalized boxes

Planning Tip Ask families to send in buttons. It is a good home/ school connection that can lead to additional math activities. You might keep a running tally of the number of buttons brought in or see how long a line of buttons can grow. You will find many uses for a button collection during the year.

A Core Activities

▶ Sorting by Attributes

Have children sit in a circle so they can see each other. Introduce the idea of attributes by asking a child to name someone who has something (an attribute) the same as he or she has. For example, "Eric has black hair like I have." Have the child who was named find something that is the same as another child. Continue for several examples.

Conduct a group sorting exercise, using the children as subjects. For example, ask all children with shoelaces to stand together. Have children with slip-on shoes stand in a second group, and children with all other types of shoes stand in a third group. Together, count the number of children in each group. Line up the children in each group and have the lines stand side by side to compare the number of children in each group. Explain that you have sorted children according to their types of shoes. Ask for volunteers to explain what *sort* means. Repeat the exercise using a different attribute.

🔗 Links to the Future

This sorting activity is an early exposure to recognizing, understanding, and consistently applying rules. Being comfortable with rules will make it easier for children to grasp numeric sequences and functions, which are Grade 1 Goals. (See "Patterns, Sequences, Functions, and Algebra," *Teacher's Reference Manual* Chapter 15.)

Show the objects and the sorting containers that you collected. Explain that there are some things that are the same and some things that are different about these objects. Place them in the Math Center for children to explore and sort. Encourage children to find new ways to sort the materials. Keep track of the different ways they have sorted (color, size, material, shape, and so on), and allow children to share sorting schemes. Over the year, add new collections for sorting.

▶ Getting to Know Numbers—Number Two (Revisit Activity 1•5, p. 54)

Focus on the number 2 as the featured number for Getting to Know Numbers activities.

B Teaching Options

READINESS

▶ Singing about Attributes

Sing and act out the following rhyme (to the tune of "Mary Wore a Red Dress"). Repeat several times, varying the attribute. Later in the year, use two attributes (long hair and long pants) or more qualified descriptions (yellow on shirt).

Children with red on, stand up, stand up, stand up.
Children with red stand up, clap hands 3 times, and sit back down.

SCIENCE CONNECTION

▶ Sorting Nature Collections

Collections such as shells, rocks, leaves, or seeds (or even apples, if your class studies them) are excellent for sorting; sorting helps children observe these items more carefully.

LITERACY CONNECTION

▶ Reading about Attributes

Read *The Button Box* by Margarette S. Reid (Dutton, 1990). Invite children to choose a favorite button and describe several of its attributes, including color, shape, and size.

Buttons with 0 Holes

Buttons with 2 Holes

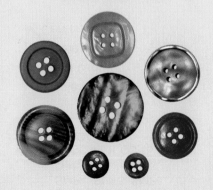

Buttons with 4 Holes

ACTIVITY 1·7

Sand and Water Play

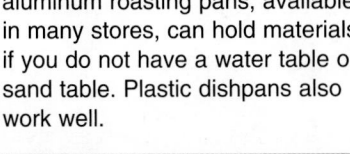

CCSS Mathematical Practices
SMP1, SMP2, **SMP3,** SMP4, SMP5, SMP6
Content Standards
K.CC.3, K.CC.4a, K.CC.4b, K.CC.4c, K.OA.3

Objective To introduce volume through sand and water play.

☐ Whole Group
☐ Small Group
☐ Partners
☑ Center

Key Concepts and Skills
- Experiment with and compare volumes and develop awareness of relative size.
  [Measurement and Reference Frames Goal 1]

Terms to Use volume, more, less, same

Materials Home Link Master (*Math Masters*, p. 4); water, sand, or dry beans; water table, sand table, or tubs to hold materials; containers of various sizes and shapes including low and wide; tall and thin

Planning Tip Disposable aluminum roasting pans, available in many stores, can hold materials if you do not have a water table or sand table. Plastic dishpans also work well.

A Core Activities

▶ Experimenting with Volume

Allow children to experiment with volume by pouring water, sand, or dry beans from one container to another. This is a natural way for children to begin making comparisons. Vary the materials and containers. After children have had ample time to explore, pose questions about volume, such as: *Which container holds more? Why do you think so? How can you find out which holds more? Can any of the containers fit inside another one?* Prompt children to explain their ideas. Listening to their responses can help you find ways to expand their thinking.

After children have had time to explore on their own, invite them to compare the volume of pairs of containers. Provide three or four pairs of containers that are not too close in capacity. Label the containers set 1A, 1B and set 2A, 2B, for example. Use containers that vary enough in shape to make it difficult to judge visually which holds more.

 **Links to the Future**

This activity is an early exposure to understanding the capacity of containers, such as measuring cups, and the idea that all 3-dimensional objects have volume. Describing and using strategies to find volume is a Grade 4 Goal. (See "Measurement," *Teacher's Reference Manual* Chapter 12.)

Show the pairs of different-size containers to children and introduce the term **volume.** Ask: *Which container holds more material or has the larger volume? How could we find out?* Encourage children to pour the contents from one container into the other to see which holds more. Also provide two containers that hold the same amount of material but have different shapes.

After the pan balance has been introduced in Activity 3-4, use it with beans and a variety of containers to provide new directions for exploration.

 Home Link 1·7 (*Math Masters*, p. 4)
Children experiment with volume at home.

▶ **Getting to Know Numbers—Number Three** (Revisit Activity 1·5, p. 54)

Focus on the number 3 as the featured number for Getting to Know Numbers activities.

B **Teaching Options**

(ENRICHMENT)

▶ **Estimating Container Capacity** (*Center Activity Cards*, 1)

Put out several 1-cup measuring cups. Show children how to determine the number of cups a container holds. Have children estimate first, then check their estimates by pouring cupfuls of material into their containers. Invite children to use this technique with several containers to figure out which ones hold the most and the least and whether any hold the same amount. Children may wish to record their findings.

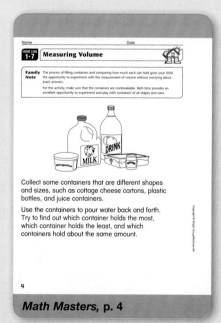

Math Masters, p. 4

Birthday Graphs

◎ **Objective** To introduce bar graphs using age and birthday information.

CCSS Mathematical Practices
SMP2, SMP3, **SMP4,** SMP6
Content Standards
K.CC.3, K.CC.4a, K.CC.4b,
K.CC.4c, **K.CC.5,** K.CC.6, K.OA.3,
K.MD.3

Key Concepts and Skills
• Construct a bar graph and a moveable graph. [Data and Chance Goal 1]
• Make comparisons and answer simple questions based on data from the graphs. [Data and Chance Goal 2]

Terms to Use graph, data, total, some, none, all, more, most

Materials index cards cut into 3-inch squares; posterboard; material to attach cards to posterboard; markers

☑ Whole Group
☐ Small Group
☐ Partners
☐ Center

Planning Tip The two graphs can be created on separate days or at the same time. You might want to have children make the cards during one session and then construct the graphs at a later time.

A **Core Activities**

▶ Graphing Birthdays and Ages

Construct two class graphs that children can refer to throughout the year.

Birthday Months Graph Have each child create a card to place on the graph to represent his or her birthday. The card might include the child's picture, a cake with his or her initials on it, or a collection of candles equal in number to the child's age. (Children can add a candle to their cards on their birthdays.) As a class, sort the birthday cards by month, and attach them to the graph. Add your birthday, too!

Discuss the information the graph presents by asking: *What did we find out?* Follow up with: *Which month has the most birthdays? The fewest? Do any months have the same number of birthdays? Do all of the children have birthdays in January? Do some of them? Do you notice that none of the children in our class were born in April?* As a class, choose a name for the graph. Children can vote for their favorite idea, and the votes can be recorded with tallies.

Birthday Bar Graph

Age Change Graph Have children draw a self-portrait on an index card. Then make a graph by having children place their pictures on the row that corresponds to their ages. On their birthdays, children move their pictures to the appropriate row (from the 5-year-old row to the 6-year-old row, for example). Discuss the changing totals in each row as children's ages change over the year.

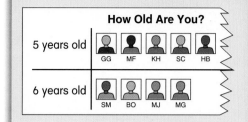

▶ Getting to Know Numbers—Number Four (Revisit Activity 1•5, p. 54)

Focus on the number 4 as the featured number for your Getting to Know Numbers activities. Also remember to use *Minute Math* during spare moments in the day.

B Teaching Options

SCIENCE CONNECTION

▶ Representing the Earth's Revolution

To represent the rotation of the Earth around the sun (a full revolution takes one year), children walk around a candle or picture of the sun one time for each year of their ages. Individual children can do this on their birthday after they move their card on the Age Change Graph.

LITERACY CONNECTION

▶ Reading Birthday Stories

Read a birthday story such as *Flower Garden* by Eve Bunting (Harcourt, 1994), *The Secret Birthday Message* by Eric Carle (HarperCollins, 1981), or *Moira's Birthday* by Robert Munsch (Annick Press, 1987).

> **NOTE** Because the "bars" on these graphs are made with discrete pictures, they can be called picture graphs or pictographs. It is important for children to see and work with both horizontal and vertical "bars." (See "Data and Chance," *Teacher's Reference Manual* Chapter 10.)

Sound and Motion Patterns

CCSS Mathematical Practices
SMP7

Content Standards
K.CC.3, K.CC.4a, K.CC.4b, K.CC.4c, K.OA.3

ACTIVITY 1·9

◎ **Objective** To introduce patterns through multisensory, experiential activities.

☑ Whole Group
☑ Small Group
☐ Partners
☐ Center

Key Concepts and Skills
• Create and extend patterns with sounds and motions. [Patterns, Functions, and Algebra Goal 1]

Terms to Use pattern, repeat

Materials none

NOTE In this activity, children experience patterns through an auditory and kinesthetic approach. Activity 1-10, p. 64, provides a more formal introduction to patterns using visual patterning with colors as the focus.

A Core Activities

▶ Discovering Patterns

Children enjoy discovering patterns through sound and movement. Using these modalities helps all children—especially auditory and kinesthetic learners—to better understand the concept of patterning. Begin by having children replicate and extend sounds in a pattern. *For example:*

▷ Hum, clap; hum, clap; ...

▷ Clap, clap, stomp, stomp; clap, clap, stomp, stomp; ...

▷ Boom, boom, chick; Boom, boom, chick; ...

▷ Ta, tee, tee; ta, tee, tee; ta, ...

Next, use body movements in a pattern. Demonstrate a pattern for children and say the words of the movement while doing the activity. See examples on the next page.

▷ Step, step, jump, jump; step, step, ...

▷ Bend over, stand up; bend over, stand up; ...

▷ Step, jump, jump; step, jump, jump; step, jump, jump; ...

▷ Stand, squat, kneel; stand, squat, ...

Then have children create patterns and invite others to join in and continue the pattern.

Continue to do sound and movement patterns often, increasing the complexity of the patterns as the year progresses. These patterning activities entice children to watch and listen, so they can help gather the class or get children's attention during transitions. They can also be incorporated into *Minute Math* activities.

▶ Getting to Know Numbers—Number Five (Revisit Activity 1•5, p. 54)

Focus on the number 5 as the featured number for Getting to Know Numbers activities.

B Teaching Options

MUSIC CONNECTION

▶ Singing a Patterned Song

Sing "B-I-N-G-O." Have the class talk about the patterns they hear, including the clapping pattern.

LITERACY CONNECTION

▶ Reading Books with Patterns

Read *Beep Beep, Vroom Vroom!* by Stuart J. Murphy (HarperCollins, 2000) or one of the many books with patterned language by Eric Carle. Invite children to chime in during repeated parts and to describe the patterns they notice in the books.

Links to the Future

Children's early experiences with repeating sound, movement, and visual patterns lay the foundation for later work with numeric patterns. At first children show they grasp patterns by extending them; later they can also describe the rules by which patterns are produced. Recognizing and describing patterns prepares children for algebra because algebraic functions are rules for producing certain patterns. (See "Patterns, Sequences, Functions, and Algebra," *Teacher's Reference Manual* Chapter 15.)

Patterns with Color

CCSS Mathematical Practices
SMP3, SMP7
Content Standards
K.CC.3, K.CC.4a, K.CC.4b,
K.CC.4c, K.OA.3

◎ **Objective** To introduce simple color patterns.

☑ Whole Group
☑ Small Group
☑ Partners
☑ Center

Key Concepts and Skills
- Create and extend color patterns. [Patterns, Functions, and Algebra Goal 1]
- Describe patterns. [Patterns, Functions, and Algebra Goal 1]

Terms to Use pattern, repeat

Materials one set of objects of different colors (cubes, crayons, beads, counters, and so on)

A Core Activities

⬤⬤⬤⬤⬤⬤

⬤⬤⬤⬤⬤⬤

Color Patterns

▶ Creating and Extending Patterns

Repeat a few of the sound and movement patterns that the class created in Activity 1-9, page 62. Ask children if they think patterns can be made with colors. Show a set of objects of different colors. Have a volunteer use the colored objects to start a pattern. Invite the other children to continue the pattern. *For example:*

▷ red, green; red, green; red, ...

▷ yellow, yellow, blue; yellow, yellow, blue; ...

▷ white, orange, orange; white, orange, ...

After they have made several examples of color patterns, ask: *What are we making? What do you notice?* Introduce the term **pattern** and ask for children's ideas about what a pattern is. Help children realize that a pattern repeats and that they can tell what comes next once they identify a pattern. Change a few colors to disrupt a pattern.

Ask: *What if we change some of the colors? Is it still a pattern? Can you tell what should come next?*

Provide materials for partners to take turns creating and extending color patterns. One child creates a pattern with six to eight objects and the other describes and continues the pattern. Place the materials in a center and invite children to continue exploring patterns on their own or with partners.

▶ Getting to Know Numbers—Number Six (Revisit Activity 1•5, p. 54)

Focus on the number 6 as the featured number for Getting to Know Numbers activities.

(Revisit Activity 1•5, p. 54)

B Teaching Options

SCIENCE CONNECTION

▶ Creating Patterns with Natural Objects (Center Activity Cards, 2)

Encourage children to use natural objects such as leaves, shells, rocks, and seeds to create patterns.

ART CONNECTION

▶ Exploring Patterns through Art Projects

Watch for and point out patterns in children's artwork. You can encourage patterning with certain materials and projects, such as making paper chains using different colored strips of paper.

Adjusting the Activity

Allow children to use additional objects to make more complicated patterns.

AUDITORY ◆ KINESTHETIC ◆ TACTILE ◆ VISUAL

Ongoing Assessment:
Informing Instruction

Watch for children who cannot create and extend a pattern. Listen to children's explanations to determine who can identify a pattern and describe it as something that repeats. For children who do not yet understand the concept of patterning, continue to provide exposure through a variety of modes: sound, movement, or manipulation of materials. Begin with simple ABAB patterns.

ACTIVITY 1·11

Coin Comparisons

Objective To provide practice with sorting and to lay groundwork for coin recognition.

CCSS Mathematical Practices
SMP2, **SMP3,** SMP6, SMP7
Content Standards
K.CC.3, K.CC.4a, K.CC.4b,
K.CC.4c, K.CC.6, K.OA.3, **K.MD.3**

☐ Whole Group
☐ Small Group
☐ Partners
☑ Center

Planning Tip You can use muffin tins or egg cartons as banks for sorting. Plan to collect plenty of coins prior to the activity. It is preferable to use real money. However, you may also use play money or a combination of the two.

Key Concepts and Skills

• Count the number of coins in each category. [Number and Numeration Goal 2]

• Compare the number of coins in each category. [Number and Numeration Goal 6]

• Notice coin features and differences among coins. [Measurement and Reference Frames Goal 2]

• Sort coins according to various attributes. [Patterns, Functions, and Algebra Goal 1]

Terms to Use sort, heads, tails, coins

Materials Home Link Master (*Math Masters*, p. 5); pennies, nickels, dimes, and quarters; muffin tins, egg cartons, or sorting trays; pencils and small strips of paper (optional)

 A **Core Activities**

▶ Sorting Coins into "Banks"

Place the sorting banks and coins in the Math Center. Remind children of the sorting activity they did previously (Activity 1-6, page 56), and invite them to sort coins by size, color, markings (heads/tails), or other characteristics. Have them place their groups into the compartments of their banks.

 **Links to the Future**

Do not expect children to know coin values at this time. Children will begin to learn coin values in Section 6. Identifying and comparing coin values is a Grade 1 Goal.

Encourage children to describe their groupings. Some children may want to label their groups using small strips of paper. For example, they might write "B" for big, "M" for medium, and "S" for small or they may draw pictures of smooth and rough edges. After children complete their sorting, ask them to count and compare the number of coins in each group. You may wish to have children count the same group of coins in different arrangements to reinforce that the number doesn't change if the coins are rearranged or counted in a different order.

 Home Link 1·11 (*Math Masters*, p. 5)
Children practice sorting using grocery items.

▶ Getting to Know Numbers—Number Seven (Revisit Activity 1·5, p. 54)

Focus on the number 7 as the featured number for Getting to Know Numbers activities. Also, remember to use *Minute Math* during spare moments in the day.

B Teaching Options

EXTRA PRACTICE

▶ Using Coins in a Feely Box or Feely Bag (*Center Activity Cards*, 3)

Put out some coins and a Feely Box in the Math Center. Working with a partner, one child puts a few coins (not more than 5 or 6) in the box, and the other child reaches in and counts the objects without looking. Children can match the number counted with a number card or record the number. After the count, both children can compare the size, color, markings, and feel of the various coins using descriptive words. The game can also focus on coin attributes: one partner tells the other to pull out a small coin or a coin with rough edges.

MATHEMATICS IN THE DRAMATIC PLAY CENTER

▶ Playing with Money and Banks

Place the money and banks in your Dramatic Play or Housekeeping Centers. Watch how quickly children incorporate them into their play.

NOTE You may wish to have children line up two sets of coins side by side and compare the number of coins in the sets using the terms *more than, less than,* or *same* (or *equal*). Ask children to describe any other strategies they have for comparing the number of coins in each group.

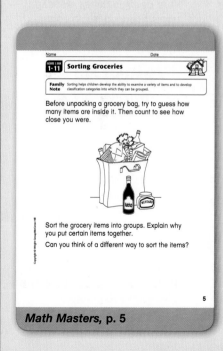

Math Masters, p. 5

ACTIVITY 1·12

Give the Next Number Game

CCSS Mathematical Practices
SMP2, **SMP6**
Content Standards
**K.CC.1, K.CC.2, K.CC.3, K.CC.4a,
K.CC.4b, K.CC.4c,** K.OA.3

Objective To develop number sense and counting skills through an oral counting game.

☑ Whole Group
☐ Small Group
☐ Partners
☐ Center

Key Concepts and Skills
• Count numbers and ordinal numbers in sequence. [Number and Numeration Goal 1]
• Represent numbers with claps or taps. [Number and Numeration Goal 2]

Terms to Use first, second, third, . . .

Materials none

A Core Activities

▶ Playing *Give the Next Number*

Warm up for the game by quickly counting from 0 to 10 as a class. Then point to children one at a time, prompting each to say the next number in sequence. For example, prompt the first child to say *one,* the next child to say *two,* and so on. If children miss a number or aren't keeping track, quickly say the number for them, have them repeat it, then continue with the next child. When you reach 10, start over so everyone has a turn. You may choose to invite a child to be the pointer. (Some teachers like to use a finger puppet to prompt children during the count.)

After children get the hang of giving the next number, turn the activity into a game. Have children form a circle. Walk around the circle slowly, counting the children (or their feet to generate larger numbers) using a soft voice. Children keep track by counting along, also using soft voices. Every so often, tap a child to stand up and say the next number clearly. Also have the standing child clap or tap the number.

Later in the year, encourage children to count silently or "in their heads" as they play the game.

Adjusting the Activity

This game can be played often and made more challenging as children's oral counting skills advance. When children are ready, vary the game by:

▷ Extending the count to higher numbers

▷ Changing the starting number

▷ Counting backward from different numbers

▷ Skip counting by 2s, 5s, or 10s

To incorporate numeral recognition, hold up a number card to prompt counting rather than saying the number. For children who need it, demonstrate how to use the number line as a reference for figuring out the next number.

AUDITORY ◆ KINESTHETIC ◆ TACTILE ◆ VISUAL

To provide practice identifying and sequencing ordinal numbers, have children take turns saying ordinal numbers in sequence. For example, prompt the first child to say *first,* the next child to say *second,* and so on. You can start over once you reach 10 or continue on through the teens and beyond, depending on children's counting skills. You can also play *Give the Next Number* using ordinal numbers. Children keep track of the ordinal numbers you say softly as you count them and then stand up and say the next ordinal number when you tap them.

▶ Getting to Know Numbers—Number Eight (Revisit Activity 1◆5, p. 54)

Focus on the number 8 as the featured number for Getting to Know Numbers activities.

Ⓑ Teaching Options

ENRICHMENT

▶ Counting On Using Number Cards (*Math Masters,* pp. 92–102)

Vary the main activity and reinforce numeral recognition by giving individual children a number card or sheet of paper with a number written on it. (You can use *Math Masters,* pages 92–102 to make number cards. Use the numbers in the range that you are practicing.) Have the child with the next number hold up his or her card and say the number out loud. You might also have children work together to line up in order of the numbers on their cards.

TECHNOLOGY

▶ Counting in Computer Games

Many computer games for young children provide practice with counting and number sequencing. For example, the dot-to-dot segments in *Piggy in Numberland* (Learning in Motion, 1998) and *Piggy's Birthday Present* (Learning in Motion, 1999) reinforce these skills. See *Resources for the Kindergarten Classroom* for other suggestions.

Ongoing Assessment:
Informing Instruction

Monitor children's accuracy and automaticity as they count. Do they say the next number correctly? How much think time do they require? Are they able to listen and follow along as the group counts?

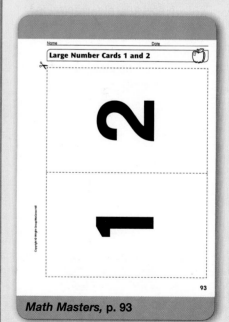

Math Masters, p. 93

Body Height Comparisons

CCSS Mathematical Practices
SMP1, SMP2, **SMP4**, SMP6
Content Standards
K.CC.3, K.CC.4a, K.CC.4b,
K.CC.4c, K.OA.3, **K.MD.1, K.MD.2**

ACTIVITY 1·13

◎ **Objective** To provide practice with comparing lengths.

☑ Whole Group
☐ Small Group
☐ Partners
☐ Center

Key Concepts and Skills

- Make a pictorial representation of class data. [Data and Chance Goal 1]
- Compare heights of objects. [Measurement and Reference Frames Goal 1]

Terms to Use longer, shorter, same length, taller, about the same

Materials classroom objects; sheet of chart paper about a foot taller than a typical kindergartner; stick-on notes; crayons or markers; four strips of paper (one long, one short, and two medium that are exactly the same length)

Planning Tip Draw a child-sized stick figure on the left side of the chart paper. Leave about a foot of blank space at the top and leave room for stick-on notes (two per child) on the right side of the figure.

A Core Activities

▶ Comparing Body Heights to Objects

Show children one of the medium-sized strips of paper, and remind them of the activity in which they looked for a partner who had the same length strip as they had (Activity 1-1, page 46). Show children the other strips you prepared: the same length strip, the shorter strip, and the longer strip. Review the terms **longer, shorter,** and the **same length** by holding up the medium strip and having the class find and describe the strips that are the same length, longer, and shorter.

Ask children to find something in the classroom that is taller than they are and to find something that is shorter. Remind children that they must line up the ends of the things they are measuring. (In this case, the object should be lined up next to children's feet at floor level.)

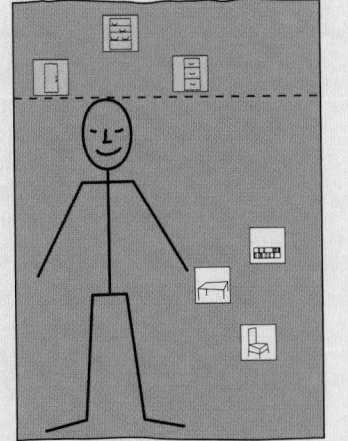

Have children draw the found objects on stick-on notes (one note for the taller object and one for the shorter object). Children should place their notes on the large sheet of paper alongside the stick figure, with the pictures of the taller objects positioned above the stick figure's head and the pictures of the shorter objects positioned below its head. As children place their stick-on notes, they report their findings to the class.

As a group, decide on a title for the data representation, and choose where to display it. Add a few sentences of explanation (in children's words) to the display.

▶ **Getting to Know Numbers—Number Nine** (Revisit Activity 1•5, p. 54)

Focus on the number 9 as the featured number for Getting to Know Numbers activities.

Teaching Options

ELL SUPPORT

▶ **Discussing the Terms *Long* and *Short***

Talk with children about things that can be described as *long* and *short*. Start the discussion by showing children three pieces of string that vary in length and ask: *Which piece of string is* short? *Which piece is* long? *What other objects in the classroom have a* short *length? What other objects in the classroom have a* long *length?* Then hold up two objects and ask which one is *shorter* and which one is *longer*.

LITERACY CONNECTION

▶ **Reading a Book and Comparing Heights**

Read *Where's My Teddy?* by Jez Alborough (Candlewick Press, 1994). Talk with children about the relative size of the boy, the bear, and the two teddies.

NOTE Children also can look for "same length" objects and add them to the correct position on the data display.

Ongoing Assessment:
Recognizing Student Achievement

Use **Body Height Comparisons** to assess children's ability to make direct comparisons of length. Children are making adequate progress if they can compare the lengths of two objects and tell which one is longer and which one is shorter.

[Measurement and Reference Frames Goal 1]

Finger Count Fun

CCSS Mathematical Practices
SMP1, **SMP2**, SMP6, SMP7, SMP8
Content Standards
K.CC.3, K.CC.4a, K.CC.4b, K.CC.4c, K.CC.5, K.CC.6

Objective To reinforce counting and recognizing numerals 0–10.

☑ Whole Group
☑ Small Group
☑ Partners
☐ Center

Key Concepts and Skills

• Count up to 10 objects. [Number and Numeration Goal 2]

• Practice reading numerals through 10. [Number and Numeration Goal 3]

• Recognize numbers as "5 and some more." [Number and Numeration Goal 5]

Materials Teaching Aid Masters (*Math Masters,* pp. 92–97)

✓ Ongoing Assessment:

Recognizing Student Achievement

Use **Showing Fingers** to assess children's abilities to recognize numerals 1–10 and to count up to 10 objects (fingers). Children are making adequate progress with numeral recognition if they are able to read the numbers on the cards.

[Number and Numeration Goal 3]

They are making adequate progress with one-to-one counting if they can show the correct number of fingers by deliberately touching and counting. Some children may be able to quickly show the correct number of fingers without one-to-one counting.

[Number and Numeration Goal 2]

A Core Activities

▶ Reviewing Numbers (*Math Masters,* pp. 92–97)

Children have explored numbers through Ongoing Daily Routines, Getting to Know Numbers activities, and other experiences in and out of school. The following activities provide review and assessment opportunities at any time. Start with number cards 0–5 and add numbers as children gain experience with the activities. You can cut large number cards 0–10 from *Math Masters,* pages 92–97.

Showing Fingers Hold up a number card and direct children to hold up that number of fingers. After playing a few times as a class, have children turn to a partner and take turns saying a number and showing the finger count.

Counting Fingers Direct children to watch your fingers. Show a number of fingers (1, 2, 3, 4, or 5) very quickly, and then hide them. Give children a moment to think, and then ask them how many fingers they saw. Show the same number again, using your fingers and a number card so that children can check. Invite children to try this with partners.

When most children can identify the numbers 1 through 5 quickly, begin using both hands to show 6 to 10 fingers. (Use 5 fingers on one hand and add to them, rather than using different combinations, such as 4 and 2 or 3 and 4.) Initially, many children will count each finger one by one. The goal is for children to move toward a strategy of counting on from 5 and later, recognizing "5 and some more" patterns.

▶ Getting to Know Numbers—Counting Book (Revisit Activity 1•5, p. 54)

Read a favorite counting book (or two) to reinforce numeration concepts. Invite children to count the pictures on each page and match them to the numeral; reinforce one-to-one correspondence and cardinality as needed. Also have children count the pictures in different orders to emphasize that the total number stays the same. Emphasize the "one more" relationship of successive numbers as you read.

B Teaching Options

READINESS

▶ Counting Beans (Center Activity Cards, 4)

Label each cup of an egg carton or muffin tin with the numbers 0 through 11 in any order. A child places the correct number of beans in each cup while his or her partner checks for accuracy.

Vary the activity by labeling the cups in order. After children fill each cup with the correct number of beans, have them verify their counts by lining up the beans from each successive cup next to one another and comparing the lines. Emphasize the "one more" pattern.

EXTRA PRACTICE

▶ Using Ten Frames (Math Masters, p. 103; Center Activity Cards, 5)

Children can choose a number card and represent the number by placing objects on a ten frame (Math Masters, page 103). Orient the ten frame horizontally. Have children fill the top row from left to right before adding objects to the bottom row to promote recognition of "5 and some more" patterns. Ten Frames are the focus of Activity 1-16.

Activity 1•14 Finger Count Fun

NOTE Immediate perception of numbers of small groups of objects is very easy for most young children. Beyond about 5 objects, this is difficult for nearly everyone, including adults. However, mental grouping of objects, especially by 5s, extends the range of rapid association of numbers with small collections.

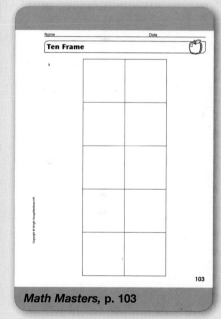

Math Masters, p. 103

NOTE The format of the ten frame helps children develop number sense—especially an awareness of quantity and of equivalent names for numbers.

ACTIVITY
1·15

Shape Puzzles

Objective To provide experiences with manipulating and combining shapes.

CCSS

Mathematical Practices
SMP1, SMP2, SMP3, SMP7
Content Standards
K.CC.6, **K.G.1, K.G.2, K.G.6**

☑ Whole Group   ☐ Partners
☑ Small Group   ☑ Center

Key Concepts and Skills
• Explore shapes in different orientations. [Geometry Goal 1]
• Combine simple shapes to form other shapes and pictures. [Geometry Goal 1]
• Describe the relative positions of shapes. [Geometry Goal 1]

Terms to Use shape, triangle, square, rectangle, above, below, next to, rotate

Materials Teaching Masters (*Math Masters,* pp. 5A–5D)

Planning Tip Copy and cut apart one set of shape cards from *Math Masters,* page 5A for each child. If possible, laminate or use cardstock for durability. Also make several sets of the Shape-Card Puzzles (*Math Masters,* pages 5B–5D) for the Math Center.

A Core Activities

▶ Combining and Creating Shapes (*Math Masters,* pp. 5A–5D)

Give each child one set of shape cards (*Math Masters,* page 5A). Introduce the shapes and have children find and hold up the shapes that match. For example, *This is a small triangle. Can you find a small triangle?* Tell children that they can rotate and combine the shapes in different ways. Hold two small triangles together so they form a larger triangle and say: *What happens if I put two small triangles together this way?* Then change the position of the two triangles so they form a square and say: *Now what shape did I make from the two small triangles?* Hold up two large rectangles and say: *What shape can I make with these rectangles if I put them next to each other? What shape can I make if I place one above the other?* Model various combinations and have children do the same with their own shapes. Next, provide children time to explore and combine the shapes in their sets to make new shapes. As children work, invite them to share their discoveries and describe their combinations using shape and position words. Help children recognize when they have combined two smaller shapes to make a larger square, triangle, or rectangle.

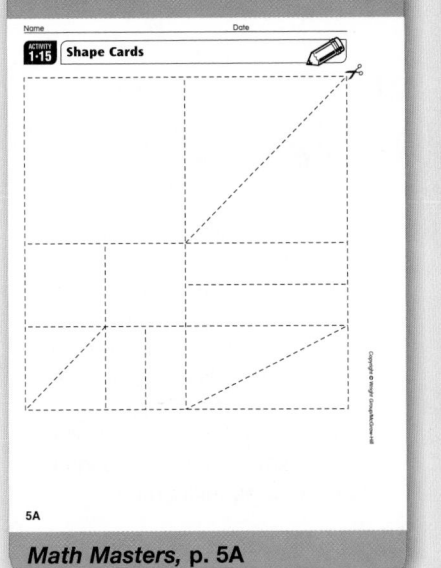

Math Masters, p. 5A

Pose new questions or challenges, such as: *Can you make a rectangle using squares? Can you find another way to make a rectangle?* Put several sets of shape cards in the Math Center for children to continue to explore. You may also want to include the Shape-Card Puzzles on *Math Masters,* pages 5B–5D. For additional challenge, make some copies of the puzzles eliminating the interior lines.

▶ Comparing Numbers (Revisit Activity 1•5, p. 54)

Use the number-collection bags that children created in Activity 1-5 to compare numbers and sets. Have children choose two number-collection bags and line up the objects from each bag next to one another, counting each set out loud as they line them up. Help them use a matching strategy to figure out which bag has more and which has fewer objects. Encourage children to share their own comparison strategies.

B Teaching Options

EXTRA PRACTICE

▶ Doing Pattern-Block Puzzles (*Math Masters,* pp. 5E–5H)

Encourage children to explore ways to combine pattern blocks to make new shapes and pictures. As a starting point, you may wish to provide the Pattern-Block Puzzles on *Math Masters,* pages 5E–5H (or similar templates). Some children might enjoy making their own puzzles for others to fill in with pattern blocks. They may need assistance tracing around the pattern blocks (or using the pattern-block template) to record outlines of the shapes and pictures they create.

ART CONNECTION

▶ Making Shape Pictures and Puzzles (*Math Masters,* p. 5A)

Invite interested children to trace around the shape cards to create their own shape pictures and puzzles. They can color or decorate their work and have other children try to use the cards to fill in the shapes and designs. Children who have difficulty tracing might glue shape cards on paper to record their pictures.

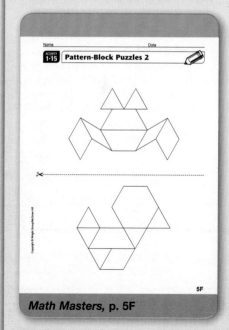

NOTE Help children recognize that the shapes do not change when you rotate them or put them in different positions. Also keep in mind that some children may still be learning to name and differentiate some shapes. To assist these children, be sure to show, in addition to name, shapes throughout this activity. Children will explore specific attributes of shapes in later activities.

Math Masters, p. 5F

Ten Frames

ACTIVITY 1·16

 **Objective** To use ten frames to explore numbers and number relationships through 10.

☑ Whole Group ☐ Partners
☑ Small Group ☑ Center

Key Concepts and Skills
- Use understanding of one-to-one correspondence and cardinality to count and create sets of objects. [Number and Numeration Goal 2]
- Represent numbers on a ten frame. [Number and Numeration Goal 3]
- Use a ten frame to explore benchmarks of 5 and 10. [Number and Numeration Goal 5]
- Compare numbers and sets. [Number and Numeration Goal 6]
- Identify pairs of numbers that add to 10. [Operations and Computation Goal 1]

Terms to Use ten frame

Materials Teaching Aid Masters (*Math Masters,* pp. 103–103B); counters

Planning Tip Make a copy of *Math Masters,* page 103 for each child. Also copy and cut apart one set of ten-frame cards (*Math Masters,* pages 103A and 103B) for every child or pair of children. If possible, laminate or use cardstock for durability.

A Core Activities

▶ Exploring Ten Frames (*Math Masters,* pp. 103–103B)

Give each child a ten frame (*Math Masters,* page 103) and ten counters. Explain that it is called a ten frame. Orient the ten frame horizontally and put one counter in each box, starting at the top left. Fill the top row from left to right, and then repeat in the bottom row. Invite children to do the same. Lead children in counting the counters aloud to reinforce the total number of 10.

Have children clear their ten frames. Then dictate and write a number between 1 and 5 and direct children to use counters to show that number on their ten frames, reminding them to start at the top left. Ask children what they notice about the ten frames. If no one brings it up, highlight that only the top row has counters. Ask: *How many more counters do you need to get to 5 (to fill the top row)? How many more do you need to get*

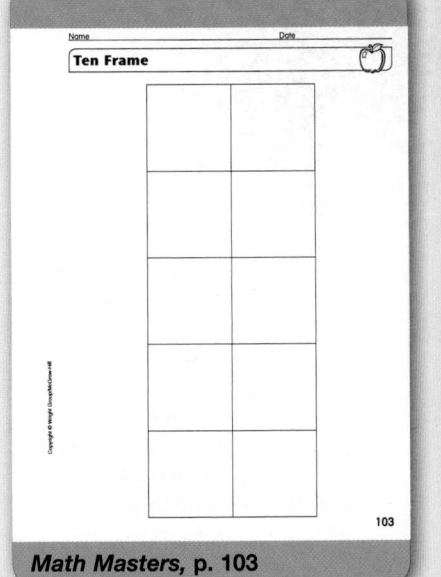

Math Masters, p. 103

to 10? How do you know? If necessary, remind them that the ten frame has 10 spaces and guide them to count the empty spaces to find how many they need to get to 10. Next, have children use counters to show a number between 6 and 10 on their ten frames. Again, ask what they notice. Ask: *Is the number more than 5? How many more than 5? How many more counters do you need to get to 10?* Repeat for several numbers.

Hold up several cards from *Math Masters,* pages 103A–103B and ask children what numbers they represent. Next, give each child or pair a set of ten-frame cards and have them do some or all of the following:

▷ Choose a card, identify the number it represents and how much more to make 10.

▷ Choose a card and identify the numbers right before and right after.

▷ Choose two cards and decide which is greater and which is less. (Discuss children's strategies for determining this.)

▷ Choose a number-collection bag from Activity 1-5 and line up the objects in the bag on the ten-frame card that matches the bag number.

Put ten-frame cards in the Math Center and encourage children to continue these activities and make up others to do with the ten-frame cards.

▶ Exploring Shape Combinations
(Revisit Activity 1•15, p. 73A; *Math Masters,* pp. 5A–5H)

Place Shape-Card Puzzles or Pattern-Block Puzzles in the Math Center.

B Teaching Options

EXTRA PRACTICE

▶ Exploring Ten Pennies with Two Hands (*Math Masters,* p. 103)

Give children 10 pennies, 2 wipe-off markers, and a laminated copy of *Math Masters,* p. 103. Model how to divide the pennies between their two hands and record their results on the ten frame. They should mark spaces in one color to match the number of pennies in their left hand and mark spaces in the other color to match the number of pennies in their right hand.

NOTE When using ten frames, routinely ask children how they know what number is represented. Promote discussion of a variety of strategies. Some children may not be ready for it yet, but look for someone to share the strategy of using benchmarks of 5 or 10 ("I noticed it was 5 and 2 more, so I said 5, 6, 7" or "I noticed that it was two less than 10").

4 pennies in the left hand and 6 pennies in the right hand

PROJECT 1

Numbers in Our World

CCSS

Mathematical Practices
SMP2, SMP4, SMP7

⊙ **Objective** To enlarge and enrich children's awareness of numbers and their uses in a variety of contexts.

Terms to Use numbers, codes, address, phone number, pattern

Materials

Number Walks
☐ chart paper

Class Telephone Book
☐ Project Master (*Math Masters,* p. 66)
☐ crayons or markers
☐ construction paper

"We Live Here" Mural
☐ large sheet of paper
☐ construction paper
☐ scissors
☐ glue sticks; markers or crayons

Introduction

Numbers are used for different purposes. Some numbers are measurements, some are counts, and some numbers, called *codes,* are used for identification. Examples of codes are: credit card numbers, phone numbers, and addresses. The Numbers in Our World project integrates the study of children's telephone numbers, addresses, and other numbers and numbering systems in and outside school. This project offers meaningful opportunities to connect mathematics with other curricular areas, most notably literacy (as children write and interpret printed symbols) and social studies (as children talk about their neighborhoods and communities). As with all projects in *Kindergarten Everyday Mathematics,* choose some or all of these activities and feel free to add or modify activities as your time and children's interests permit.

To begin this project, discuss numbers children know and use. The numbers might include their age, birthday, phone number, address, classroom number, or time or channel of a favorite TV show. Write down the numbers children suggest, along with a description of their use. Post the list where children can add to it.

NOTE For further discussion of the use of numbers, see Number and Counting, in the *Teacher's Reference Manual,* Chapter 8.

NOTE You might want to remind children about the number walks they took as part of Home Link 1-5 and discuss their findings.

Activity Options

▶ # Number Walks

☑ **Whole Group** ☑ **Small Group**

Increasing children's awareness of numbers helps build comfort and sense of ownership. Children begin to look for numbers around them, and their interest and curiosity about numbers leads to further inquiry and understanding.

School Walk Take children on a number walk in your school. Encourage them to look for numbers on signs, displays, clocks, calendars, doors, and so on. Talk about the numbers on different classrooms. Ask children how the number on their classroom door relates to the numbers on adjacent classroom doors. If there is more than one floor in your school, help children recognize the number pattern on different floors (for example, numbers on second-floor classrooms may begin with 2). Encourage children to discuss and share their observations. You may want to make a record of the classroom numbers and draw a simple map showing the numbering system in your school.

Neighborhood Walk Take children on a walk around the block or neighborhood. Include parents if possible. Encourage children to look for numbers on license plates, traffic signs, or billboards and to observe street signs and building numbers. Ask children to read the numbers, digit by digit. Have them try to figure out if the numbers are getting bigger or smaller. Ask: *Is there a pattern?* Consider writing down the addresses and making a simple map of your walk. Children can draw the buildings and label them.

○ **Literature Link** Show and discuss *Arlene Alda's 1 2 3* by Arlene Alda (Tricycle Press, 1998), which "finds" numeral shapes in innovative photographs of everyday objects and settings.

NOTE Project 6, which begins on page 316, focuses on maps and mapping.

▶ Class Telephone Book

☑ **Whole Group** ☑ **Small Group** ☑ **Center**

(Math Masters, p. 66)

Learning telephone numbers is one way for children to recognize that numbers have different uses. This activity invites children to write, read, and learn their own telephone numbers, which has practical as well as safety implications. The Class Telephone Book also promotes communication between class members and serves as a handy reference for families.

Children can use *Math Masters,* page 66, to make their own phone book pages. Each child's page should include his or her self-portrait, first name, and telephone number with area code. To make the telephone numbers easy to read, you may want to write children's numbers on the bottom of the pages or write the numbers using a highlighter for children to trace.

Make enough copies so that each child will have one page from everyone in the class. Make one additional copy of each page to make a classroom telephone book. One way to assemble the books is to lay out the copies of children's pages in piles, in alphabetical order. Over the next few days, help (or ask a parent to help) children collect one page from each pile to make a book. Children can make and decorate construction paper covers and write titles for their books.

NOTE You may want to send a note home to families describing the activity and requesting their phone numbers and addresses, as well as permission to include the information in the book. Families who do not have a phone or do not want their number published can use the school phone number instead.

Children can have fun entering telephone numbers on calculators, and then using the calculators as pretend telephones to make "calls" to each other.

Math Masters, p. 66

▶ "We Live Here" Mural

☑ Whole Group   ☑ Small Group   ☑ Center

A child's home address is a meaningful number to him or her. As children examine their addresses, they begin to recognize that digits can be used and combined to help locate a particular place. They also begin to recognize patterns in addresses. For example, children may observe that all the buildings on a block have a 53 at the beginning of each address.

Have children draw their houses or apartment buildings on construction paper as preparation for constructing a large mural. Help children label their buildings with their names and addresses. This is a good opportunity for children to memorize their addresses. Discuss the different parts of an address, such as house number, street name, and geographic designation (N, S, E, and W).

Discuss how to arrange individual drawings on the mural. Children can add streets, trees, and other features they decide upon. Encourage lively discussions. Strong differences of opinion can be settled by voting. (You might use tally marks to record votes.)

You may wish to bring in a large map of the area and help children locate streets. Can they find a pattern in the way the streets are laid out?

Help children write their addresses on the mural.

Section 2

Overview

Section 2 has a number of main areas of focus:

- ◆ To explore 2-dimensional shapes,
- ◆ To reinforce spatial relations vocabulary and concepts,
- ◆ To introduce the concept of symmetry,
- ◆ To develop understanding of teen numbers,
- ◆ To develop counting and numeral recognition skills,
- ◆ To lay groundwork for number writing through tactile and kinesthetic activities,
- ◆ To introduce estimation,
- ◆ To introduce number stories, and
- ◆ To continue patterning, graphing, and measurement comparison activities.

Maintaining Ongoing Daily Routines

Doing the Routines

In addition to Section 2 activities, continue to do the following Ongoing Daily Routines each day:

- ◆ Number of the Day
- ◆ Attendance
- ◆ Job Chart
- ◆ Monthly Calendar
- ◆ Daily Schedule
- ◆ Weather Observation
- ◆ Recording Daily Temperature
- ◆ Survey

Many children in your class are probably beginning to demonstrate independence with the Ongoing Daily Routines; others may still need considerable help carrying out the routines and making sense of the underlying mathematics. Make sure that you are consistent in implementing the routine activities. Children's independence—as well as their ability to apply and extend the mathematics embedded in the routines—will develop from continuous, repeated exposure.

Adjusting the Routines

Each Ongoing Daily Routine can be adjusted periodically according to children's progress and interest. Use Ongoing Daily Routines as powerful tools for practicing and reinforcing the skills that are introduced in the activities. If you haven't already done so, use the following routines to introduce new ideas and ask different questions during and after Section 2:

- ◆ **Monthly Calendar** Dismantle and rebuild your calendar with children at the end of each month using clues such as those suggested on page 20.
- ◆ **Survey** From time to time, children can take the survey questions home and record family responses. Later, you can compile, display, and discuss the group's results.

Using Routines for Ongoing Assessment

All of the Ongoing Daily Routines offer opportunities for ongoing assessment of a variety of skills and concepts. You might want to use the following routines for ongoing assessment during Section 2:

- ◆ **Attendance** Can children count the number of children present and absent from the attendance recording system? Do they say the correct number in sequence as they "count off" to verify the attendance record?
- ◆ **Survey** Can children count the number of each type of response and describe the results?

Learning in Perspective

Core Activities

Activity	Objective	Revisit Activity	Page
2·1	**Shape Collages** To introduce circles, triangles, squares, and rectangles.	**Playing *Give the Next Number*** (Activity 1-12, p. 68) **Links to the Past** Children played *Give the Next Number* with numbers through 10 in Activity 1-12. They may now be ready for higher numbers.	88
2·2	**Shapes by Feel** To develop understanding of shapes using the sense of touch.	**Adding to Shape Collages** (Activity 2-1, p. 88) **Links to the Past** Children began shape collages for circles, squares, triangles, and rectangles in Activity 2-1.	90
2·3	**Which Way Do I Go?** To review spatial vocabulary and concepts. **Links to the Future** Children apply position and spatial relations concepts as they learn about transformational geometry in Grades 4 through 6.	**Adding to Shape Collages** (Activity 2-1, p. 88)	92
2·4	***Spin a Number* Game** To reinforce counting and reading numbers 1–10 using a game.	**Reviewing Visual Patterns** (Activity 1-10, p. 64) **Links to the Past** Children worked with sound, movement, and color patterns in Section 1.	94
2·5	**Patterns All Around** To reinforce recognition of patterns through a pattern search activity.	**Using Pattern Blocks** (Activities 1-2 and 1-15, pp. 48 and 73A) **Links to the Future** Children will use pattern blocks throughout Kindergarten.	96
2·6	**Playful Oral Counting Games** To develop oral counting skills through movement activities.	**Using Pattern Blocks** (Activities 1-2 and 1-15, pp. 48 and 73A)	98
2·7	**Preparation for Number Writing** To lay groundwork for number writing through kinesthetic and tactile stroke-formation activities. **Links to the Future** Children will be formally introduced to number writing in Activity 3-1.	**Getting to Know Numbers, 1–9** (Activity 1-5, p. 54) **Links to the Past** Children participated in various Getting to Know Numbers activities in Section 1.	100

Core Activities, *continued*

Activity	Objective	Revisit Activity	Page
2•8	**Matching Coin Game** To promote coin recognition using a game. 🔗 **Links to the Future** In Section 6, children will begin to learn coin names and values.	**Exploring Ten Frames** (Activity 1-16, p. 73C; *Math Masters*, pp. 103A–103B)	104
2•9	**Number Board** To reinforce the meaning of numbers by constructing a class number board.	**Playing** *Give the Next Number* (Activity 1-12, p. 68)	106
2•10	**Tricky Teens** To introduce and provide practice with counting and recognizing teen numbers.	**Sorting Objects** (Activity 1-6, p. 56) 🔗 **Links to the Past** Children were introduced to sorting in Activity 1-6.	108
2•11	**Listen and Do (10–19)** To reinforce oral counting and recognizing teen numbers through a movement activity.	**Playing** *I Spy* (Home Link 2-1 from Activity 2-1, p. 89)	110
2•12	**Teen Partners** To introduce the concept that teen numbers represent "10 and some more."	**Arranging Objects by Length** (Activity 1-13, p. 70) 🔗 **Links to the Past** Children compared the lengths of objects in Activities 1-1 and 1-13.	112
2•13	**Estimation Jars** To introduce the concept of estimation. 🔗 **Links to the Future** Each section in Kindergarten includes at least one estimation activity as part of the revisit activities.	**Arranging Objects by Length** (Activity 1-13, p. 70)	114
2•14	**Number Stories: Stage 1** To introduce addition and subtraction number stories. 🔗 **Links to the Future** Activities 4-15 and 7-3 focus on later stages of developing, solving, and modeling number stories.	**Playing Counting Games with Teens** (Activity 2-6, p. 98)	116
2•15	**Symmetry Painting** To introduce symmetry.	**Combining and Creating Shapes** (Activity 1-15, p. 73A; *Math Masters*, p. 5A)	120
2•16	**Symmetry in Nature** To develop understanding of symmetry by looking for symmetry in natural objects.	**Creating a Bar Graph** (Activity 1-8, p. 60) 🔗 **Links to the Future** Children will have opportunities to create bar graphs in every section in Kindergarten.	122

Section Opener

Ongoing Learning and Practice

Practice through Games

Games are an essential component of practice in the *Everyday Mathematics* program. Games offer skills practice and promote strategic thinking. These games are introduced in this section:

Activity	Game	Skill Practiced
2◆1	*I Spy*	Using attributes to identify shapes [Geometry Goal 1]
2◆4	*Spin a Number*	Reading numbers 1–10 and counting spaces on a gameboard [Number and Numeration Goals 2 and 3]
2◆6	*Follow the Leader*	Counting movements by ones [Number and Numeration Goal 1]
2◆6	*Count and Sit*	Counting children by ones [Number and Numeration Goal 1]
2◆8	*Matching Coin Game*	Recognizing and matching pictures of coins with actual coins [Measurement and Reference Frames Goal 2]
2◆10	*Tricky Teens*	Recognizing and ordering teen numbers [Number and Numeration Goals 3 and 6]
2◆10	*Teen Tangle*	Recognizing teen numbers [Number and Numeration Goal 3]

Home-School Connection

Home Links provide homework and home communication. The following activities contain Home Links: 2-1, 2-5, 2-8, 2-13.

Home Connection Handbook provides more ideas to communicate effectively with parents. ▶

◀ *Mathematics at Home* Books **1–4** provide additional ideas for enjoyable mathematics activities that families can do together, as well as lists of children's books related to topics in each strand area. Families can do activities from *Mathematics at Home* Book **1** during Section 2.

Balanced Assessment

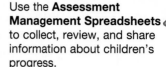

Use the **Assessment Management Spreadsheets** to collect, review, and share information about children's progress.

Ongoing Assessment

 Recognizing Student Achievement

Opportunities to assess children's progress toward Kindergarten Goals:

Activity	Content Assessed
2♦2	Identify and name a triangle and circle. [Geometry Goal 1]
2♦4	Count 1–10 objects and recognize numerals 1–10. [Number and Numeration Goals 2 and 3]
2♦16	Identify symmetrical objects. [Geometry Goal 2]

 Informing Instruction

To anticipate common trouble spots and to highlight problem-solving strategies:

Activity 2♦1
Visually discriminate between shapes

Activity 2♦6
Count fluently

Activity 2♦7
Make prewriting strokes

Activity 2♦11
Read and sequence teen numbers

Activity 2♦14
Tell and solve number stories

Periodic Assessment

Baseline assessment tasks were completed in Section 1. Mid-Year assessment tasks will be completed in Sections 4 and 5.

Portfolio Opportunities

◆ Shape prints or pictures, **Activity 2-2** Teaching Option

◆ Buildings with a teen number of blocks, **Activity 2-11** Teaching Option

◆ Number stories, **Activity 2-14** Teaching Option

Assessment Handbook

◆ Kindergarten Goals, pp. 27–33

◆ Section 2 Assessment Overview, pp. 52–53

◆ Assessment Overviews by Strand, pp. 66–75

◆ Individual Profile of Progress and Class Checklist (Sections 1–2), pp. 77–78

◆ Cumulative Individual Profile of Progress (Sections 1–4), pp. 97–98

Differentiated Instruction

Teaching Options

Use optional Part B activities as time permits to meet individual and class needs and to integrate mathematics throughout the Kindergarten classroom and schedule.

ELL SUPPORT

2•8   Sorting coins
2•15   Making fold-and-cut symmetrical shapes
2•16   Finding symmetrical objects in books

READINESS

2•3   Reading direction stories
2•6   Singing counting songs
2•9   Counting with concrete materials

CONNECTIONS

Literacy
2•1   Reading about shapes
2•6   Reading counting books
2•9   Reading *Bat Jamboree*
2•14   Modeling number stories

Science
2•1   Looking for shapes in nature
2•16   Sorting natural objects

Art
2•2   Printing or gluing shapes
2•7   Making sandpaper number rubbings

Art *continued*
2•8   Making coin rubbings
2•12   Creating paper chains
2•15   Creating symmetrical faces

Music
2•3   Singing directional songs

Cooking
2•7   Preparing cookie or modeling dough

Movement
2•10   Playing *Teen Tangle*

ENRICHMENT

2•12   Representing tens and ones
2•13   Comparing sizes to estimate
2•14   Creating stories for particular numbers

EXTRA PRACTICE

2•4   Counting on a life-size game mat
2•5   Going on a pattern hunt
2•10   Playing oral counting games with teens
2•11   Sequencing teen cards in the Math Center
2•13   Making handful estimates

CENTERS

Math Snack
2•2   Nibbling Shapes

Block Center
2•5   Building with patterns
2•11   Constructing teen buildings

Writing Center
2•14   Drawing and writing number stories

TECHNOLOGY

2•4   Playing *Spin a Number* on the computer

HALF-DAY AND FULL-DAY PROGRAMS   ◆   CROSS-CURRICULAR INTEGRATION   ◆   CENTERS-BASED LEARNING

Language Support

Everyday Mathematics provides activity-specific suggestions to help *all* young children develop the language necessary to acquire, process, and express mathematical ideas. Activities that provide additional support for non-native English speakers are marked by **ELL SUPPORT** and **ELL**.

Connecting Math and Literacy

Activity 2◆3 *Rosie's Walk* by Pat Hutchins (Simon & Schuster, 1968); "The Three Bears" and "The Three Billy Goats Gruff"

Activity 2◆9 *Bat Jamboree* by Kathi Appelt (HarperCollins, 1996)

Activity 2◆14 *Mouse Count* by Ellen Stoll Walsh (Harcourt, 1991); *Splash!* by Ann Jonas (Greenwillow, 1995)

See page 89 for more literature suggestions.

Using the Projects

Use Mathematics and Our Bodies (Project 2, page 124) during or after Section 2 to reinforce skills and concepts related to measurement, counting, and symmetry.

Adjusting the Activity

| AUDITORY | ◆ | KINESTHETIC | ◆ | TACTILE | ◆ | VISUAL |

Activity 2◆2 Locating, identifying, and describing a shown shape **ELL**

Activity 2◆3 Acting out and using standard gestures for position words **ELL**

Activity 2◆4 Using a higher or lower range of numbers in a game

Activity 2◆6 Varying counting in a game

Activity 2◆12 Using craft sticks or straws to represent "10 and some more"

Language & Vocabulary

Use these terms informally.

about	more
above	most
add	next to
all together	nickel
around	number story
behind	outside
below	over
beside	pattern
between	penny
circle	rectangle
coins	remove
corner	right
curve	round
curved	same
digit	shape
dime	side
down	square
equal	straight
estimate	subtract
flat	symmetrical
in front of	symmetry
inside	take away
join	teen
least	top
left	triangle
less	2-dimensional
line	under
match	up

Planning Tips

Pacing

Pacing depends on a number of factors, such as children's individual needs and how long your school has been using *Everyday Mathematics*. Use the optional Part B activities throughout Section 2 if you have extended mathematics instructional time. See page 84 for a list of these activities.

	← MOST CLASSROOMS →	
SEPTEMBER	OCTOBER	NOVEMBER

Teaching Resources

Resources for the Kindergarten Classroom provides additional teaching ideas, including suggestions for bringing mathematics into thematic instruction as well as using games, literature, technology, and rhymes to support mathematics learning. ▶

Minute Math provides brief activities for transition times and for spare moments throughout the day. During Section 2, use the activities in Part 1, pages 5–66.

NCTM Standards

Content Standards: 1 Number and Operations, **2** Algebra, **3** Geometry, **4** Measurement, **5** Data Analysis and Probability
Process Standards: 6 Problem Solving, **7** Reasoning and Proof, **8** Communication, **9** Connection, **10** Representation

Section 2 Activities	2•1	2•2	2•3	2•4	2•5	2•6	2•7	2•8	2•9	2•10	2•11	2•12	2•13	2•14	2•15	2•16
NCTM Standards	3, 8, 9	3, 7, 8	3, 9	1	2, 9	1	1,10	1, 4, 5, 7	1, 2, 10	1, 10	1, 10	1, 6, 10	1, 6, 10	1, 6, 8	3	3, 9

Professional Development

Teacher's Reference Manual Links

Activity	Topic	Section	Activity	Topic	Section
2•3	Transformations and Symmetry	11.7, 11.8	2•13	Estimation	14.1
			2•15	Symmetry	11.8

Materials

Activity	Masters	Materials	
2·1	Home Link Master, p. 6	• large shapes (square, circle, triangle, and rectangle) cut from cardstock or posterboard	• magazines and catalogs • scissors • glue
2·2		• a variety of shapes • selected attribute blocks* (circles, squares, rectangles, triangles) • Feely Box	• large posterboard shapes/shape collages from Activity 2-1 • tape
2·3		• a variety of manipulatives	
2·4	Game Master, p. 136	• paper reinforcements • large paper clips	• pencils • permanent marker
2·5	Home Link Master, p. 7	• magazines with pictures • scissors	• glue sticks • large piece of paper or posterboard
2·6			
2·7	Teaching Masters, pp. 8 and 9	• sand or salt in trays • shaving cream on trays • finger paint in resealable plastic bags	• cotton swabs • sandpaper numbers and strokes
2·8	Home Link Master, p. 10 Teaching Aid Master, p. 104	• coin stickers (optional) • a collection of pennies, nickels, and dimes • several eight-cup muffin tins, egg	cartons or other sorting trays • several one-inch cubes*

Activity	Masters	Materials	
2·9	Teaching Master, p. 11	• posterboard • stickers, pictures, or lightweight objects	• glue or tape • coins*, counters*, or other small objects
2·10	Teaching Aid Masters, pp. 97–102 (optional)	• large pieces of cardstock, each labeled on both	sides with a number between 10 and 19
2·11		• Large Teen Number Cards, each with a number	10–19 on both sides (one per child)
2·12		• Large Teen Number Cards each with a number	10–19 on both sides (one per child)
2·13	Home Link Master, p. 12	• two identical clear containers • collections of small objects, such as counters* or cubes*	
2·14		• counters* • paper (optional)	• markers or crayons (optional)
2·15		• paper • paint • cotton swabs, small paintbrushes, eye	droppers, or squeeze bottles
2·16		• magazines with photographs of natural objects (such as leaves and flowers) and/or a collection of natural objects	• scissors • glue sticks • crayons or markers • large paper or posterboard

Technology

Assessment Management Spreadsheets, Section 2
See the *iTGA*.

* Indicates items in the Kindergarten manipulative kit.

ACTIVITY
2·1

Shape Collages

⊚ **Objective** To introduce circles, triangles, squares, and rectangles.

CCSS Mathematical Practices
SMP2, **SMP4,** SMP6, SMP7
Content Standards
K.CC.1, K.CC.2, K.MD.3, K.G.1, K.G.2, K.G.3, K.G.4

☑ Whole Group ☐ Partners
☑ Small Group ☑ Center

Key Concepts and Skills
• Find and sort shapes. [Geometry Goal 1]
• Identify and name shapes. [Geometry Goal 1]
• Describe attributes of shapes. [Geometry Goal 1]
• Compare and relate 2-dimensional (flat) and 3-dimensional shapes. [Geometry Goal 1]

Terms to Use circle, square, triangle, rectangle, shape, straight, side, curved, corner, flat, 2-dimensional

Materials Home Link Master (*Math Masters,* p. 6); large shapes (square, circle, triangle, and rectangle) cut from cardstock or posterboard; magazines and catalogs; scissors; glue

Planning Tip You may want to introduce just one or two shapes per day. Plan to do the introductory activities during a group time. Invite children to add to the collages in a center over the course of a few days (or as long as children's interest lasts).

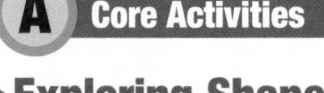

A **Core Activities**

▶ Exploring Shapes

Present the large posterboard shapes. For each shape, have children try the following activities:

▷ Draw the shape in the air with large arm motions.

▷ Walk around the outline of the shape. (Encourage children to identify things like straight sides, curved sides, and turns or corners.)

▷ Describe and name the shape. (Prompt children to tell the number of sides and corners, compare lengths of sides, and notice if sides are straight or curved.)

▷ Think of objects that look like or remind them of each shape. Encourage children to give examples, such as a clock for a circle or a ramp-shaped block for a triangle. If children

Shape Collages

mention 3-dimensional objects, highlight the difference between a 2-dimensional (flat) shape and the 3-dimensional object and point out the 2-dimensional shapes that are part of the object. For example, note the two triangle faces on a ramp-shaped block and ask what other flat shapes, such as rectangles, are part of the block.

▷ Find or draw objects that match the shape. (Drawings, magazine pictures, or actual objects can be taped to the posterboard shapes.) Use this activity to introduce creating shape collages.

Place the large posterboard shapes, magazines, scissors, and tape or glue in the Art or Math Center. Children can cut out geometric shapes from magazines, then tape or glue them to the corresponding posterboard shape. Save the posterboard shape collages to use as shape models in the next activity and for a classroom display.

 Home Link 2·1 (*Math Masters,* p. 6)
Children play *I Spy* to look for shapes at home.

▶ **Playing *Give the Next Number*** (Revisit Activity 1·12, p. 68)
Go beyond 10 or count backward from 10 as you play *Give the Next Number.*

B **Teaching Options**

SCIENCE CONNECTION
▶ **Looking for Shapes in Nature**
Encourage children to look for and share natural objects of various shapes.

LITERACY CONNECTION
▶ **Reading about Shapes**
Invite children to find shapes as you read *Circus Shapes* by Stuart J. Murphy. (HarperCollins, 1998). (See *Resources for the Kindergarten Classroom* for more shape books.)

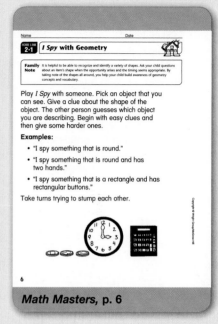

Math Masters, p. 6

 Ongoing Assessment:
Informing Instruction

Watch for children who are unable to visually discriminate between shapes. Try to work one on one with these children to help them find pictures to add to the collage. Children who are having difficulty may benefit from additional tactile and kinesthetic experiences with shapes.

Shapes by Feel

ACTIVITY 2·2

◎ **Objective** To develop understanding of shapes using the sense of touch.

☑ Whole Group
☑ Small Group
☐ Partners
☑ Center

Key Concepts and Skills

• Explore, recognize, and identify shapes by feel. [Geometry Goal 1]

• Describe attributes of shapes. [Geometry Goal 1]

Terms to Use shape, corner, side, round, curve, circle, triangle, square, rectangle, flat, 2-dimensional

Materials a variety of shapes; selected attribute blocks (circles, squares, rectangles, triangles); Feely Box; large posterboard shapes/shape collages from Activity 2•1; tape

Planning Tip See the Mathematics Extension in Activity 1-3, page 51, for information about making a Feely Box (or Feely Bag).

A Core Activities

▶ Identifying Attributes of Shapes

Show each of the large posterboard shapes or shape collages from the previous activity. Pass around an attribute block of each shape for children to feel. Ask children to describe one of the shapes without giving its name. Review the previous activity and prompt children to describe one thing about the shape, such as the number of corners or sides. Record the properties that children describe on the reverse side of the shape collage. Ask children if they know the name of the shape, and write the name on the back of the shape collage. Repeat this for all four shapes. Emphasize that these are all flat (2-dimensional) shapes.

Put several matching pairs of attribute block shapes into a Feely Box. Have a child reach in and pick out two shapes that feel the same. Ask the child to show the shapes to the group, name them, and replace them for the next child. Ask: *How did you know that the shapes were the same?* Repeat several times, then put the Feely Box and shapes in the Math Center for free exploration and play.

Ongoing Assessment:
Recognizing Student Achievement

Use **Shapes by Feel** to assess children's ability to name shapes and describe some of their attributes. Children are making adequate progress if they correctly identify and name a triangle and a circle. Some children may be able to recognize the difference between squares and rectangles.

[Geometry Goal 1]

Adjusting the Activity ⬆⬇ [ELL]

For children who need more practice or a simpler introduction, hold up a shape and ask children to locate the same shape in the Feely Box without looking. Then have them identify and describe the shape. For a slightly more difficult task, name a shape, and then have a child reach in and try to find that shape by feel. Prompt children to explain how they identified the correct shape.

AUDITORY ◆ **KINESTHETIC** ◆ **TACTILE** ◆ **VISUAL**

▶ Adding to Shape Collages (Revisit Activity 2•1, p. 88)

Put the shape collages and magazines from the previous activity in the Art or Math Center and invite children to add to them. When the collages are complete, punch a hole near the top and hang them with string so that both sides will be visible.

B Teaching Options

ART CONNECTION

▶ Printing or Gluing Shapes

Portfolio Ideas Cut small sponges into geometric shapes for children to use for printing. Children dip the sponges into paint and use them to print patterns, pictures, other shapes, or designs. Children can also make pictures by cutting shapes from colored paper (or using pre-cut shapes), then gluing them onto construction paper. You might show a collage-based picture book by Lois Ehlert to inspire children's artwork.

MATH SNACK

▶ Nibbling Shapes

Have children nibble crackers or cookies to create different shapes. Encourage children to "show and tell" about the different shapes they make.

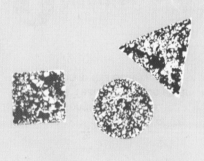

Shape Prints

Which Way Do I Go?

Objective To review spatial vocabulary and concepts.

CCSS

Mathematical Practices
SMP4, **SMP6,** SMP7
Content Standards
K.MD.3, **K.G.1,** K.G.2, K.G.4

☑ Whole Group
☑ Small Group
☐ Partners
☐ Center

Key Concepts and Skills

• Use spatial vocabulary and concepts in everyday situations. [Geometry Goal 1]

Terms to Use top, below, next to, between, behind, in front of, around, over, under, inside, outside, above, beside, up, down, left, right

Materials a variety of manipulatives

Planning Tip Use one of the books or songs listed in the Readiness Teaching Option as an introduction to this activity.

A   Core Activities

▶ Completing an Obstacle Course

Give each child a counter or other small object. Use spatial vocabulary as you give directions to position the object. For example, say: *Place your block on top of your head, below your foot, next to your friend,* or *between your knees.* Children can model spatial relationships with their bodies. For example, direct two children to line up next to each other, one child to stand between two others, and another child to move behind or in front of a designated classmate.

Create an obstacle course that children complete by following directions. For example, if outdoors, have children go around a tree, step over a rock, crawl under a branch, and walk next to a flower. Indoors, children might walk around the rug, climb over a chair, go between two hollow blocks, and then crawl under a desk. Also incorporate directional words such as *left* and *right* into the directions.

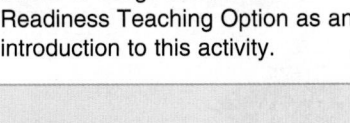

Adjusting the Activity   ELL

If children have difficulty with position words, spend additional time modeling and having children act out these concepts and provide assistance as they complete the obstacle course. Note that prepositions and position words may be difficult for English language learners. It may be helpful to develop standard gestures to indicate common position words.

AUDITORY ◆ KINESTHETIC ◆ TACTILE ◆ VISUAL

When they finish the obstacle course, have children describe the directions they followed. Invite children to collaborate to create and describe other obstacle courses that they can then move through.

▶ Adding to Shape Collages (Revisit Activity 2•1, p. 88)

Children can continue to add to the shape collages from Activity 2-1 using cutouts from magazines. When the collages are finished, display them in the classroom. Also remember to use *Minute Math* during spare moments in the day.

B Teaching Options

READINESS

▶ Reading Direction Stories

Read and act out *Rosie's Walk* by Pat Hutchins (Simon and Schuster, 1968), or a version of "The Three Bears" or "The Three Billy Goats Gruff." Ask children to help you list the words that tell "where" characters go. See *Resources for the Kindergarten Classroom* for other stories that emphasize spatial relationships and vocabulary.

MUSIC CONNECTION

▶ Singing Directional Songs

Sing "Going on a Bear Hunt" and have children act out the directions. See *Resources for the Kindergarten Classroom* for the lyrics.

Play a modified version of the "Hokey Pokey." Change the directions to include spatial vocabulary such as: *above, below, under, over,* and *next to.* (Model right/left hand and foot motions for children, but don't expect all children to know the difference yet.)

NOTE To provide practice using ordinal numbers, draw a picture of each step of the obstacle course on a large piece of paper. Then label each step with an ordinal number. You may also wish to discuss the children's ordinal positions as they line up to complete the obstacle course.

Links to the Future

Understanding position and spatial relation concepts prepares children to learn transformational geometry (translations, reflections, and rotations) in Grades 4 through 6. (See "Geometry," *Teacher's Reference Manual* Chapter 11.)

ACTIVITY 2·4

Spin a Number Game

Mathematical Practices
SMP2, **SMP6**, SMP7

🎯 **Objective** To reinforce counting and reading numbers 1–10 using a game.

☐ Whole Group ☑ Partners
☑ Small Group ☑ Center

Key Concepts and Skills
• Count and move between 1 and 10 spaces on a gameboard. [Number and Numeration Goal 2]
• Read numbers 1–10. [Number and Numeration Goal 3]

Materials Game Master (*Math Masters,* p. 136); paper reinforcements; large paper clips; pencils; permanent marker

NOTE Add a paper reinforcement to the center of the spinner to help children know where to place their pencil and to help prevent the pencil from slipping.

A Core Activities

▶ Making and Playing *Spin a Number* (*Math Masters,* p. 136)

Show children how to make and use spinners using *Math Masters,* page 136 and a large (2 inch) paper clip and pencil. (A standard-size paper clip will also work, but doesn't spin as well.) Using a permanent marker, make a dot at one end of the paper clip to serve as a pointer. (This mark helps children see more clearly what number the pointer has stopped on.) To spin, place the pencil point through the paper clip at the center of the circle. Then use your finger to flick the paper clip about halfway between the center of the circle and the tip of the paper clip.

Children play in pairs or small groups. They spin to get a number and move that number of spaces on the gameboard. The game ends when a child reaches the square marked "End." For a more difficult game, children's last numbers must take them exactly to the final square. Children can add illustrations to make it a game about helping a bird find its nest, moving a car toward a garage, or another goal. Leave the game out in the Math Center. You might make copies of the *Spin a Number* gameboard for children to take home to play.

NOTE Games such as *Spin a Number* provide important practice for children throughout *Kindergarten Everyday Mathematics.* Many teachers create game bags (containing game materials and directions) that children can "check out" to play at home with their families.

▶ Reviewing Visual Patterns (Revisit Activity 1•10, p. 64)

Review the concept of patterns. During a group or transition time, try the following suggestions: point out and describe color patterns on children's clothing or on the classroom carpet; line children up in a boy/girl or other pattern; draw a pattern on the board and ask children to describe and extend it. Children will have additional opportunities to practice patterns in Activity 2-5.

B Teaching Options

EXTRA PRACTICE

▶ Counting on a Life-Size Game Mat

Make a large game mat by taping paper squares on the floor or drawing with chalk on a rug to make the spaces. Two or more children can be the game markers. The other children take turns reading the spinner and announcing the number for players to move. (The game can be based on a theme such as cars or dinosaurs.)

TECHNOLOGY

▶ Playing *Spin a Number* on the Computer

Children can play a version of *Spin a Number* on the computer using *Everyday Mathematics EM Games*. See *Resources for the Kindergarten Classroom* for other software suggestions.

ACTIVITY
2·5

Patterns All Around

CCSS

Mathematical Practices
SMP4, **SMP7**

Content Standards
K.G.2, K.G.4, K.G.6

🎯 **Objective** To reinforce recognition of patterns through a
pattern search activity.

☑ Whole Group   ☐ Partners
☑ Small Group   ☑ Center

Key Concepts and Skills

• Notice and describe patterns in surroundings. [Patterns, Functions, and Algebra Goal 1]

• Extend patterns. [Patterns, Functions, and Algebra Goal 1]

Terms to Use pattern

Materials Home Link Master (*Math Masters*, p. 7); magazines with pictures; scissors; glue sticks; large
piece of paper or posterboard

 **A** **Core Activities**

▶ Looking for Patterns

Quickly review patterns by asking one or two volunteers to describe what a pattern is.
Then prompt children to look around the room to find patterns. For example, they might
notice patterns in floor tiles, bookshelves, door panels, vent grids, or windowpanes. If
possible, take a walk around the school to look for more patterns. (See the Teaching
Options on the next page.) Use the examples children find to reinforce the concept that
once a part of a pattern is identified, it is possible to figure out what comes next and to
extend the pattern indefinitely. If children have difficulty identifying or extending
patterns, it may help to ask them to verbalize what they see. (For example, "black line,
space, blue line; black line, space, blue line; …")

Place a large piece of paper or posterboard labeled "Patterns All Around" on a table or
low bulletin board. Encourage children to look in magazines to find examples of patterns

Patterns in a Tie

NOTE Many people make a
distinction between repeating patterns
(e.g., ABABAB… or ABBABBABB…)
and growing patterns (e.g., ☐ ☐☐
☐☐☐ ☐☐☐☐… or 0, 5, 10, 15, 20…).
Encourage children to look for and
discuss both types of patterns.

in nature, architecture, clothing, and so on. Children can cut out or draw pictures to add to the posterboard collage. Allow children to add to this group collage over time as they find more examples. The collage can become the basis for a pattern display in the classroom.

Vent and Tiles

Laundry Basket

 **Home Link 2·5** *(Math Masters,* p. 7)
Children look for patterns at home and share their findings with the class.

▶ Using Pattern Blocks (Revisit Activities 1·2 and 1·15, pp. 48 and 73A)

Set out pattern blocks in the Math Center. As children use the blocks to create and extend patterns, reinforce the names of the pattern block shapes: square, triangle, rhombus, trapezoid, and hexagon. Challenge children to combine the pattern blocks to compose larger shapes, as they did with the shape cards in Activity 1-15.

B Teaching Options

EXTRA PRACTICE

▶ Going on a Pattern Hunt

Go on a "Pattern Hunt" around the building or playground. If possible, take photos of patterns that children find and include the photos in a class "Pattern Hunt Book."

MATHEMATICS IN THE BLOCK CENTER

▶ Building with Patterns

Encourage children to incorporate patterns in their block buildings. You might prompt them to look for patterns on your school building, their homes, or on other architecture.

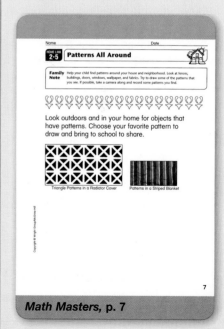

Math Masters, p. 7

Playful Oral Counting Games

ACTIVITY 2·6

CCSS **Mathematical Practices**
SMP2, **SMP5**, SMP6, SMP7
Content Standards
**K.CC.1, K.CC.2, K.CC.4a,
K.CC.4b, K.CC.4c, K.CC.5,**
K.G.2, K.G.4, K.G.6

◎ **Objective** To develop oral counting skills through movement activities.

☑ Whole Group
☐ Small Group
☐ Partners
☐ Center

Key Concepts and Skills
• Practice oral counting forward by ones. [Number and Numeration Goal 1]

Materials none

Planning Tip Play the games on separate days if you think it will confuse children to learn both games at once. Consider using a counting song to introduce this activity. (See Teaching Options.)

A Core Activities

▶ Playing Counting Games

Play several rounds of each of these games as a class.

Follow the Leader Have children sit in a circle on the floor and talk with them about ways they can move their bodies while sitting. Explain and demonstrate a counting game similar to *Follow the Leader*. Tap your head or wiggle your fingers, and have the children join in. Direct them to begin counting (while continuing the movement) and go around the circle, with each child saying the next number. Invite the child who says *ten* to change the movement. Start the count over from *one* with the new movement. Repeat as long as interest lasts.

Count and Sit Have children stand in a circle and choose a target number, such as eight. Begin counting with *one* and go around the circle with each child saying the next number in sequence. The child who says the target number sits down and the count begins again at *one*. The seated child is skipped as the count continues around the circle with another child sitting each time the target number is reached. Keep counting around the circle until all children are sitting. Some children may enjoy trying to figure out who will be the last person left standing. Repeat, using different target numbers.

Adjusting the Activity

Both games can be played using higher numbers, counting backward, or skip counting as children are ready.

AUDITORY ♦ KINESTHETIC ♦ TACTILE ♦ VISUAL

Ongoing Assessment: Informing Instruction

Listen to find out where children have difficulty in counting. When they stumble, do they need to start over from one? Have they developed other strategies to pick up the counting? Some children may benefit from a visual reference such as a number line to help them keep track or make sense of counting patterns.

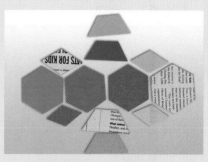

A Pattern-Block Design

▶ **Using Pattern Blocks** (Revisit Activities 1•2 and 1•15, pp. 48 and 73A)

Keep pattern blocks in the Math Center for continued exploration. As children share their designs and talk about them, introduce ways to record and preserve their work. You might provide paper and pattern-block stickers or pattern-block shapes cut out of construction paper, newspaper, fabric, or wallpaper. You can also photograph children's creations and post them in the classroom for inspiration. (The Pattern-Block Template is introduced in Activity 4-3, p. 192.)

B **Teaching Options**

READINESS

▶ **Singing Counting Songs**

Sing and act out counting songs such as "Ten Little Penguins." When possible, substitute higher numbers in songs ("Eight Little Monkeys," instead of "Five Little Monkeys," for example). See *Resources for the Kindergarten Classroom* for song suggestions.

LITERACY CONNECTION

▶ **Reading Counting Books**

Read and compare various counting books. See *Resources for the Kindergarten Classroom* for a list of good counting books, but you or your students may have other favorites!

NOTE Use counting songs and books to reinforce foundational counting principles, including one-to-one correspondence, cardinality, and the "one more" (or "one less") pattern of adjacent numbers. Counting books are also useful for discussing how the number of objects is the same no matter what the objects are, how they are arranged, or in what order they are counted.

Preparation for Number Writing

ACTIVITY 2·7

CCSS Mathematical Practices
SMP2, **SMP6**
Content Standards
K.CC.3, K.CC.4a, K.CC.4b, K.CC.5, K.CC.6

◎ **Objective** To lay groundwork for number writing through kinesthetic and tactile stroke-formation activities.

☑ Whole Group   ☐ Partners
☑ Small Group   ☑ Center

Key Concepts and Skills

- Identify numbers. [Number and Numeration Goal 3]
- Develop stroke formation skills to prepare for writing numbers. [Number and Numeration Goal 3]

Terms to Use stroke, line, curve, circle

Materials Teaching Masters (*Math Masters,* pp. 8 and 9); sand or salt in trays; shaving cream on trays; finger paint in resealable plastic bags; cotton swabs; sandpaper numbers and strokes

Planning Tip In addition to helping with number formation, these activities provide practice for number recognition. Make the materials available in centers over the course of several days or weeks.

A Core Activities

▶ Introducing Strokes with Stories (*Math Masters,* pp. 8 and 9)

Begin by telling children the action stories below. Encourage children to use large hand and arm movements to draw the actions (strokes) in the air.

- *You've blown bubbles on a wand. Trace the bubbles all around you.* (circular strokes)

- *You are a cloud. Make the shapes of your puffs against the sky.* (curved strokes)

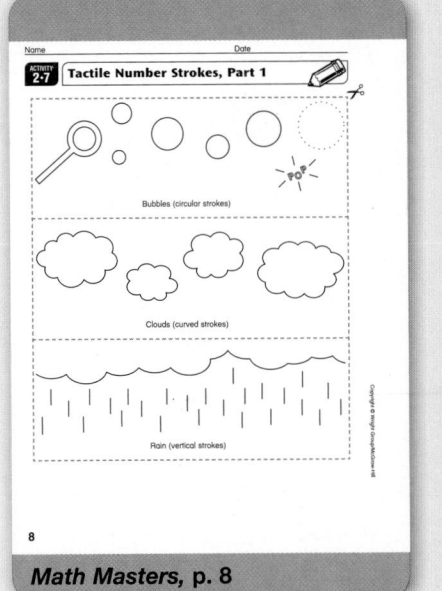

Math Masters, p. 8

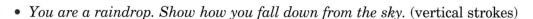

- *You are a raindrop. Show how you fall down from the sky.* (vertical strokes)

- *You are walking sideways. Draw the steps you take as you move.* (horizontal strokes)

- *You are on a slide. Show the movement you make as you slide down.* (diagonal strokes)

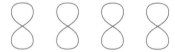

- *You are an ice skater. Trace figure 8s in the air.* (figure 8s)

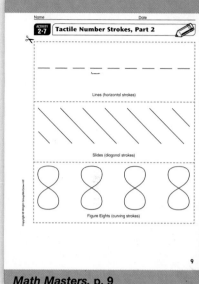

Math Masters, p. 9

🔗 Links to the Future

Practicing the formation of pre-writing strokes—including circles, curves, and diagonal, horizontal, and vertical lines—helps children develop fine motor skills and builds a foundation for writing numbers. Children will be formally introduced to number writing in Activity 3-1, page 138.

Practicing Strokes

Children can practice strokes using the materials on the next page. Place the number stroke guides (*Math Masters,* pages 8 and 9) at one or more centers to provide models of stroke designs. After children have had time to practice the pre-writing strokes, you can provide models of numbers for them to copy or trace. Children will also enjoy creating designs and other figures in each medium.

▷ **Sand/Salt Trays** Children use their fingers to draw strokes or numbers in sand or salt in a box top or tray.

▷ **No-Mess Finger Painting** Fill sealable bags with just enough paint to form an even layer when laid flat. Children use the bag like a piece of paper, drawing with their fingers or cotton swabs to make strokes or numbers by displacing the paint. Place the bag on a contrasting sheet of paper to achieve the most visible results. Then "erase" and start over.

▷ **Shaving Cream** Children use their fingers to form strokes or numbers in a small amount of shaving cream in a tray.

▷ **Sandpaper** Cut out strokes and numbers from sandpaper and glue them onto cards, or write the figures in glue and then sprinkle with sand. (Prepared sandpaper strokes and numbers are also available for purchase.) Children trace the sandpaper strokes or numbers with their fingers. Add a dot to the starting point of each number to help children know where to start forming the numbers. Children can also close their eyes and try to identify the sandpaper numbers by touch.

Ongoing Assessment: Informing Instruction

Watch for children who are having trouble forming strokes. Repeat various tactile activities to give them further practice. Also keep in mind that fine motor skills vary tremendously at this age, so many children simply require additional time and experience.

0 1 2 3 4 5 6 7 8 9

▶ Getting to Know Numbers, 1–9 (Revisit Activity 1•5, p. 54)

Do a Look and Find number activity. Give individuals or pairs of children a card with a number between 1 and 9 written on it. Have them search the room to find that number of objects, then trade their objects and number cards with someone else to check their counting. If time permits, each child or pair can share the objects they found with the class, and the class can put the collections in order from smallest to largest. Or, children can compare their objects with those of another child or pair to see who has more or fewer. If children have difficulty comparing the sets, model how to use a matching and counting strategy.

Also remember to use *Minute Math* during spare moments in the day.

B Teaching Options

ART CONNECTION

▶ Making Sandpaper Number Rubbings

Children can make crayon rubbings of the sandpaper numbers.

COOKING CONNECTION

▶ Preparing Cookie or Modeling Dough (*Center Activity Cards*, 6)

Use your favorite recipe to make cookies or modeling dough with children. Invite them to form shapes and numbers with the dough. Cooking provides wonderful counting and measuring opportunities for children!

Matching Coin Game

 Objective To promote coin recognition using a game.

CCSS **Mathematical Practices**
SMP2, SMP3, **SMP6,** SMP7
Content Standards
**K.CC.3, K.CC.4a, K.CC.4b,
K.CC.4c, K.CC.5, K.CC.6,**
K.OA.4, **K.MD.3**

☐ Whole Group
☐ Small Group
☐ Partners
☑ Center

Planning Tip Use the coins from *Math Masters,* page 104, or coin stickers to label the cubes. Make sure that both sides of a penny and dime are represented on the cubes. For nickels (and later, quarters) you might want to use two pictures of the heads side (no tails) to avoid problems with multiple versions of the tails sides of these coins. Discuss these variations with children.

Key Concepts and Skills
• Compare numbers of coins. [Number and Numeration Goal 6]
• Consider the likelihood of outcomes on a toss of a money cube. [Data and Chance Goal 3]
• Recognize and match pictures of coins with actual coins. [Measurement and Reference Frames Goal 2]
• Identify coin features and begin to use coin names. [Measurement and Reference Frames Goal 2]

Terms to Use match, penny, nickel, dime, coins, most, least

Materials Home Link Master (*Math Masters,* p. 10); Teaching Aid Master (*Math Masters,* p. 104) or coin stickers; a collection of pennies, nickels, and dimes; several eight-cup muffin tins, egg cartons or other sorting trays; several one-inch cubes

A Core Activities

▶ **Playing the *Matching Coin Game*** (*Math Masters,* p. 104)

Place a collection of coins and several money cubes and sorting trays in the Math Center. Show children how to roll the money cube, find the corresponding coin, and then put the coin in the correct section of their trays. After several rounds, children can compare how many of each type of coin they have. The winner can be the child with the most dimes, or the least pennies, or some other agreed-upon goal. Many children will enjoy solitary play by rolling the cube and collecting and sorting coins.

NOTE To provide practice ordering sets of objects according to quantity, you may wish to have children order sets of each coin from the most to the least or from the least to the most.

Once children understand the game, have them examine their cubes and discuss whether they are more or less likely to roll one type of coin than another. (Each cube gives two chances of rolling each coin: all outcomes are equally likely.)

Place the game in the Math Center for free play. As the year progresses, create cubes and trays that include quarters. (Note that this will change the chances of rolling one coin or another, since some coins will be represented only once on the cube and others twice. Some children will be interested in thinking about this.)

 Home Link 2·8 (*Math Masters*, p. 10)
Children continue their exploration of coins at home.

▶ **Exploring Ten Frames** (Revisit Activity 1•16, p. 73C; *Math Masters*, pp. 103A–103B)

Give each child or pair of children a set of ten-frame cards (*Math Masters*, pp. 103A–103B) to do one or more of the activities suggested on page 73D. For example, you might have them say the number represented on each card and identify how many more to make 10. Or, they can choose a card and say two numbers, one that comes right before and one that comes right after the number shown on the card. Invite children to think of other activities to do with the cards.

 **Teaching Options**

ELL SUPPORT

▶ **Sorting Coins** (*Center Activity Cards*, 7)

Children may benefit from sorting a collection of coins to focus on coin attributes and differences among coins (see Activity 1-6, page 56). Display and label each of the coins in the classroom for reference.

ART CONNECTION

▶ **Making Coin Rubbings**

Children can use paper and unwrapped crayons to make crayon rubbings of coins.

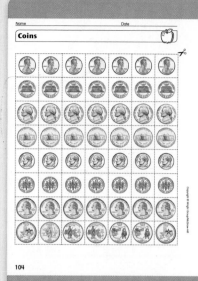

Math Masters, p. 104

Math Masters, p. 10

Number Board

ACTIVITY 2·9

CCSS Mathematical Practices
SMP2, SMP6, **SMP7**

Content Standards
K.CC.1, K.CC.2, K.CC.4a,
K.CC.4b, K.CC.4c, K.CC.5

◎ **Objective** To reinforce the meaning of numbers by constructing a class number board.

☑ Whole Group
☐ Small Group
☐ Partners
☑ Center

Key Concepts and Skills
- Count objects using one-to-one correspondence. [Number and Numeration Goal 2]
- Represent numbers with concrete materials. [Number and Numeration Goal 3]
- Discover that the digits 0–9 can be used to write any number. [Number and Numeration Goal 3]
- Recognize a visual pattern of numbers. [Patterns, Functions, and Algebra Goal 1]

Terms to Use pattern, digit

Materials Teaching Master (*Math Masters,* p. 11); posterboard; stickers, pictures, or lightweight objects; glue or tape; coins, counters, or other small objects

Planning Tip Prepare a blank number board by marking a posterboard with 11 rows and 11 columns (rows should be numbered 0 through 10). You can fill in the number board during group time over several days.

A Core Activities

▶ **Building a Number Board** (*Math Masters,* p. 11)

With children, count out and add the appropriate number of stickers, small pictures, or small objects to each row on the blank number board you prepared. Talk to children about what should go next to the number 0. If necessary, remind them that 0 is a number that means "none."

Once the number board is complete, ask children to describe things they notice about the board. They may point out that it looks like steps or a triangle, or that there is a pattern of adding one thing for each row. Validate all observations.

Introduce the term **digits** and mention that the digits 0–9 can be used to write any counting number, no matter how large. For example, 16 is formed with a 1 and a 6.

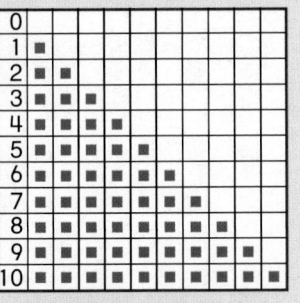

Number Board, 0–10

One hundred is formed with a 1 and two 0s. Ask children to name some big numbers while you write them using the digits from the number board. Ask if anyone can think of a number that cannot be written using 0–9.

Laminate several copies of the blank number board on *Math Masters,* page 11 and place them in the Math Center. Invite children to cover the spaces with the appropriate number of coins, counters, or other small objects. Children might also invent games to play on the number board.

▶ **Playing *Give the Next Number*** (Revisit Activity 1•12, p. 68)

Play a few rounds of *Give the Next Number* with the class. Go beyond 10 in preparation for the next several activities which focus on the teen numbers.

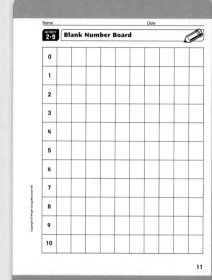

Math Masters, p. 11

B **Teaching Options**

READINESS

▶ **Counting with Concrete Materials**

Children who need more experience with counting and representing numbers through 10 can use interlocking cubes, links, beads on strings, or various commercial puzzles to reinforce these skills.

NOTE Encourage children to line up two sets of objects side by side and compare them using the terms *more than, less than,* or *same* (or *equal*).

LITERACY CONNECTION

▶ **Reading *Bat Jamboree***

Read *Bat Jamboree* by Kathi Appelt (HarperCollins, 1996). Help children see the connection between the items on the number board and the number of bats on each page of the book. Count the total number of objects on the number board together and compare this to the total number of bats in the story. (They are the same.)

Tricky Teens

Objective To introduce and provide practice with counting and recognizing teen numbers.

CCSS Mathematical Practices
SMP2, SMP6, **SMP7**
Content Standards
K.CC.2, K.CC.5, K.CC.6, K.MD.1, K.MD.3

☑ Whole Group
☑ Small Group
☐ Partners
☑ Center

Key Concepts and Skills
- Count orally from 10 through 19. [Number and Numeration Goal 1]
- Recognize teen numbers. [Number and Numeration Goal 3]
- Sequence numbers from 10 through 19. [Number and Numeration Goal 6]

Terms to Use tricky teens

Materials Teaching Aid Masters (*Math Masters*, pp. 97–102, optional); large pieces of cardstock, each labeled on both sides with a number between 10 and 19

Planning Tip You can use *Math Masters,* pages 97–102 to add the numbers to both sides of the cardstock pieces. Laminate them if possible. You will need additional sets of teen cards for *Teen Tangle* (see Teaching Options) and subsequent activities, so you may want to make two or three sets of cards at this time.

A Core Activities

▶ Introducing the *Tricky Teens Game* (Math Masters, pp. 97–102)

Count from 1 to 10 together. Ask: *What number comes after 10?* Show the portion of the number line that displays 10 through 19 to introduce the teen numbers. Ask: *Where else can we find these numbers?* If children don't mention them, you might refer to the calendar, locker numbers, room numbers, or the 11 and 12 on the clock.

Display one set of the large number cards with the numbers 10–19 on them. Ask: *What is the same about these numbers? How are they different from the numbers 1 through 9?* Point out that all teen numbers are written with the numeral 1 going first. You might also introduce the label "tricky teens." Ask children why they think the teens might be called "tricky." (Later in the year, you might ask whether they think 10, 11, and 12 are "teens" or not.)

Mix up one set of teen cards and work as a class to arrange the cards in order on the floor. Then introduce the *Tricky Teens Game* to the group. Mix up the cards again, so that they are randomly placed on the floor in close proximity to one another. One at a time, call on children to jump from one number to another in sequence, and say the numbers out loud. After a few children have had a turn, re-shuffle the numbers and give other children a chance to jump. After playing the game as a group, place the cards in the Math Center for free play. Children can also play the game outdoors.

▶ Sorting Objects (Revisit Activity 1•6, p. 56)

Set out a collection of objects and sorting trays in the Math Center. You might use leaves, rocks, shells, acorns, buttons, or counters. Add strips of paper and pencils to encourage labeling. After children sort, have them count the numbers of objects in each category and compare these numbers. Ask children to order the categories according to the number of objects in each and to identify which has the most and which has the fewest objects. Have collections available as long as interest remains high.

B Teaching Options

(EXTRA PRACTICE)

▶ Playing Oral Counting Games with Teens

Play *Give the Next Number* (Activity 1-12, page 68), *Follow the Leader,* and *Count and Sit* (Activity 2-6, page 98) using teen numbers.

(MOVEMENT CONNECTION)

▶ Playing *Teen Tangle* (Math Masters, pp. 98–102 and 139)

Place multiple sets of teen cards from *Math Masters,* pages 98–102, close together on the floor in random order. Have one child spin a spinner with the numbers 11–20 (*Math Masters,* page 139) while the other children (one at a time) place a finger, foot, or other body part on each number the spinner points to. The goal is for children to touch as many numbers as they can without falling.

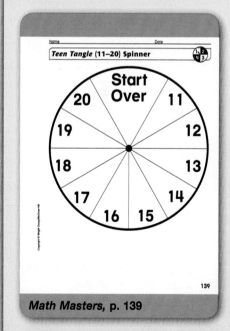

Math Masters, p. 139

Listen and Do (10-19)

ACTIVITY 2·11

@ **Objective** To reinforce oral counting and recognizing teen numbers through a movement activity.

☑ Whole Group
☑ Small Group
☐ Partners
☐ Center

Key Concepts and Skills

• Orally count by ones through 19. [Number and Numeration Goal 1]

• Use one-to-one correspondence to count movements. [Number and Numeration Goal 2]

• Recognize numerals 10–19. [Number and Numeration Goal 3]

• Sequence numerals 10–19. [Number and Numeration Goal 6]

Terms to Use teen

Materials Large Teen Number Cards, each with a number 10–19 on both sides (one per child)

Planning Tip You can use the teen cards from the previous activity or make new ones using *Math Masters,* pages 97–102.

A Core Activities

▶ Counting and Moving

Shuffle the Teen Number Cards and give each child a card.

Have children stand in a circle. Tell them they must listen very carefully and follow your directions. Call out a number and an action. For example, say: *10s, kick with your foot (10 times). 19s, clap your hands (19 times).* Children holding the number called should perform the action the number of times that is on their cards.

Then have children arrange themselves in numerical order (duplicate numbers stand together).

Below are some other ideas for using the teen cards during group time:

▷ Hold up a number card. Ask children who are holding the numbers that come before and after to stand and show their cards.

▷ Give a clue about a mystery teen number. For example, say: *I'm thinking of a teen number with a five in it,* or *I'm thinking of a teen number that comes between 10 and 12.* If children think they are holding the mystery number, they stand up and show their cards.

▶ Playing *I Spy* (Revisit Home Link 2•1 from Activity 2•1, p. 89)

Play *I Spy*, the game introduced in Home Link 2-1, perhaps while waiting in line during a transition time. Focus your clues on shapes but feel free to incorporate other attributes, such as size and color. For example, say: *I spy with my little eye something round and red. What could it be?* Allow children to give clues, too.

B   Teaching Options

EXTRA PRACTICE

▶ Sequencing Teen Cards in the Math Center (*Center Activity Cards,* 8)

Place a set of teen cards in the Math Center for sequencing. Children can also choose a teen card and count out that number of objects to place on top of the card.

MATHEMATICS IN THE BLOCK CENTER

▶ Constructing Teen Buildings

Have children build something using an identified (teen) number of blocks. Take pictures to record the buildings and compare the creations.

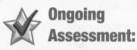

Ongoing Assessment:
Informing Instruction

Watch for children who are not able to read and sequence the teen numbers or count objects into the teens. Children will gain confidence with the teen numbers through repeated exposure and practice.

ACTIVITY
2·12

Teen Partners

Objective To introduce the concept that teen numbers represent "10 and some more."

☑ Whole Group
☑ Small Group
☑ Partners
☐ Center

Key Concepts and Skills
• Identify the numbers 0–19. [Number and Numeration Goal 3]
• Use concrete materials to represent the numbers 10–19. [Number and Numeration Goal 3]
• Recognize each teen number as 10 + a digit. [Number and Numeration Goal 5]

Terms to Use teen

Materials Large Teen Number Cards, each with a number from 10 through 19 on both sides (one per child)

Planning Tip Use the teen cards from previous activities.

A Core Activities

▶ Representing Teen Numbers

This activity helps children understand the idea that 11 means "10 and 1 more"; 15 means "10 and 5 more," and so on. Refer to your Concrete Number Count from the Growing Number Line Routine (page 8) and discuss how the 10s and 1s representations have changed since school began. Use it to quickly review the concept of 10s and 1s. (Not all children will understand this.)

Hold up the 10 card and ask all children to hold up 10 fingers. Ask them what number comes next. Hold up the 11 card and ask if anyone can think of a way to show 11 fingers. If no one suggests it, call on two children to work together. Choose one child to be the 10 (holding up all 10 fingers). Ask the other child how many more fingers he or she must hold up so that together the partners show 11 fingers.

Adjusting the Activity ELL

Use craft sticks and straws (singles and bundles of 10) to reinforce the concept of "10 and some more" and make a connection with your Concrete Number Counts routine.

AUDITORY ♦ KINESTHETIC ♦ TACTILE ♦ VISUAL

Have all children work with a partner. Hold up a number card between 10 and 19 and have each set of partners hold up the correct number of fingers as "10 and some more." Continue with different teen numbers. Children take turns as the 10. After several rounds, discuss how teen numbers can be thought of as "10 and some more." Ask a few children to explain what they think this means.

▶ Arranging Objects by Length (Revisit Activity 1•13, p. 70)

In the Math Center, put out a collection of objects (pencil, crayon, paper clip, and book, for example) and direct children to arrange the objects in order by length. Encourage children to make a drawing to record their findings. Have children compare their drawings and resolve any discrepancies.

B Teaching Options

ENRICHMENT

▶ Representing Tens and Ones (*Center Activity Cards*, 9)

Have children choose a number card and represent the number with craft sticks or straws (singles and bundles of 10). Children who have a good grasp of teens can represent higher numbers.

ART CONNECTION

▶ Creating Paper Chains

Put out strips of paper (at least two colors) and show children how to loop the strips through one another to create paper chains. Have children create chains with 11 to 19 links. They should use one color for the first 10 links, then a second color to continue the chain. Label the chains with the total number of links, and hang them around the classroom. (Children might also use the colored strips to create patterned chains.)

> **NOTE** Children should not use other finger combinations (such as 9 and 6) to make the numbers for this activity.

Estimation Jars

ACTIVITY 2·13

CCSS **Mathematical Practices**
SMP1, SMP2, SMP3, SMP5, SMP6
Content Standards
K.MD.1, K.MD.2

◎ **Objective** To introduce the concept of estimation.

☑ Whole Group   ☐ Partners
☐ Small Group   ☐ Center

Planning Tip Place 10 identical objects in one container. Place 15 of the same type of object in the second container. There should be a clear distinction between the amounts in the containers; the objects in the second container should fill more of the container.

Key Concepts and Skills
• Estimate the number of objects in a collection. [Number and Numeration Goal 2]
• Count objects in a collection. [Number and Numeration Goal 2]

Terms to Use estimate, about

Materials Home Link Master (*Math Masters*, p. 12); two identical clear containers; collections of small objects, such as counters or cubes

A Core Activities

▶ Making an Estimate

Show children the container with 10 objects and ask them how many objects they think are inside. After getting responses, count the objects with children and label the container with the number. Show the second container to children and ask how many objects they think are in this container. Prompt them to give reasons for their answers. Discuss how it is sometimes hard to count objects—particularly when they are mixed together—and that it is important to be able to estimate, or determine *about* how many objects there are. Point out that sometimes you need an exact number, but sometimes an **estimate,** or a "smart guess," is enough.

NOTE Estimation is an important tool in mathematics. Many children worry that estimating is somehow wrong, but, in reality, it requires good number sense and is an important aid to understanding and solving problems.

Some teachers set up an "Estimation Station" in their classroom. They change the contents of the estimation jar at the beginning of each week and invite children to record estimates during the week. The class counts the contents of the jar on Friday.

Let children examine and handle the jars. Remind them to estimate how many are in the container and not try to get an exact count. After children make their estimates, count the objects with the class. Repeat this activity periodically with different numbers of objects in the second container. Keep the same number of objects in the first container so children have a frame of reference. (This discourages wild guessing.)

Home Link 2·13 (Math Masters, p. 12)

Children begin a penny collection and use it to practice estimating and counting.

▶ Arranging Objects by Length (Revisit Activity 1·13, p. 70)

In the Math Center, add to the collection of objects to arrange in order of length. (See Arranging Objects by Length, page 113.) Invite children to find additional objects. Continue to encourage children to record and compare findings.

B Teaching Options

EXTRA PRACTICE

▶ Making Handful Estimates

Have each child take a handful of small objects (such as pennies or marbles), guess the total, and then count the objects. Compare results. Ask: *Are all handfuls the same? How different are they? Would it be fair to divide objects by handfuls?*

ENRICHMENT

▶ Comparing Sizes to Estimate

Place 12 to 16 identical objects in a clear container and label it with the number of objects inside. In a second identical container, use a different object (smaller or larger) and fill the container to approximately the same height as the first container. Have children use the first container as a reference for estimating the amount in the second container. Discuss reasons for their estimates.

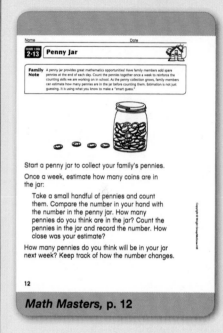

Math Masters, p. 12

CCSS **Mathematical Practices**
SMP1, SMP2, SMP4, SMP5, SMP6
Content Standards
K.CC.1, K.CC.2, K.OA.1, K.OA.2, K.OA.3, K.OA.4

Number Stories: Stage 1

ACTIVITY 2·14

◎ **Objective** To introduce addition and subtraction number stories.

☑ Whole Group
☐ Small Group
☑ Partners
☐ Center

Key Concepts and Skills
- Use concrete materials and pictures to represent and solve addition and subtraction stories.
  [Operations and Computation Goal 1]
- Begin to distinguish between joining (addition) and take-away (subtraction) stories.
  [Operations and Computation Goal 2]

Terms to Use number story, all together, join, add, take away, subtract, remove, equal, more, less, the same

Materials counters; paper (optional); markers or crayons (optional)

A Core Activities

▶ Telling and Acting Out Number Stories

Number stories provide a natural bridge from spoken to mathematical symbolic language. Children cross this bridge in stages, at first using everyday language to tell number stories, then gradually incorporating mathematical language, and ultimately using mathematical symbols to model their stories. Each stage should be introduced casually and developed over time so children gain experience with the language, concepts, and skills involved. This activity focuses on the earliest part of this process. (Activities 4-15 and 7-3, on pages 218 and 336, focus on later stages.)

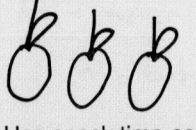

Use snack time as a basis for number stories.

Tell stories that are short, simple, and interesting to children. Use children's names and characteristics, classroom events, or other real-life situations as the basis for number stories. There is no "right" way to tell number stories. The goal is to make them meaningful and to include a variety of problem-solving strategies. *For example:*

- Mary and Jane are wearing blue tops today. Joe is wearing a blue top too. How many children in our class are wearing blue tops?

- Marcos and Sam made a block tower that was 9 blocks high. The top block fell off. How many blocks high is the tower now?

- This morning some squirrels were playing in my yard. Five were chasing each other and 2 were eating acorns. How many squirrels were there in all?

- Dayon was snack helper today. He carried 3 apples to the table. Then he got 2 more apples. How many apples did he have?

- Today 2 children are absent. There are 22 children when everyone is at school. How many children are here today?

Invite children to act out a story or use counters to show the action as you tell it. You might draw pictures on the chalkboard or chart paper to represent the story. Model how to include units (squirrels, children, or apples, for example) when you solve or draw number stories, and reinforce this whenever the class does number stories. After you and the children have created and solved several number stories together, have children work in pairs to tell each other number stories and use counters to model the action. Allow children to draw one or more of their stories if they wish.

When the class seems ready, begin to use mathematical vocabulary to describe what is happening in a number story. For example, *When you said 2 squirrels joined the group of 5 squirrels, you were adding!* or *You told a subtraction story—you started with 9 helicopters and took 2 away to have 7 left.*

Ongoing Assessment:

Informing Instruction

Listen to the language children use as they tell number stories, as well as the strategies they use to solve them (acting out, counters, drawings, mental math, and so on). Note whether children have difficulty with particular types of stories, such as addition, subtraction, comparison, or "missing number" stories. Provide extra practice and support for the story types that seem the trickiest. Subsequent activities address different types of problems more specifically.

Over the course of the year, progress through the following stages as you use number stories to help children develop problem-solving skills and build a solid understanding of addition and subtraction. Move through the stages gradually and informally, introducing and reinforcing new concepts and ideas at a pace that is comfortable for your students. Although each stage is detailed in a single activity, provide many intervening experiences to reinforce development. Use *Minute Math,* as well as children's ideas, as an ongoing source for number stories.

Stage 1: Telling and Acting Out Stories	Children use simple, everyday language to tell number stories and model them with play acting, counters, and/or simple drawings.	Described in Activity 2-14, pp. 116–119.
Stage 2: Using Mathematical Language and Symbols	Children categorize number stories as addition or subtraction and begin to relate the +, −, and = symbols to the actions in the stories.	Described in Activity 4-15, pp. 218–219.
Stage 3: Modeling with Number Sentences	Children use number sentences to model number stories.	Described in Activity 7-3, pp. 336–339.

▶ Playing Counting Games with Teens (Revisit Activity 2◆6, p. 98)

Play a few rounds of *Count and Sit* or *Follow the Leader* using teen numbers as your target numbers.

B Teaching Options

MATHEMATICS IN THE WRITING CENTER (*Center Activity Cards,* 10)

▶ Drawing and Writing Number Stories

Portfolio Ideas

Provide supplies so that children can tell and solve number stories using their drawing and emergent writing skills. Create a space where children's number stories can be posted for all to read and enjoy!

▶ Modeling Number Stories

Have children use counters to model number stories based on picture books. For example, give each child 10 counters and a container and have children move the counters appropriately as you read *Mouse Count* by Ellen Stoll Walsh (Harcourt, 1991). You can also use *Mouse Count* to explore combinations of numbers that total up to 10. As you read each page, ask children to use their counters to show and count how many mice are in the jar and how many mice are outside of the jar. You might keep track of these numbers in a simple table. Discuss that the total number of mice is always 10, and ask children what they notice about the numbers in the table. (For example, they may notice that when the numbers "in the jar" go down, the numbers "out of the jar" go up.) Children can record these combinations of 10 total mice with numbers and pictures.

Splash! by Ann Jonas (Greenwillow, 1995) also provides opportunities for posing and modeling number stories with counters. (See *Resources for the Kindergarten Classroom* for additional books to use for modeling number stories.)

▶ Creating Stories for Particular Numbers

Invite children to work on pages for class number story books about particular numbers. For example, you might have children draw and write number stories whose answer is 10 and compile these into a "Number Stories About 10" book. Discuss the different ways they get to the target number in their stories. This can be an ongoing project, with children adding new pages throughout the year. As the year progresses, encourage children to write number models for their stories.

ACTIVITY 2·15

Symmetry Painting

 Objective To introduce symmetry.

CCSS

Mathematical Practices
SMP1, SMP6, SMP7
Content Standards
K.CC.5, K.G.1, K.G.2, K.G.6

☑ Whole Group
☑ Small Group
☐ Partners
☑ Center

Key Concepts and Skills
• Explore symmetry by using paint and folded paper. [Geometry Goal 2]
• Begin to define the concept of symmetry. [Geometry Goal 2]

Terms to Use symmetry, symmetrical

Materials paper; paint; cotton swabs, small paintbrushes, eye droppers or squeeze bottles

A **Core Activities**

▶ Making Symmetrical Paintings

Demonstrate symmetry painting to the whole class or to small groups at a center. Fold a sheet of paper in half and then unfold it. On one half of the paper, place small drops or dabs of paint. Refold the paper while the paint is still wet. Gently press and smooth. Open the paper. Ask the children what they notice when they look at both sides of the paper. Introduce the word **symmetry** to describe something that has the same size and shape on both sides of a dividing line, such as the painting. Ask what will happen if you put more drops on the paper and fold it again. Test their ideas by repeating the process.

Put materials in the Art Center and invite children to create their own symmetry paintings. Children might experiment by adding paint to different sides of the paper before folding, painting representational pictures instead of blobs on one side of the paper, or trying other innovations.

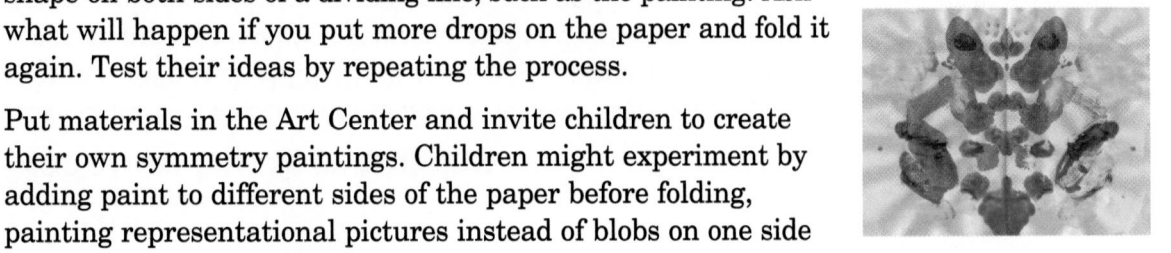

Planning Tip You may want to pre-fold sheets of paper for this activity.

NOTE Some children may describe the two halves of the picture as "the same"; others may note that they are "opposite" or "face in different directions." At this point, children should begin to recognize symmetry and describe it in their own words. Children will explore symmetry more formally in later grades of *Everyday Mathematics.*

Combining and Creating Shapes

(Revisit Activity 1•15, p. 73A; *Math Masters*, p. 5A)

Give children a set of shape cards (*Math Masters,* page 5A) and invite them to explore shape combinations. You might provide prompts such as the following: *What shape can you make with your two small squares? Can anyone find a way to make a triangle using two of their shapes? Can you combine three shapes to make another shape?* Encourage children to show and describe their discoveries after each prompt. Also provide time for free exploration with the shapes. This activity can be done in a whole group or small groups.

Also remember to use *Minute Math* during spare moments in the day.

 **B** **Teaching Options**

ELL SUPPORT

► Making Fold-and-Cut Symmetrical Shapes

Show children how to fold paper in half and then cut through both layers of paper, starting at the folded edge and cutting away from the fold. Open the paper and ask children to describe what they see. Encourage use of the word **symmetrical.**

ART CONNECTION

► Creating Symmetrical Faces

Children can look in a mirror or at a partner to explore whether bodies and faces are symmetrical. Then have children create faces using pre-cut geometric shapes, paper, markers, and glue. Discuss whether the faces they make are symmetrical.

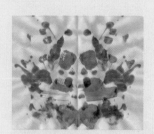

> **NOTE** Children's symmetry paintings make a beautiful display. Label the display with the word *symmetry* and include some of children's words to describe the concept of symmetry.

Symmetry in Nature

 **Objective** To develop understanding of symmetry by looking for symmetry in natural objects.

CCSS

Mathematical Practices
SMP4, SMP6, SMP7

Content Standards
K.CC.5, K.CC.6, K.MD.3

☑ Whole Group
☑ Small Group
☐ Partners
☑ Center

Key Concepts and Skills
• Look for symmetry in nature. [Geometry Goal 2]
• Describe symmetrical objects. [Geometry Goal 2]

Terms to Use symmetry, symmetrical

Materials magazines with photographs of natural objects (such as leaves and flowers) and/or a collection of natural objects; scissors; glue sticks; crayons or markers; large paper or posterboard

A Core Activities

▶ Making a Group Symmetry Collage

Set a large piece of paper or posterboard labeled "Symmetry in Nature" on a table, floor, or low bulletin board. Remind children of the symmetry paintings they made and review what *symmetry* means. Encourage children to talk about symmetry and how they know an object is symmetrical. Ask questions such as: *What do symmetrical objects look like? How can you make sure that something is symmetrical?* (Fold it in half.) *How would you know if it is not symmetrical?* (The sides would not be the same.)

Have children look outdoors or in magazines to find examples of symmetry in nature (for example, butterflies, animal markings, flowers, or snowflakes). Children can cut out and glue pictures to the posterboard, draw objects, or attach real-life examples. Invite children to add to the collage as they find more examples.

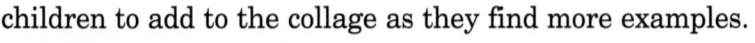

▶ Creating a Bar Graph (Revisit Activity 1•8, p. 60)

With the class, create a bar graph that shows each child's favorite school activity (center time, music, story time, recess, and so on). Write each activity (with a small picture to illustrate it, if possible) along the side or bottom of a sheet of chart paper. Add a title at the top. Consider these methods of collecting and graphing data:

▷ Collect the data by writing each child's response on a class list, then use Xs, halved index cards, paper squares, or stick-on notes to record the data in the appropriate row or column on the graph.

▷ Give each child a halved index card, square of paper, or self-stick note to add to the appropriate row or column on the graph.

Have children count and compare the results for each activity on the graph. Together, use the totals to rank the activities from least popular to most popular. Ask children what other information they know from the graph. Post the graph in the classroom or hallway.

B Teaching Options

ELL SUPPORT

▶ Finding Symmetrical Objects in Books

As you read picture books aloud, point out examples of symmetry you notice in the illustrations. Invite children to look for and share other examples of symmetry. Help them describe the pictures.

SCIENCE CONNECTION

▶ Sorting Natural Objects

Begin a class collection of natural objects. (Invite children to find objects while on a walk or on the playground.) Have children sort the objects into two piles: symmetrical and non-symmetrical. (Later, they can sort by other attributes.) After each sort, have children count and compare the numbers of objects in each category.

Ongoing Assessment:

Recognizing Student Achievement

Use **Symmetry in Nature** to assess children's ability to identify symmetrical objects. Children are making adequate progress if they are able to recognize line symmetry in objects.

[Geometry Goal 2]

NOTE After children have sorted the class collection of natural objects, you may wish to construct a real-object graph based on how the class has grouped the objects.

Mathematics and Our Bodies

CCSS

Mathematical Practices
SMP1, SMP2, SMP3,
SMP4, SMP5, SMP6, SMP7

◎ **Objective** To provide opportunities for children to use their bodies as tools for understanding and applying mathematical skills and concepts.

Terms to Use digit, yard, hand, hand span, measure, body measures, height, weight, length, symmetry, symmetrical

Materials

Our Bodies Help Us Count
☐ None

Our Bodies Help Us Measure
☐ markers or crayons; paper (optional)

Our Bodies Can Be Described with Numbers
☐ string, adding machine tape, or tape measure
☐ mirrors
☐ paper; markers or crayons
☐ Home Link (*Math Masters*, p. 67) (optional)

Our Bodies Are Symmetrical
☐ mirrors
☐ cutout paper doll

Introduction

In the distant past, measurement, comparison, and counting were directly related to the human body. For young children, the body remains an important tool for experiencing, understanding, and applying various mathematical skills and concepts. In this project, children explore some of these physical counts and measures to expand and consolidate their developing mathematical ideas and number sense. The project activities informally introduce ideas about circumference, nonstandard measurement, and how people in different countries represent numbers. This project also offers meaningful opportunities to connect mathematics with social studies as children talk and learn about the past and about the conventions of different countries. Choose the topics and activities in this project that most interest you and your class.

Activity Options

▶ **Our Bodies Help Us Count** ☑ **Whole Group** ☑ **Small Group** ☑ **Partners**

Explain that *digit,* the term we use to talk about the numbers 0–9, also means "finger." Fingers were among the first objects people used for counting and are still a useful way to show and keep track of a simple count. Explain to children that if they travel to a country where they don't speak the language, they may need to show "how many" by holding up their fingers.

Finger Counting in Africa Have children pretend they are in a village in East Africa and want to buy 3 oranges. Ask them to show the number using fingers on just one hand. Then have them show the same number using fingers on both hands (1 finger and 2 fingers).

Now have them pretend that they want to buy 8 bananas. Ask: *How many hands do you need to show eight?* Then say: *Show 8 in two different ways on your fingers* (4 and 4; 5 and 3). *Are there any other finger combinations for 8?* Explain that the Maasai (Maa sî) people of East Africa show 8 by waving 4 fingers of their right hand twice (4 + 4). The Kamba (Kaam-bû) people show 8 a different way. The right hand holds 3 fingers of the left hand. (Five fingers on the right and 3 fingers on the left make 8.)

Invite children to think of other numbers to show. When they reach the teens, they may need a partner. Have them think about using different rules. For example, ask: *What if the rule is that each person can only hold up one finger?* Ask a child to show the class the number 3 using this rule. Ask someone else to show 8. (They'll need to call helpers for both.)

⭕ **Literature Link** Read and discuss *Count On Your Fingers African Style* by Claudia Zaslavsky (Black Butterfly Children's Books, 2000). If you wish to pursue African counting further, see *Africa Counts* by Claudia Zaslavsky (Lawrence Hill Books, 1999).

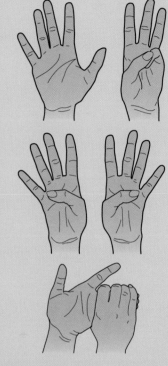

Different ways to show the number 8

▶ Our Bodies Help Us Measure
✔ **Whole Group** ✔ **Small Group**

In early times, before standard measurements were agreed upon, people used different parts of their bodies as measuring devices. A **yard** was about the distance from the nose to the tips of the fingers of an outstretched arm. Fingers, besides being useful for counting, were used to measure. A **digit** is about the width of a finger. A **hand** is about the width of the palm; a **hand span** is about the width of the outstretched fingers.

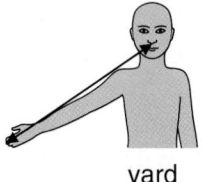   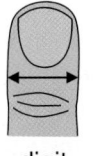   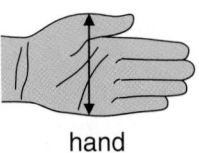   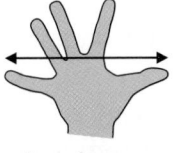

| yard | digit | hand | hand span |

Introduce some of these common "body measures" to your class. Encourage children to try them out. For example, demonstrate how to measure a block building with hand spans or a classroom plant with digits. Encourage children to compare their measurements and think about why the measurements might be different from one another.

You might have children find something longer, shorter, and about the same length as a digit, then a hand span. Consider having them record their findings with drawings.

▶ Our Bodies Can Be Described with Numbers
✔ **Whole Group** ✔ **Small Group**

Children can collect numbers related to their bodies and include them in their own record books. They might include some or all of the following:

Linear Measurements Help children measure height, fathom (the length between outstretched arms), and foot or leg length. Measure and record several times during the year, and track and compare the results over time. Children can use standard or nonstandard measuring units or measure with lengths of string or adding machine tape.

Circumference Measurements Prompt children to discuss how the distance around the waist, head, neck, or wrist might be measured. After children share and try their ideas, you can show them how to use string or measuring tape, if these haven't been suggested.

NOTE Children will have more experiences measuring with their bodies and using this as a basis for understanding the need for standard units of measure in Section 5. For additional information on personal measures and measurement, see "Measurement" in the *Teacher's Reference Manual,* Chapter 12.

Number of Teeth This is a topic of great interest in Kindergarten! Children can look in mirrors and examine their teeth and try to count them. Some classrooms keep a running tally of the total number of missing (and/or loose) teeth in the class. Some classes create other types of "tooth graphs."

Heart Beat (Pulse) Help children find a wrist or neck pulse point and count their resting pulse rate (the resting pulse of a six-year-old is usually about 90 to 100 beats per minute). Have children do 20 jumping jacks and then check again. (This is easier to manage if extra adults are on hand, or if children do the activity at home and bring the results to school.)

Sizes Discuss shoe size or clothing size. Talk with children about how numbers help them choose clothes and shoes that fit.

Home Link Suggestions (*Math Masters,* p. 67)
Children can weigh and measure themselves at home, then compare their weight and height to other objects. You might use *Math Masters,* page 67, which suggests some measurement ideas.

▶ Our Bodies Are Symmetrical
✔ Whole Group ✔ Small Group

Remind children of the symmetry activities in Section 2 (Activities 2-15 and 2-16, pages 120 and 122). Ask: *Is your body symmetrical?* Prompt them to think about their entire body, as well as its individual parts. Discuss children's ideas and conclusions. Count fingers, toes, eyes, and so on. Encourage children to look in the mirror and at each other to find body parts that are symmetrical, such as noses and mouths. Show them a paper doll. Fold it along the line of symmetry. What would happen if they were able to fold themselves?

Literature Link These two books complement all of the project activities: *Me and My Amazing Body* by Joan Sweeney (Crown Publishers, Inc., 1999); *If You Hopped like a Frog* by David M. Schwartz (Scholastic Press, 1999).

NOTE There are 20 baby teeth and 32 permanent teeth. These include sharp-edged teeth for biting (incisors and canines) and flatter, bumpy-surfaced teeth for chewing and grinding (bicuspids and molars).

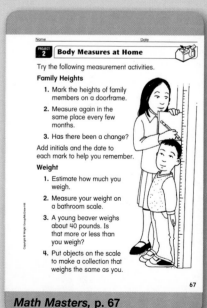

Body Measures at Home

Try the following measurement activities.

Family Heights
1. Mark the heights of family members on a doorframe.
2. Measure again in the same place every few months.
3. Has there been a change?

Add initials and the date to each mark to help you remember.

Weight
1. Estimate how much you weigh.
2. Measure your weight on a bathroom scale.
3. A young beaver weighs about 40 pounds. Is that more or less than you weigh?
4. Put objects on the scale to make a collection that weighs the same as you.

Math Masters, p. 67

Section 3

Overview

Section 3 has a number of main areas of focus:

◆ To introduce the concepts of addition and subtraction through concrete activities,

◆ To introduce number writing,

◆ To reinforce and extend counting, numeral recognition, and number comparison skills,

◆ To introduce skip counting by 10s,

◆ To introduce the pan balance,

◆ To introduce non-standard measurement tools and units for measuring length,

◆ To introduce the basic language of probability,

◆ To continue shape recognition, patterning, and graphing activities, and

◆ To continue estimation and number story activities.

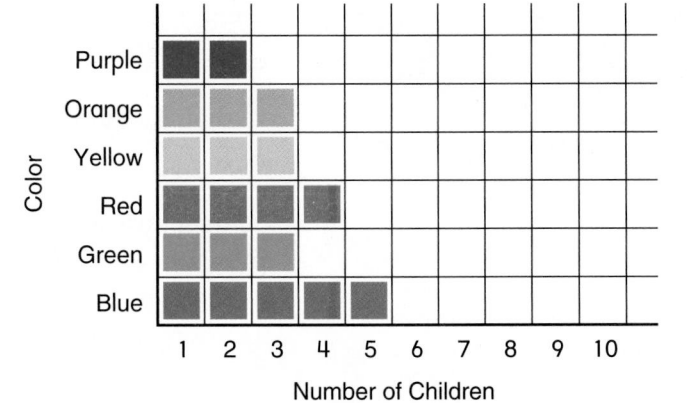

Number of Children
Favorite Colors Graph

Maintaining Ongoing Daily Routines

Doing the Routines

In addition to Section 3 Activities, continue to do the following Ongoing Daily Routines each day:

- Number of the Day
- Attendance
- Job Chart
- Monthly Calendar
- Daily Schedule
- Weather Observation
- Recording Daily Temperature
- Survey

Adjusting the Routines

Each Ongoing Daily Routine can be adjusted periodically according to children's progress and interests. Ongoing Daily Routines are a powerful tool for practicing and reinforcing the skills that are introduced in the activities. If you haven't already done so, use the following routines to introduce new ideas and ask different questions during and after Section 3:

- **Weather Observation and Recording Daily Temperature** Have children look at the weather and temperature data for the month and describe and discuss the compiled observations. *How many sunny days were in November? Were there more sunny than cloudy days this month? How did the temperature change this month?*

- **Attendance** Use the attendance data as a source for number stories and problem solving. For example, ask: *Are there more boys or girls at school today? Can you figure out how many more?*

Using Routines for Ongoing Assessment

All of the Ongoing Daily Routines offer opportunities for ongoing assessment of a variety of skills and concepts. You might want to use the following routines for ongoing assessment during Section 3:

- **Weather Observation and Recording Daily Temperature** Can children correctly add daily data to the weather and temperature records? Can they interpret and compare the weather and temperature data? Do they understand that a thermometer is a tool for measuring temperature?

- **Attendance** Can children answer questions or solve number stories based on the attendance data?

Section Opener

Learning in Perspective

Core Activities

Activity	Objective	Revisit Activity	Page
3·1	**Number Books** To provide practice with writing and representing numbers.	**Reviewing Color Patterns** (Activity 1-10, p. 64) ⬭ **Links to the Past** In Section 1, children worked with sound, movement, and color patterns.	**138**
3·2	**Macaroni Necklaces** To provide practice with creating and describing patterns through an art project.	**Estimating Pennies** (Activity 2-13, p. 114) ⬭ **Links to the Past** In Activity 2-13, children learned about estimation. They will have opportunities to estimate in every section in Kindergarten.	**140**
3·3	**Roll and Record** To review counting and number recognition through a graphing activity.	**Continuing Number Books** (Activity 3-1, p. 138)	**142**
3·4	**The Pan Balance** To introduce the pan balance as a tool to compare the weights of objects.	**Playing *Give the Next Number*** (Activity 1-12, p. 68)	**144**
3·5	***Domino Concentration* Game** To introduce a game that involves matching numbers of dots to written numbers.	**Continuing Number Books** (Activity 3-1, p. 138)	**148**
3·6	***Monster Squeeze* Game** To introduce a game that reinforces number relationships and number recognition.	**Telling and Drawing Number Stories** (Activity 2-14, p. 116) ⬭ **Links to the Past** Children were introduced to number stories in Activity 2-14.	**150**
3·7	**Measurement with Objects** To introduce measurement techniques using interlocking cubes or other nonstandard measuring devices.	**Continuing Number Books** (Activity 3-1, p. 138)	**152**
3·8	**Pocket Problems** To develop children's understanding of addition and subtraction using concrete experiences. ⬭ **Links to the Future** Children will learn more formal addition and subtraction procedures beginning in Grade 1.	**Graphing Dice Rolls** (Activity 3-3, p. 142; *Math Masters*, p. 26 or 27) ⬭ **Links to the Past** Children learned to graph dice rolls in Activity 3-3.	**156**

Core Activities, *continued*

Activity	Objective	Revisit Activity	Page
3·9	**Number Card Games** To review counting, number recognition, and sequencing numbers 0–20 through number card activities.	**Continuing Number Books** (Activity 3-1, p. 138)	158
3·10	**Probability Stories** To introduce the basic language of probability. ⌖ **Links to the Future** Children work with qualitative descriptions of probability in Grades K-2. They begin to calculate quantitative representations of probability in Grade 3.	**Creating Shape Art** (Activities 1-15 and 2-1, pp. 73A and 88) ⌖ **Links to the Past** In Section 2, children participated in a variety of introductory shape activities with circles, squares, triangles, and rectangles.	160
3·11	**Probability Tray** To develop children's understanding of probability.	**Creating Shape Art** (Activities 1-15, 2-1, and 3-10, pp. 73A, 88, and 160)	162
3·12	**Pan Balance 2: Leveling** To review the use of the pan balance and introduce the concept of balancing objects.	**Playing *Count and Sit*** (Activity 2-6, p. 98) ⌖ **Links to the Past** Children learned to play *Count and Sit* in Activity 2-6. They may be ready for higher numbers.	164
3·13	**Train Games** To introduce a series of games that provide practice with counting and concrete addition and subtraction.	**Playing *I Spy* Patterns** (Activity 2-5, p. 96) ⌖ **Links to the Past** Children looked for patterns in their surroundings in Activity 2-5.	166
3·14	**Favorite Colors Graph** To provide practice with making and analyzing a bar graph.	**Measuring with Objects** (Activity 3-7, p. 152) ⌖ **Links to the Past** Children learned to measure with uniform-length objects in Activity 3-7.	168
3·15	**Count by 10s** To introduce skip counting by 10s. ⌖ **Links to the Future** Children will learn to count by 5s in Activity 5-8 and to count by 2s in Activity 6-10.	**Solving Pocket Problems** (Activity 3-8, p. 156)	170
3·16	***Teen Frame* Game** To introduce a game that provides practice with teen numbers and builds number sense.	**Choosing from a Probability Tray** (Activity 3-11, p. 162)	172

Ongoing Learning and Practice

Practice through Games

Project 3, Fun with Games, includes a variety of mathematics-related games, including strategy games from around the world and games for addition and subtraction facts practice. In addition, these games are introduced in this section:

Activity	Game	Skill Practiced
3◆3	*Dice Race*	**Counting dots and graphing dice rolls** [Number and Numeration Goal 2; Data and Chance Goal 1]
3◆5	*Domino Concentration*	**Counting and matching numbers of dots to written numerals** [Number and Numeration Goals 2 and 3]
3◆6	*Monster Squeeze*	**Comparing and ordering numbers** [Number and Numeration Goal 6]
3◆11	*Stick Pick-Up*	**Recording and analyzing outcomes and counting and comparing results** [Data and Chance Goals 1 and 3]
3◆13	Train Games	**Counting cubes, adding and subtracting cubes, and complements of 10** [Number and Numeration Goal 2; Operations and Computation Goals 1 and 2]
3◆16	*Teen Frame*	**Reading, counting, and comparing teen numbers** [Number and Numeration Goals 2, 3 and 6]

Home-School Connection

Home Links provide homework and home communication. The following activities contain Home Links: 3-2, 3-6, 3-7, 3-12, 3-15.

Home Connection Handbook provides more ideas to communicate effectively with parents. ▶

◀ *Mathematics at Home* Books 1–4 provide additional ideas for enjoyable mathematics activities that families can do together. Families can do activities from **Book 2** during Section 3.

Balanced Assessment

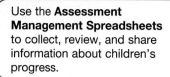

Use the **Assessment Management Spreadsheets** to collect, review, and share information about children's progress.

Ongoing Assessment

 ### Recognizing Student Achievement

Opportunities to assess children's progress toward Kindergarten Goals:

Activity	Content Assessed
3◆1	Represent numerals 1–10 using the correct number of objects. [Number and Numeration Goal 2]
3◆2	Create and describe a pattern. [Patterns, Functions, and Algebra Goal 1]
3◆5	Count 1–12 objects and match numbers with numerals. [Number and Numeration Goals 2 and 3]
3◆16	Count and compare teen numbers. [Number and Numeration Goals 2 and 6]

Informing Instruction

To anticipate common trouble spots and highlight problem-solving strategies:

Activity 3◆6
Compare and order numbers

Activity 3◆9
Count, read, represent, and order numbers through 20

Activity 3◆11
Predict or describe the probability of an event

Activity 3◆12
Use a pan balance

Activity 3◆13
Understand the difference between addition and subtraction

Activity 3◆14
Use information from graphs to answer questions

Periodic Assessment

Baseline assessment tasks were completed in Section 1. Mid-Year assessment tasks will be completed in Sections 4 and 5.

Portfolio Opportunities

◆ Number books, **Activity 3-1**
◆ Patterned necklaces, **Activity 3-2**
◆ Pan balance drawings or records, **Activity 3-4**
◆ Measurement Records, **Activity 3-7**
◆ Roll and Record sheets, **Activity 3-8**

Assessment Handbook

◆ Kindergarten Goals, pp. 27–33
◆ Section 3 Assessment Overview, pp. 54–55
◆ Assessment Overviews by Strand, pp. 66–75
◆ Individual Profile of Progress and Class Checklist (Sections 3–4), pp. 79–80
◆ Cumulative Individual Profile of Progress (Sections 1–4), pp. 97–98

Differentiated Instruction

Teaching Options

Use optional Part B activities as time permits to meet individual and class needs and to integrate mathematics throughout the Kindergarten classroom and schedule.

ELL SUPPORT

3•4 Understanding *heavier* and *lighter*
3•10 Understanding *certain* and *impossible*

READINESS

3•1 Writing on backs
3•5 Matching dominoes and number cards
3•13 Making a train of children

CONNECTIONS

Literacy
3•7 Reading about measurement
3•10 Using probability vocabulary
3•12 Reading a book about weight
3•13 Counting passengers on a train
3•14 Graphing hat colors
3•15 Reading a book about counting by 10s

Science
3•4 Comparing weights of natural objects
3•7 Measuring blue whales with body measures

Art
3•2 Making pattern prints
3•6 Making symmetrical monsters
3•10 Creating class probability collages
3•16 Creating number art

Music
3•15 Counting to rhythms and music

Social Studies
3•14 Learning color names in different languages

ENRICHMENT

3•3 Varying Roll and Record
3•7 Measuring with different units
3•12 Weighing objects with nonstandard units

EXTRA PRACTICE

3•1 Writing on slates
3•2 Creating pattern strips
3•3 Playing *Dice Race*
3•4 Predicting and testing weights of objects
3•5 Playing dominoes
3•6 Playing *Monster Squeeze* (Mini Version)
3•9 Playing with number cards
3•11 Playing *Stick Pick-Up*
3•16 Using a 10 Die

CENTERS

Dramatic Play
3•8 Playing with pockets and counters

Writing Center
3•9 Tracing numbers

TECHNOLOGY

3•8 Playing addition and subtraction computer games

Language Support

Everyday Mathematics provides activity-specific suggestions to help *all* young children develop the language necessary to acquire, process, and express mathematical ideas. Activities that provide additional support for non-native English speakers are marked by (ELL SUPPORT) and (ELL).

Connecting Math and Literacy

Activity 3◆10 *And to Think That I Saw It on Mulberry Street* by Dr. Seuss, *Wacky Wednesday* by Theo LeSieg (Random House, 1989; 1974)

Activity 3◆14 *Caps for Sale* by Esphyr Slobodkina (HarperTrophy, 1987)

Activity 3◆15 *One Hundred Is a Family* by Pam Munoz Ryan (Hyperion, 1994)

See pages 154, 165, and 167 for more literature suggestions.

Using the Projects

Use Fun with Games (Project 3, page 174) during or after Section 3 to incorporate a variety of mathematics-related games into your classroom, including games for addition and subtraction facts practice.

Adjusting the Activity

AUDITORY ◆ **KINESTHETIC** ◆ **TACTILE** ◆ **VISUAL**

Activity 3◆1 Revisiting strokes and prewriting activities

Activity 3◆9 Adding dots to number cards and varying the numbers

Activity 3◆13 Using smaller or larger numbers of cubes in games

Language & Vocabulary

Use these terms informally.

1s, 10s	match
add	maybe
all	measure
approximate	might happen
balance	more
bar graph	most
bigger	none
certain	number line
chance	order
column	pan balance
compare	pattern
count back	possible
count on	predict
counting by 10s	probably
equal	remove
forward	repeat
half	row
heavier	same
high	skip counting
how many	smaller
impossible	some
least	subtract
less	take away
level	teen
lighter	ten
likely	unlikely
low	weight

Planning Tips

Pacing

Pacing depends on a number of factors, such as children's individual needs and how long your school has been using *Everyday Mathematics*. Use the optional Part B activities throughout Section 3 if you have extended mathematics instructional time. See page 134 for a list of these activities.

OCTOBER	←——— MOST CLASSROOMS ———→	
	NOVEMBER	DECEMBER

Teaching Resources

Resources for the Kindergarten Classroom provides additional teaching ideas, including suggestions for bringing mathematics into thematic instruction, as well as using games, literature, technology, and rhymes to support mathematics learning. ▶

Minute Math provides brief activities for transition times and for spare moments throughout the day. During Section 3, use activities in Part 2, pages 67–196.

NCTM Standards

Content Standards: 1 Number and Operations, **2** Algebra, **3** Geometry, **4** Measurement, **5** Data Analysis and Probability
Process Standards: 6 Problem Solving, **7** Reasoning and Proof, **8** Communication, **9** Connection, **10** Representation

Section 3 Activities	3•1	3•2	3•3	3•4	3•5	3•6	3•7	3•8	3•9	3•10	3•11	3•12	3•13	3•14	3•15	3•16
NCTM Standards	1, 10	2, 9	1, 5, 7, 8	4, 6, 7, 8	1, 10	1, 6, 7, 8	4, 6, 8	1, 7, 8	1, 10	5, 8	5, 7, 8	4, 7, 8	1, 9	5, 10	1, 2, 6, 8	1, 6, 10

Professional Development

Teacher's Reference Manual Links

Activity	Topic	Section	Activity	Topic	Section
3•10	Probability	10.1	3•15	Plain and Fancy Counting and Sequences	8.2.2 and 15.1.3

Materials

Activity	Masters	Materials	
3·1	Teaching Masters, pp. 13–24	• pencils	• markers or crayons
3·2	Home Link Master, p. 25	• tube-shaped macaroni or other hollow pasta • string	• food coloring • rubbing alcohol (optional)
3·3	Teaching Masters, pp. 26 and 27	• dice* • pencils, crayons, or markers	
3·4		• one or more pan balances* • two identical clear containers each filled with a different material (paper	clips, counters, or sand) • interesting objects to weigh • blank paper and pencils (optional)
3·5	Teaching Aid Masters, pp. 105 and 106 Game Masters, pp. 121–123	• sets of double-six dominoes*	
3·6	Home Link Master, p. 28 Game Masters, pp. 126 and 127	• number line* • metersticks* (optional)	
3·7	Home Link Master, p. 29	• set of interlocking cubes*, plastic links, or other interlocking objects of uniform length, such as paper clips	• several small items of different lengths, such as a piece of chalk, a pencil, a crayon, a straw*, a spoon, and a block
3·8		• 10 counters* • bag or box with a pocket design	drawn or pasted on the front

Activity	Masters	Materials	
3·9	Teaching Aid Masters, pp. 105–107	• scissors • large paper clips or small plastic bags	
3·10		• a book that features unlikely or impossible events	
3·11		• tray • red and blue connecting cubes*	(or other counters* in two colors)
3·12	Home Link Master, p. 30	• one or more pan balances* • various objects to weigh	• clay (or similar material)
3·13		• interlocking cubes* • green die* (marked 1, 2, 3, 1, 2, 3) • red die* (marked 1, 2, 3, 1, 2, 3)	• die colored red on four sides* (marked 1, 2, 3, 3) and green on two sides* (marked 1, 2)
3·14		• posterboard • squares of white paper	• markers, crayons, or colored pencils • tape or glue stick
3·15	Home Link Master, p. 31	• Growing Number Line • Concrete Number Counts containers	• additional straws* or sticks* (optional)
3·16	Game Masters, pp. 137, 138, and 139	• large paper clips • pencils • counters* for the	gameboard • scoring counters*

Technology
Assessment Management Spreadsheets,
Section 3: See the *iTGA*.

* Indicates items in the Kindergarten manipulative kit.

Number Books

CCSS Mathematical Practices
SMP1, **SMP2,** SMP3,
SMP4, SMP6, **SMP7**
Content Standards
K.CC.3

ACTIVITY 3·1

◎ **Objective** To provide practice with writing and representing numbers.

☑ Whole Group ☐ Partners
☑ Small Group ☑ Center

Key Concepts and Skills
• Draw the correct quantity of items to represent numbers. [Number and Numeration Goal 2]
• Practice writing numerals. [Number and Numeration Goal 3]
• Discuss and reinforce the concept of zero. [Number and Numeration Goal 3]

Terms to Use number

Materials Teaching Masters (*Math Masters,* pp. 13–24); pencils; markers or crayons

Planning Tip Introduce one number at a time and take as many days as needed for your class. *Math Masters,* page 24 is a blank number book sheet, which some children may use to make pages for larger numbers.

A Core Activities

▶ Writing Numbers 0–10 (*Math Masters,* pp. 13–24)

Introduce each number by giving explicit directions as you model how to write the number on the board. For example: *Start at the dot on the top line, come straight down, and stop at the bottom line.* Children can write with their fingers in the air as you demonstrate the process. Large writing motions and verbal prompts are helpful for many children.

After you introduce a number, children write the number in pencil in the top section of the *Math Masters* page. Then they use markers or crayons to draw a corresponding number of objects in the box below. The objects do not need to be the same, and they do not need to be elaborate. For example, one child might draw a tree, a house, and a person for the number 3; another might draw three Xs. When children work on the 0 page, start a discussion with the question: *What goes in the picture box to show zero?*

Name _____ Date _____

ACTIVITY 3·1 Number Book (1)

14

Math Masters, p. 14

Some children will want to leave the box empty; others may want a "0" in the box. Discuss whether a box with "0" is empty.

 Collect each child's pages. When the pages for numbers 0–10 are completed, children can compile them, think of titles for their books, and decorate the covers. Send the books home or save them for portfolios or other assessment purposes. Some teachers have children make number books at the year's end to note their progress.

Portfolio Ideas

▶ Reviewing Color Patterns (Revisit Activity 1•10, p. 64)

Use markers, colored chalk, or connecting cubes to start several color patterns of varying levels of complexity. Allow children to take turns continuing the patterns. Ask for volunteers to describe each pattern. For example, *"one red, one blue; one red, one blue; …"* or *"red, red, green; red, red, green; …"*

B Teaching Options

READINESS

▶ Writing on Backs

Children take turns writing a number on a partner's back with a finger. The partner then identifies the number orally or in writing on a slate.

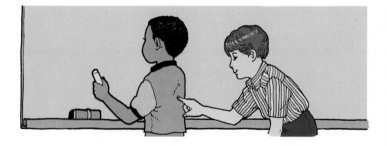

EXTRA PRACTICE

▶ Writing on Slates (*Math Masters*, pp. 13–24)

Provide slates in the Math Center and use *Math Masters,* pages 13–24 as a guide for children to practice writing numbers.

Adjusting the Activity

Revisit the strokes and pre-writing activities from Activity 2-7, page 100, to help children who need additional practice before making their pages.

AUDITORY ◆ KINESTHETIC ◆ TACTILE ◆ VISUAL

Ongoing Assessment:

Recognizing Student Achievement

Use **Number Books** to assess children's ability to represent the numeral with the correct number of items. Children are making adequate progress if they draw the correct number of pictures on each page. Some children may still have difficulty with handwriting and number formation at this point; this will improve with maturation and practice.

[Number and Numeration Goal 2]

Macaroni Necklaces

CCSS
Mathematical Practices
SMP1, SMP2, **SMP3,**
SMP4, SMP5, SMP6, **SMP7**

◎ **Objective** To provide practice with creating and describing patterns through an art project.

☐ Whole Group   ☐ Partners
☐ Small Group   ☑ Center

Key Concepts and Skills
• Create and describe a pattern. [Patterns, Functions, and Algebra Goal 1]

Terms to Use pattern, repeat

Materials Home Link Master (*Math Masters*, p. 25); tube-shaped macaroni or other hollow pasta; string; food coloring; rubbing alcohol (optional)

Planning Tip Dye pasta by gently shaking it in a jar with food coloring or liquid watercolors. Add rubbing alcohol to the food coloring for more vivid colors.

A **Core Activities**

▶ Making Macaroni Necklaces

Provide a large quantity of one type of stringable pasta, dyed in several different colors. Have children string the colored pasta in patterns to make necklaces. Ask them to describe the pattern they created. (For example: *red, blue; red blue; ...* or *yellow and two blues; yellow and two blues; ...*) Encourage children to note similarities and differences in their patterns. Leave the materials in a center until all children have a chance to make at least one necklace.

✔ **Ongoing Assessment:**
Recognizing Student Achievement

Use **Making Macaroni Necklaces** to assess children's ability to create, extend, and describe patterns. Children are making adequate progress if they are able to independently make a patterned necklace and describe the pattern.

[Patterns, Functions, and Algebra Goal 1]

Portfolio Ideas

After children have made necklaces with one type of pasta, provide a mixture of pasta shapes in different colors to use to create necklaces with more complex patterns. You might put photographs of children's necklaces in their portfolios, if you use portfolio assessment.

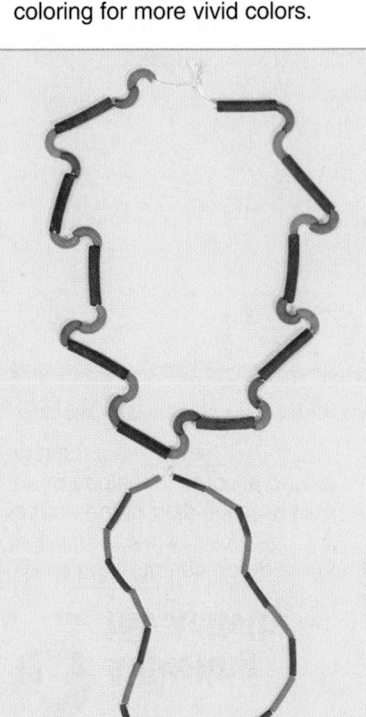

Home Link 3·2 (*Math Masters*, p. 25)

Children create shape and color patterns at home with cereal or pasta.

▶ Estimating Pennies (Revisit Activity 2·13, p. 114)

Put 20 pennies in a clear jar and ask children to estimate how many pennies are inside. Provide an identical "reference jar" with 10 pennies in it for comparison (mark the number on the jar). Have each child record his or her estimate on an index card or stick-on note. Provide help as needed. Work with the class to order the cards from lowest to highest estimate. Count the pennies and compare the actual number to the children's estimates. Children's estimate cards can be arranged in a non-permanent bar graph, with all of the "way too low" estimates in a column on the left, all of the "pretty close" estimates in the middle column, and all of the "way too high" estimates in a third column on the right. Discuss what range of numbers should be considered "pretty close." The steps in this activity provide practice with writing, ordering, and comparing numbers; you might repeat them each time you do an estimation activity.

B Teaching Options

EXTRA PRACTICE

▶ Creating Pattern Strips (*Center Activity Cards*, 11)

Use the Pattern-Block Template and markers to begin patterns of varying complexity on sentence strips. Leave space for children to use pattern blocks to extend the pattern on the strips. Keep the strips in the Math Center.

ART CONNECTION

▶ Making Pattern Prints

Children can make pattern prints by dipping a variety of different-shaped sponges or cookie cutters into different-colored paints and pressing them onto paper.

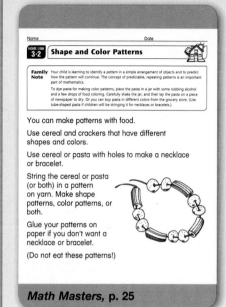

Math Masters, p. 25

---

141 **Activity 3·2** Macaroni Necklaces

ACTIVITY 3·3

Roll and Record

CCSS

Mathematical Practices
SMP2, SMP4, SMP6
Content Standards
K.CC.3, K.CC.4a, K.CC.4b

Objective To review counting and number recognition through a graphing activity.

☑ Whole Group
☑ Small Group
☐ Partners
☑ Center

Key Concepts and Skills
• Count dots on a single die. [Number and Numeration Goal 2]
• Read and write numbers 1–6. [Number and Numeration Goal 3]
• Create a simple graph of dice rolls. [Data and Chance Goal 1]
• Make predictions about dice throws and discuss results. [Data and Chance Goal 3]

Terms to Use count, numbers, graph, row, column, predict

Materials Teaching Masters (*Math Masters,* pp. 26 and 27); dice; pencils, crayons, or markers

Planning Tip To demonstrate this activity you may want to enlarge a copy of *Math Masters,* page 26, or create a large version of the Roll and Record sheet on the board or chart paper.

A Core Activities

▶ **Graphing Dice Rolls** (*Math Masters,* pp. 26 and 27)

Invite children to look closely at various classroom graphs (birthday graph, age change graph, weather graphs, and so on). Point out that graphs often include information in rows that go across the page and/or columns that go from top to bottom. To support English language learners, use gestures and the graphs to discuss the terms *row* and *column.* Discuss the information each graph shows.

Tell children they will make their own graphs that show how many times they roll each number on a die. Model the procedure by inviting volunteers to roll a single die. Solicit their input as you fill in the appropriate squares on the Roll and Record sheet.

Give each child one die and a copy of the Roll and Record sheet (*Math Masters,* page 26 or page 27). Children roll the die, count the dots to find the number, and fill in the next

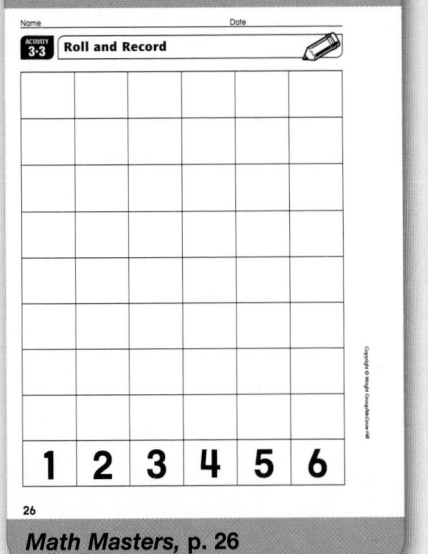

Math Masters, p. 26

open box above that number on their graphs. They continue rolling and marking until one column is filled. Have children circle the number that reaches the top first.

As children work, ask them if they think they are more likely to roll one number than another. Through observation and discussion, help them realize that each number is represented the same number of times (once) on the die.

You might compile class data from the activity. Children report the number that "won" on their graphs as you tally or graph the class results. Compare and discuss the differences between the class data and children's individual outcomes.

▶ **Continuing Number Books** (Revisit Activity 3•1, p. 138)

Provide time and assistance for children to continue their number book pages. Also remember to use *Minute Math* during spare moments in the day.

B Teaching Options

ENRICHMENT

▶ **Varying Roll and Record** (*Math Masters*, p. 26)

Children can repeat the activity using spinners or customized dice (with higher numbers, multiple instances of the same number, or other variations). Modify the *Math Masters* page to create a sheet that corresponds to the spinner or dice used. Discuss the probability of various outcomes on the spinners or customized dice.

EXTRA PRACTICE

▶ **Playing *Dice Race*** (*Math Masters*, p. 26)

Children can play *Dice Race* with a partner or in a small group. Players agree on a target number and each player circles it on his or her copy of *Math Masters*, page 26. Using one die, they take turns rolling and marking only the target number column. The child who completes the column first wins the race.

NOTE To incorporate number-writing practice, show children how to write the number in the appropriate box, rather than just shading it. You may want to use *Math Masters*, page 27, which has dotted numbers for tracing. All children can move to the number-writing variation as the year progresses.

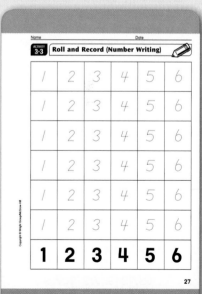

Math Masters, p. 27

The Pan Balance

Objective To introduce the pan balance as a tool to compare the weights of objects.

CCSS Mathematical Practices
SMP2, SMP3, SMP4, **SMP5, SMP6,** SMP8
Content Standards
K.CC.1, K.CC.2, **K.MD.1, K.MD.2**

☑ Whole Group
☑ Small Group
☑ Partners
☑ Center

Key Concepts and Skills

• Investigate the use of the pan balance and weighing techniques. [Measurement and Reference Frames Goal 1]

• Use a pan balance to compare and describe the weights of various objects.
  [Measurement and Reference Frames Goal 1]

Terms to Use weight, compare, heavier, lighter, pan balance, level, balance, balanced, equal

Materials one or more pan balances; two identical clear containers each filled with a different material (paper clips, counters, or sand); interesting objects to weigh; blank paper and pencils (optional)

Planning Tip Use containers that will fit in the trays or pans of your pan balance. Make sure the pan balance is leveled before using it with children. Show them the mechanism for leveling your type of balance.

A Core Activities

▶ Introducing the Pan Balance

Hold up two identical containers that are filled with different objects. One container should be noticeably heavier than the other. Pass them around and ask children if the containers feel different. How would they describe the difference? Through discussion, elicit that the **weights** of the containers feel different, which means that one feels heavier than the other. Ask children which container feels heavier. Ask if anyone knows of a tool to compare the weights of the containers.

Show the pan balance and have children describe what they notice about it. Explain that a pan balance is a type of scale that is used to compare the weights of objects. Discuss the meaning of the word *balance.* Be sure children realize that there are two empty pans and that they are at the same height, or **level.** Put one container in the pan and solicit observations.

Ask: *Why do you think the pan with the container is lower? What happens to the other pan when one goes down? What do you think will happen if we add the other container to the other side? Why do you think so?* Add the second container to the other side of the pan balance and ask children to describe what they see. Explain that the lower pan contains the heavier objects. Ask children what they think it means if both pans are level, or balanced. To summarize, review how the pan balance looks when objects in each pan are heavier, lighter, or equal weights. To support English language learners, draw and label two pictures on the board: a pan balance in which objects in one pan are heavier, and a pan balance in which the objects in both pans are the same weight.

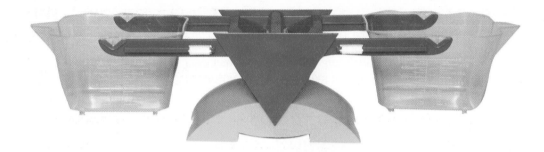

Display a variety of items. Call on a child to select two items and tell which one feels heavier (or lighter). Have the child pretend to be a pan balance by using outstretched arms to show the differing weights. Use a pan balance to check the prediction. Repeat with a few more volunteers, or have children work with a partner if you have enough objects and pan balances.

Make sure that children put one arm up to show the lighter object and one arm down to show the heavier object when they enact the arms of the pan balance. Children often will move one arm but not the other.

Portfolio Ideas

Place one or more pan balances and a collection of objects to weigh in the Math Center. Invite children to draw the balance and its contents (showing the relative level of each arm) or to record their findings in some other way. Look for opportunities to encourage children to use the pan balance.

▶ Playing *Give the Next Number* (Revisit Activity 1•12, p. 68)

Play a few rounds of *Give the Next Number* using numbers at least in the 20s and 30s. Children can refer to the Growing Number Line to help them count.

B Teaching Options

EXTRA PRACTICE

▶ Predicting and Testing Weights of Objects

Periodically, pose questions for discussion and testing such as: *Is a pencil lighter than a crayon? Which seems heavier, a marker or a glue stick?* With experience, children will become more adept at predicting, testing, and describing weight comparisons.

ELL SUPPORT

▶ Understanding *Heavier* and *Lighter*

Ask children to draw a picture representing *heavier* and a picture representing *lighter*. Children can depict these concepts in different ways.

SCIENCE CONNECTION

▶ Comparing Weights of Natural Objects

Put a pan balance in the Science Center for comparing the weights of various natural objects (rocks, shells, pine cones, or other objects children are studying). Encourage children to record their findings with drawings.

Domino Concentration Game

CCSS
Mathematical Practices
SMP1, SMP2, SMP4, SMP6
Content Standards
K.CC.3, K.CC.4a, K.CC.4b

ACTIVITY 3·5

◎ Objective To introduce a game that involves matching numbers of dots to written numbers.

☑ Whole Group   ☐ Partners
☑ Small Group   ☑ Center

Key Concepts and Skills

- Count numbers of dots on dominoes. [Number and Numeration Goal 2]
- Match numbers of dots to written numerals. [Number and Numeration Goal 3]
- Become aware of equivalent names for numbers. [Number and Numeration Goal 5]

Terms to Use half, match

Materials Teaching Aid Masters (*Math Masters*, pp. 105 and 106) to make number cards 0–12; Game Masters (*Math Masters*, pp. 121–123); sets of double-six dominoes

Planning Tip If you do not have dominoes, use additional copies of the *Math Masters*, pages 121–123, for playing the game. You might create multiple sets of number cards and dominoes and color code each set using colored dots or markers.

A   Core Activities

▶ **Playing *Domino Concentration*** (*Math Masters,* pp. 105 and 106; 121–123)

Show children a domino and point out that it is divided in half. Then show them the Domino Cards and explain that the cards look just like dominoes, but they are bigger. Explain that in this activity all the dots (from both halves) should be counted together. Show several dominoes with the same total number of dots, and note that, although they look different, they all represent the same number.

Place the Small Number Cards (0–12) in a row where everyone can see them. Mix up the Domino Cards and place them facedown in a pile. Call on children, one at a time, to choose a Domino Card and set it under the correct number. (Allow enough space for children to place all possible combinations under each number.)

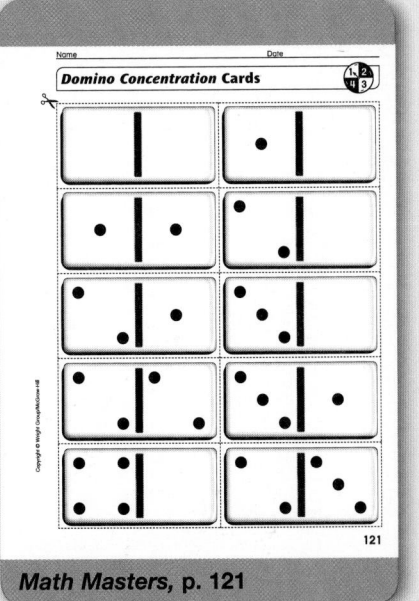

Math Masters, p. 121

After children are familiar with the dominoes, demonstrate the following concentration game. (For the game, use only one domino for each number.) Partners shuffle one set of Small Number Cards (0–12) and place the cards facedown in two rows. They also arrange the dominoes (or Domino Cards) facedown in two rows. The first player turns over one number card and one domino. If the number card matches the total number of dots on the domino, the player keeps the card-and-domino pair and continues playing. If the card and the domino do not make a pair, the player puts them back in their original places. Players try to remember which cards and dominoes they have seen so they can find matching pairs on their turns. After introducing the game, move it to the Math Center. Vary it by adding new pairs; you might use dominoes that show different combinations to make the same number.

▶ Continuing Number Books (Revisit Activity 3•1, p. 138)

Provide time and assistance for children to continue their number book pages.

B Teaching Options

READINESS

▶ Matching Dominoes and Number Cards (Center Activity Cards, 12)

Some children may need to keep dominoes and number cards faceup as they play.

EXTRA PRACTICE

▶ Playing Dominoes

Mix up a set of double-six dominoes and place them facedown. Each player draws seven tiles (for 2 players) or five tiles (for 3 or 4 players) and keeps them hidden from other players. The players confer to determine who has the highest double tile, and that tile is played to begin the game. Players take turns trying to match a domino with an end of a domino that has been played. If a player cannot match a tile, she draws from the pile until she can play. Doubles are placed crosswise. The game ends when a player uses all of his or her dominoes or no more tiles can be played. The player with no tiles left or the fewest tiles left wins.

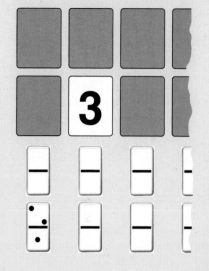

Monster Squeeze Game

CCSS
Mathematical Practices
SMP1, SMP2, SMP3,
SMP4, SMP5, SMP6, SMP8
Content Standards
K.CC.7, K.OA.1, K.OA.2

ACTIVITY
3·6

◎ **Objective** To introduce a game that reinforces number relationships and number recognition.

✔ Whole Group
✔ Small Group
☐ Partners
☐ Center

Key Concepts and Skills

• Read numbers. [Number and Numeration Goal 3]

• Compare and order numbers. [Number and Numeration Goal 6]

Terms to Use number line, big, bigger, small, smaller, more, less, high, low

Materials Home Link Master (*Math Masters,* p. 28); Game Masters (*Math Masters,* pp. 126 and 127) colored, cut out, and laminated; number line; metersticks (optional)

Planning Tip You may want to have children help you prepare the monsters. Attach each monster to a meterstick handle if it is necessary for children to reach a number line posted high on the wall.

A **Core Activities**

▶ **Playing *Monster Squeeze*** (*Math Masters,* pp. 126 and 127)

Place monsters facing each other at either end of a 0–10 number line. (You can use the 0–10 section of your Growing Number Line or hang up a new number line.) Say: *I'm thinking of a mystery number between 0 and 10.* Children take turns guessing. If the number they guess is too large, reply: *Your number is too big.* Move the right-hand monster along the number line until it covers that number. If the number they guess is too small, say: *That number is too small,* and move the left-hand monster to cover that number. Children continue guessing numbers until the correct number has been guessed, or "squeezed," between the two monsters. The child who guesses the correct answer thinks of the next number and whispers it to you. That child then responds to each guess with "too big" or "too small" and moves the monsters accordingly (with help, if necessary). As children become familiar with the game, they can respond and move the monsters without assistance.

NOTE When children identify the mystery number, the class can celebrate (and reinforce counting and numeral formation) by chanting and acting out the rhyme: *Clap it, Tap it, Write it in the air!*

Play *Monster Squeeze* frequently during the school year. As the year goes on and children become more adept at playing the game, use higher numbers on the number line, as well as a bigger range of numbers between the monsters. Also play *Monster Squeeze* as a mental math game giving only oral clues ("too big" or "too small") after each guess, without using the number line and the monsters.

Children can play a computer version of *Monster Squeeze* using *Everyday Mathematics EM Games.*

Home Link 3·6 *(Math Masters,* p. 28)

Children teach family members how to play *Monster Squeeze.* You may want to save this Home Link until children have had more practice with the game.

▶ Telling and Drawing Number Stories (Revisit Activity 2·14, p. 116)

Have children tell a number story for a partner to draw and solve. Children should have a turn telling their own story and drawing and solving someone else's story.

B Teaching Options

EXTRA PRACTICE

▶ Playing *Monster Squeeze* Mini Version *(Math Masters,* p. 128)

Use *Math Masters,* page 128 to create (or have children create) a set of mini monsters and number lines that can be used in the Math Center.

ART CONNECTION

▶ Making Symmetrical Monsters

Children can create pairs of monsters by folding a sheet of paper in half, painting a monster on one side, then refolding and rubbing. Remind children of their symmetry paintings (Activity 2-15, page 120). Ask if their monsters are symmetrical.

Ongoing Assessment:
Informing Instruction

As children become proficient with the game, watch for those who cannot provide or use clues to narrow in on a mystery number. These children may benefit from additional number-comparing activities.

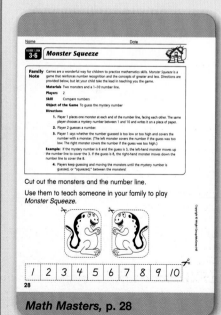

Math Masters, p. 28

Measurement with Objects

CCSS Mathematical Practices
SMP1, **SMP2,** SMP4,
SMP5, SMP6
Content Standards
K.CC.3, **K.MD.1, K.MD.2**

◎ **Objective** To introduce measurement techniques using interlocking cubes or other nonstandard measuring devices.

☑ Whole Group
☑ Small Group
☐ Partners
☑ Center

Key Concepts and Skills
• Measure items using objects of uniform length. [Measurement and Reference Frames Goal 1]
• Compare lengths and arrange items by length. [Measurement and Reference Frames Goal 1]

Terms to Use measure, about, approximate

Materials Home Link Master (*Math Masters*, p. 29); set of interlocking cubes, plastic links, or other interlocking objects of uniform length, such as paper clips; several small items of different lengths, such as a piece of chalk, a pencil, a crayon, a straw, a spoon, and a block

Planning Tip For the activity, use only one type of device for measuring so children have a consistent unit of length. (See the Enrichment activity in which children measure the same object with different devices.)

A Core Activities

▶ Measuring with Nonstandard Units

Display the items you collected where everyone can see them. Have a few children take turns picking out one item and then finding another that is longer, shorter, or about the same length. Children can test their choices by comparing the lengths side by side from a common base.

When children have shared a number of comparisons with the group, show the class the interlocking cubes (or links or paper clips). Ask if there is a way they can use the cubes to measure the lengths of the objects. Have a few children try out their ideas with one or more of the collected items. Demonstrate important measuring techniques. Line up the end of the interlocking cube stack with the end of the object being measured. Then count

NOTE The same directions apply for cubes, links, or paper clips. If children use links or paper clips, demonstrate that they should be connected end to end without gaps or overlaps.

the number of cubes in the stack that matches the length or height of the measured object. Discuss that this is an approximate measure and that the stack of cubes might be a little longer or shorter than the object. To support English language learners, discuss the meaning of the word *approximate* and provide examples.

Ask children to find something in the room and bring it back to the group. (You might want to specify that it can't be longer than the length from their elbow to their fingertips.) Have children measure the object using the interlocking cubes and draw their findings. Then, children work in small groups to compare the lengths of their objects by placing them side by side. Have the groups put their objects in order from shortest to longest. If time permits, have the class sort all of the items they measured according to the number of cubes that correspond to their lengths: items that were 10 cubes long, 11 cubes long, and so forth.

Place interlocking cubes or similar devices in the Math Center and encourage children to use them for measuring. Provide materials to record measurements.

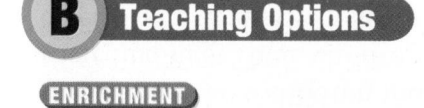 **Home Link 3·7** (*Math Masters*, p. 29)
Children use pennies to measure objects.

▶ Continuing Number Books (Revisit Activity 3·1, p. 138)

Provide time and assistance for children to continue their number book pages. Also remember to use *Minute Math* during spare moments in the day.

B Teaching Options

ENRICHMENT

▶ Measuring with Different Units (*Center Activity Cards,* 13)

Some children may wish to measure a single object using different devices (cubes, links, or small and large paper clips) and record, compare, and explain results.

LITERACY CONNECTION

▶ Reading about Measurement

Read and discuss *The Best Bug Parade* by Stuart J. Murphy (HarperTrophy, 1996).

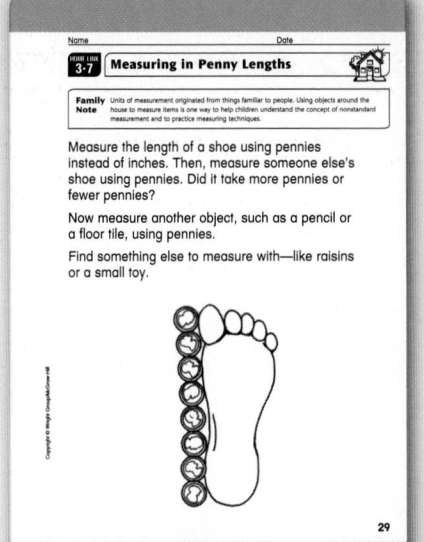

Math Masters, p. 29

▶ Measuring Blue Whales with Body Measures

Children can visualize the length of a blue whale (at about 100 feet, the largest mammal ever known) using their own bodies as measurement units. In the hallway or outdoors, mark the beginning and end of a 100-foot span. Have children stand side by side, holding hands with outstretched arms between the two points. You can count the number of children between the two points and report the results as "A blue whale is about as long as _____ Kindergarten children with outstretched arms." Repeat for dinosaurs or other large animals for which you, or children, can find measurements.

CCSS **Mathematical Practices**
SMP1, SMP2, SMP3, SMP4, SMP6, SMP7
Content Standards
K.CC.4a, K.CC.4b, **K.OA.1, K.OA.2, K.OA.5**

ACTIVITY 3·8

Pocket Problems

◎ **Objective** To develop children's understanding of addition and subtraction using concrete experiences.

☑ Whole Group
☑ Small Group
☐ Partners
☐ Center

Key Concepts and Skills
- Develop and use strategies for solving addition and subtraction problems using concrete objects. [Operations and Computation Goal 1]
- Begin to understand the meanings of addition and subtraction. [Operations and Computation Goal 2]

Terms to Use how many, more, less, add, take away, subtract

Materials 10 counters; bag or box with a pocket design drawn or pasted on the front

Planning Tip Prepare your pocket so it is easy to slip counters in and out of the top. It should also be durable because you will use it frequently in later activities. A cloth bag works very well.

A Core Activities

▶ Solving Pocket Problems

Show children three objects, and count them aloud with the class. Put the objects into the pocket you made. Show children another counter and ask them what will happen if you put it in the pocket. Do they think there will be more or less? Put the object in and ask: *How many do you think I have in my pocket now?* Invite a child to take all the objects out of the pocket and lead a class count. Ask: *Is the number more or less than when we started?* Repeat several times, varying the number of objects that are in the pocket and added to the pocket. Discuss what is happening with each step. Call on children to pose and act out pocket problems using the counters and pocket. Keep the tone playful. *For example:*

- What if we add 2 more now, without emptying the pocket? How many will we have?

- If we start with 1 and add 5 more, will we have more or less? How many will we have all together?

Informally use the word *add* in your clues and discussions. Some children may recognize that these actions always increase the number.

You might also pose subtraction pocket problems by beginning with a specified number in the pocket and then taking out objects. For example, say: *I have 7 buttons in my pocket and I'm taking away (or subtracting) 3. How many are in my pocket now?* As children become comfortable, begin to intersperse addition and subtraction situations. Use your pocket and counters to pose pocket problems frequently. They work well as quick activities in spare moments.

▶ **Graphing Dice Rolls** (Revisit Activity 3•3, p. 142; *Math Masters*, pp. 26 or 27)

Set out dice and Roll and Record sheets in the Math Center. Encourage children to work on a Dice Roll graph independently or play *Dice Race* (from the Teaching Options on page 143) with a friend. Provide dice and record sheets with different numbers for children who are ready.

B **Teaching Options**

MATHEMATICS IN THE DRAMATIC PLAY CENTER

▶ **Playing with Pockets and Counters**

Put out counters and some old wallets or purses for children to use for pocket play in the Dramatic Play Center. You might encourage them to record the amounts on a notepad for number writing practice.

TECHNOLOGY

▶ **Playing Addition and Subtraction Computer Games**

Many computer games for young children feature visual representations that reinforce the meanings of addition and subtraction and support children as they solve addition and subtraction problems. See *Resources for the Kindergarten Classroom* for software suggestions.

Links to the Future

Pocket problems and other concrete problem-solving activities give children a chance to develop a solid understanding of the meanings of addition and subtraction. They also help children develop a range of problem-solving strategies. Expect children to use a variety of techniques, such as counting objects or fingers, counting on and counting back, and mental arithmetic. Children's strategies for solving addition and subtraction problems will evolve over the course of the year and in later grades. Fluently adding and subtracting within 5 is a Kindergarten goal that will be emphasized toward the end of the year. Prior to that, children will have a variety of experiences to develop their understanding of the concepts of addition and subtraction and to explore a variety of solution strategies.

Number Card Games

Objective To review counting, number recognition, and sequencing numbers 0–20 through number card activities.

☐ Whole Group ✔ Partners
✔ Small Group ✔ Center

Key Concepts and Skills
- Practice oral counting. [Number and Numeration Goal 1]
- Practice one-to-one counting (objects and claps). [Number and Numeration Goal 2]
- Recognize numerals and represent numbers with objects. [Number and Numeration Goal 3]
- Compare and order numbers. [Number and Numeration Goal 6]

Terms to Use number cards, order, smaller, bigger

Materials Cardstock number cards from *My First Math Books* or Teaching Aid Masters (*Math Masters,* pp. 105–107) to make decks of Number Cards 0–20 (laminated or mounted on heavy paper if possible); scissors; large paper clips or small plastic bags

Planning Tip Have children cut out the cards or prepare decks for them ahead of time. (Alternately, you can detach the cardstock number cards from your class set of *My First Math Books*.) Children will need space to spread out with their cards, so you may want to conduct this in small groups over the course of one or more days. Save the decks for future use.

A Core Activities

▶ **Playing Number Card Games** (*Math Masters,* pp. 105–107)

Give each child a deck of Small Number Cards (0–20), and have them arrange their decks in numerical order. Circulate and observe children as they work. Then, use the number cards to play some games with the group. Here are a few game suggestions to use in this activity and later:

▷ Say a number and have children pick out the corresponding card.

▷ Say a number and have children pick out the number that comes before or after.

▷ Count orally together (forward, backward, skip counts) as children touch the appropriate cards.

Ongoing Assessment:
Informing Instruction

Watch for children who are not comfortable working with numbers above 10. Activity 3-16, page 172, provides additional practice with counting, reading, representing, and ordering teen numbers.

▷ Clap a number of times while children silently count and then pick out the appropriate card.

▷ Working as partners, have one child say a number and the other find the corresponding card.

▷ Working as partners, have one child show a number and the other collect that number of objects. (These collections can be put on temporary display if desired.)

Encourage children to think of additional games to play with the cards and to teach them to each other in the Math Center.

▶ Continuing Number Books (Revisit Activity 3•1, p. 138)

Provide time and assistance for children to continue their number book pages.

B **Teaching Options**

EXTRA PRACTICE

▶ Playing with Number Cards (Center Activity Cards, 14)

▷ Put a deck of number cards and a timer in the Math Center. Children can try to beat the timer as they order the cards. Begin with five minutes and move to shorter intervals as children are interested and able.

▷ Children can use two sets of cards to play *Concentration*.

MATHEMATICS IN THE WRITING CENTER

▶ Tracing Numbers

Provide additional copies of Small Number Cards for children to write on. Children can choose three colors of crayons and trace each number to create a rainbow effect. Children can take their rainbow cards home to play games with their families.

Adjusting the Activity

Tailor the range of cards used to the needs of individuals in your group. You might help some children add dots to their decks for additional support.

AUDITORY ◆ KINESTHETIC ◆ TACTILE ◆ VISUAL

Name _____ Date _____
Small Number Cards (16–20)

16 17 19

18 19

20

107

Math Masters, p. 107

ACTIVITY 3·10

Probability Stories

◎ **Objective** To introduce the basic language of probability.

CCSS Mathematical Practices
SMP1, SMP2, **SMP3,** SMP4, **SMP6**
Content Standards
K.G.1, K.G.2, K.G.4, K.G.6

☑ Whole Group
☐ Small Group
☐ Partners
☐ Center

Key Concepts and Skills
• Think of and categorize likely, unlikely, certain, and impossible events. [Data and Chance Goal 3]
• Use the basic language of probability to describe single events. [Data and Chance Goal 3]

Terms to Use possible, impossible, certain, might happen, maybe, likely, unlikely, chance

Materials a book that features unlikely or impossible events

Planning Tip Books such as *And To Think That I Saw It on Mulberry Street* (Dr. Seuss, Random House, 1989) and *Wacky Wednesday* (Theo. LeSieg, Random House, 1974) feature fun and interesting examples of unlikely or impossible events.

A Core Activities

▶ Thinking about Probability: Can Pigs Fly?

Choose a book that features unlikely events and read it aloud to the class. Give children an opportunity to share which parts of the book they liked or didn't like and why. Many children will find parts of the book to be funny. Encourage discussion about why they found them to be funny. Ask children if they think this is a true story. *Why or why not? Which events in the book are possible and which are impossible? Are there some things in the story that might have happened but might not have?* Expand the discussion beyond the book by encouraging children to use their own real-life experiences to think about the chance of things happening. Record the group's ideas in three lists:

▷ Things that are **certain,** like leaving school today or the sky getting dark tonight.

▷ Things that are **impossible,** such as seeing flying pigs or a green sun.

▷ Things that **might happen** (are **possible**), such as having pizza for dinner or seeing a cat on the way home from school.

Links to the Future

Probability—the likelihood of a given event—is a mathematical concept with many applications in everyday life. Children should begin by using their own experiences to describe probability in qualitative terms (certain, likely, possible, and unlikely). This exposure to probability builds a foundation for calculating and understanding quantitative representations of probability beginning in Grade 3.

As children discuss this final category of things, prompt them to think and talk about whether an event probably will or probably won't happen (is **likely** or **unlikely**) and to give reasons for their suggestions. Model and encourage the use of words such as **certain, maybe, possible,** and **impossible**. (See the Literacy Connection below.)

▶ Creating Shape Art (Revisit Activities 1◆15 and 2◆1, pp. 73A and 88)

In the Art or Math Center, provide a variety of pre-cut geometric shapes for children to use to create other shapes or pictures. Talk with children about the shapes they use and create, reinforcing shape names and properties, as well as positional words (above, below, next to, and so on).

B Teaching Options

ELL SUPPORT

▶ Understanding *Certain* and *Impossible*

Ask children to draw a picture representing *certain* and a picture representing *impossible*.

ART CONNECTION

▶ Creating Class Probability Collages

Have children find and/or draw pictures that illustrate definite, likely, unlikely, or impossible events. They can attach the pictures to large sheets of paper (one category of pictures per sheet). Magazine ads are a good source of pictures.

LITERACY CONNECTION

▶ Using Probability Vocabulary

Brainstorm with children different ways of saying *certain, likely, unlikely,* and *impossible*. Encourage informal as well as formal language. Some ideas might be— "no way," "definitely not," and "zero chance," to mean *impossible;* or "for sure," "definitely," and "100 percent" to mean *certain*. Use real-life events to spark children's thinking.

Probability Tray

🎯 **Objective** **To develop children's understanding of probability.**

CCSS **Mathematical Practices**
SMP1, SMP2, SMP3,
SMP4, SMP6, SMP7
Content Standards
K.G.1, K.G.2, K.G.4, K.G.6

✔ Whole Group
✔ Small Group
☐ Partners
✔ Center

Key Concepts and Skills

• Use the basic language of probability to describe predictions. [Data and Chance Goal 3]

Terms to Use certain, likely, unlikely, more likely, possible, impossible, probably, chance, some, none, all, more, less

Materials tray; red and blue connecting cubes (or other counters in two colors)

A **Core Activities**

▶ Using a Probability Tray

Remind children of the previous discussion about events that are certain, possible (likely and unlikely), and impossible. Place several red counters on a tray and ask children whether all of the counters are red. Have children take turns closing their eyes and then picking up a counter from the tray. Before each child chooses ask: *What color do you think you will pick? Why? How sure are you?* After children choose a counter, check and discuss their responses and results.

Remove all of the red counters and put several blue counters on the tray. Ask: *Are there any red counters on the tray now? Are they all blue?* Call on children to close their eyes and choose a counter. Ask children what color they think they will pick. *Is it certain, possible, or impossible that it will be blue? Red?*

After several children have had turns, change the tray so that it has two red and two blue counters, and repeat the procedures. Each time, ask children whether it is certain, possible, or impossible that they will get each color. Encourage a discussion about

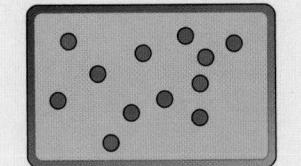

whether one outcome is more likely than another, and why. Repeat several times, varying the proportion of the two colors of counters on the tray (for example, one red and two blues, one red and nine blues, equal reds and blues, and so on). Before children make their predictions, ask them about the counters on the tray: *Are all the counters the same color, or are there some of each color? Are there more red than blue?* Encourage children to give reasons for their predictions and to use probability words to describe their thinking. For example, before picking from a tray that has two blues and ten reds, a child might say, "I might get a blue but most likely I will pick a red."

Move the materials to the Math Center for small-group or partner play. It is important to use a tray during group time so that all children can see. However, a clear plastic bag might work better at the center for holding and mixing up the counters.

▶ Creating Shape Art (Revisit Activities 1•15, 2•1, and 3•10, pp. 73A, 88, and 160)

Continue to encourage children to do the Shape Art activity described on page 161.

B Teaching Options

(EXTRA PRACTICE)

▶ Playing *Stick Pick-Up*

Use markers to color one side of three craft sticks blue and the other side red. Divide a sheet of paper into two sections, one labeled "S" or "Same" and the other labeled "D" or "Different." (All players use the same sheet to track their combined results.) Players take turns dropping the three sticks and noting how they fall. If they all land with the same color facing up (either color), the player marks an X or a tally in the "Same" section of the record sheet. If they land with mixed colors (any combination), the player marks the "Different" section of the record sheet. After several rounds, players count and compare how many "Same" and "Different" outcomes they got. Discuss the results. *Did the sticks land more often with the same color or with mixed colors? Why do you think you got those results?*

Ongoing Assessment:
Informing Instruction

Watch for children who are unable to predict or describe, in general terms, the probability of picking a particular color. Continue to provide experiences and use language to reinforce the concepts of *certain, definite, impossible,* and *possible.* However, don't worry if children have difficulty describing possible events as likely or unlikely.

Some children may be interested in figuring out and recording (perhaps through drawings) the various possible outcomes and/or different ways of getting each combination of colors.

Pan Balance 2: Leveling

ACTIVITY 3·12

◎ **Objective** To review the use of the pan balance and introduce the concept of balancing objects.

☐ Whole Group
✔ Small Group
✔ Partners
✔ Center

Key Concepts and Skills
- Use clay and a pan balance to experiment with adding and removing weight.
  [Measurement and Reference Frames Goal 1]
- Balance objects with lumps of clay. [Measurement and Reference Frames Goal 1]

Terms to Use level, compare, heavier, lighter, balance, equal, weight

Materials Home Link Master (*Math Masters,* p. 30); one or more pan balances; various objects to weigh; clay (or similar material)

Ongoing Assessment:
Informing Instruction

Watch for children who do not seem to understand that the pan balance is a tool for measuring weight or who are unable to use the pan balance to compare and then describe objects of different weights. Provide meaningful opportunities for these children to compare weights and describe their results. For example, help them compare the weights of two rocks they've collected or two types of crackers. It might help to begin comparing objects with great differences in weight and gradually decrease the difference.

A **Core Activities**

▶ Balancing Objects with Clay

Show a pan balance to children. Review what it means when one pan is lower than the other and what it means when the pans are level. Show children the clay and the objects you selected for weighing. Ask them for ideas about what they might do with these materials. Give them some time to experiment with the clay and the objects on the pan balance. Children might compare the weights of two lumps of clay or make different-sized clay balls and compare various combinations of balls (for example, one large and several small). As children explore, help them become familiar with the effect (on weight) of adding to and taking away from a lump of clay.

Look for children who put clay on one side of the pan balance and an object on the other side. As you notice children doing this, encourage them to add and remove bits of clay until the pan balance is level. Ask children what it means when the pans are level, and reiterate that it means the lump of clay weighs the same as the object on the other side of the balance. Once children have balanced the scale, they might want to predict and then test the effects of adding (or removing) bits of clay again. Invite children to work together to balance several different objects with lumps of clay. Leave the materials out in the Math Center for children to explore further.

Home Link 3·12 (*Math Masters*, p. 30)

Children compare the weights of objects and record their findings with a drawing.

▶ Playing *Count and Sit* (Revisit Activity 2·6, p. 98)

Play a few rounds of *Count and Sit*. Choose numbers in the teens, twenties, and thirties as your starting and target numbers. Also remember to use *Minute Math* during spare moments in the day.

 **Teaching Options**

ENRICHMENT

▶ Weighing Objects with Nonstandard Units (*Center Activity Cards*, 15)

Some children might be interested in using nonstandard units for weighing objects on the pan balance. Demonstrate how to balance an object using washers, cubes, pennies or another unit of measure with constant weight. (Children will explore this further in Activity 8-15.)

LITERACY CONNECTION

▶ Reading a Book about Weight

Read *Mighty Maddie* by Stuart J. Murphy (HarperTrophy, 2004) and talk about the weight of items in the book.

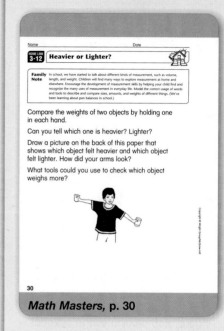

Math Masters, p. 30

Train Games

[handwritten: 1 spinner for 2 players]

CCSS **Mathematical Practices**
SMP1, **SMP2**, SMP3,
SMP4, **SMP6**, SMP7, SMP8
Content Standards
K.CC.4a, K.CC.4b, K.CC.4c,
K.CC.5, K.OA.1, K.OA.4, K.OA.5

Objective To introduce a series of games that provide practice with counting and concrete addition and subtraction.

☐ Whole Group
☑ Small Group
☐ Partners
☑ Center

Key Concepts and Skills

• Count objects using one-to-one correspondence. [Number and Numeration Goal 2]

• Add and subtract within 10 using a collection of objects. [Operations and Computation Goal 1]

• Identify pairs of numbers that add up to 10. [Operations and Computation Goal 1]

• Distinguish between addition and subtraction. [Operations and Computation Goal 2]

Terms to Use count on, forward, add, count back, backward, subtract, remove, take away

Materials interlocking cubes; green die (marked 1, 2, 3, 1, 2, 3); red die (marked 1, 2, 3, 1, 2, 3); die colored red on four sides (marked 1, 2, 3, 3) and green on two sides (marked 1, 2)

Planning Tip Prepare the dice ahead of time: color cubes with markers or use colored dots; then write the numbers on the dice. Introduce these games over the course of several days.

A Core Activities

[handwritten: Students take turns better when they share spinners]

▶ Playing Train Games

Begin by teaching children the *Growing Train Game*. Starting with zero cubes, children "grow" a train by taking turns rolling the green die. They take the rolled number of cubes and add them to the train. The game ends when one child reaches 10 cubes. To provide practice with complements of 10, at the end of each turn children say how many cubes they have on their train and how many more cubes they need to get to 10 cubes.

Introduce the *Disappearing Train Game* (description follows) in a separate session shortly afterwards. Once children are comfortable playing each game separately, introduce the *Growing and Disappearing Train Game*. Leave the materials in the Math Center for individual or group play.

Technology

Children can play versions of the *Train Games* on the computer using *Everyday Mathematics EM Games*.

NOTE See Project 3 for other games that provide opportunities to explore and practice addition and subtraction.

▷ In the *Disappearing Train Game* (subtracting only) children begin by making a train of 10 cubes. Then they take turns rolling a red die labeled 1, 2, 3, 1, 2, 3, and taking away the rolled number of cubes from the train. The game ends when someone's train disappears (no cubes are left).

▷ In the *Growing and Disappearing Train Game* (adding and subtracting) players start with a train of 10 cubes. They take turns rolling the mixed red and green die and either subtracting cubes from or adding cubes to their trains. For example, if a red 2 is rolled, the child removes two counters from the train. If a green 2 is rolled, two counters are added to the train. The first child whose train disappears is the winner. Players must roll the exact number of cubes to remove in order to win.

▶ Playing *I Spy* Patterns (Revisit Activity 2•5, p. 96)

Play *I Spy* with a focus on patterns, perhaps while waiting in line during a transition time. Allow children to take turns spying patterns and giving clues.

B Teaching Options

READINESS

▶ Making a Train of Children

Familiarize children with the dice for the train games by rolling the green die and calling on that number of children to line up. Keep rolling until the class (or smaller group) becomes part of the train. Roll the red die to remove (subtract) children from the train. You can also use the mixed die to add and subtract from the train. Periodically have children count off to determine how many are in the train.

LITERACY CONNECTION

▶ Counting Passengers on a Train

Read *Chugga-Chugga Choo-Choo* by Kevin Lewis (Hyperion, 1999). Note and discuss how the number of passengers on the train changes as animals get on.

Adjusting the Activity

As children are ready, they can write number sentences to describe their turns. For example, if they have 4 cubes and roll a green 3, they would write $4 + 3 = 7$. (The "+" and "−" symbols are formally introduced in Section 4.) You can also provide practice with fluently adding and subtracting within 5 by ending/starting with a 5-cube train and having children say or write a number sentence for each turn.

AUDITORY ◆ KINESTHETIC ◆ TACTILE ◆ VISUAL

Ongoing Assessment:
Informing Instruction

Watch for children who confuse addition and subtraction as they play. Continue to play *Growing Train Game* and *Disappearing Train Game* separately with them. Provide additional support as they move to the *Growing and Disappearing Train Game*.

Favorite Colors Graph

🎯 **Objective** To provide practice with making and analyzing a bar graph.

CCSS **Mathematical Practices**
SMP1, **SMP2,** SMP3, **SMP4,** SMP5, SMP6, SMP8
Content Standards
K.CC.5, K.CC.6, K.MD.1, **K.MD.3**

☑ Whole Group
☐ Small Group
☐ Partners
☐ Center

Key Concepts and Skills

• Count children in each sorted group and count items in each category on a bar graph.
  [Number and Numeration Goal 2]

• Compare the numbers in each group/category. [Number and Numeration Goal 6]

• Construct a class bar graph. [Data and Chance Goal 1]

• Discuss information presented in a bar graph and answer questions. [Data and Chance Goal 2]

• Sort children according to their favorite colors. [Patterns, Functions, and Algebra Goal 1]

Terms to Use bar graph, some, none, all, most, least, more, less

Materials posterboard; squares of white paper; markers, crayons, or colored pencils; tape or glue stick

---

Planning Tip Prior to the activity, prepare small squares of white paper that fit on the posterboard. You will use these for the class graph. You can also use stick-on notes.

A Core Activities

▶ Graphing Favorite Colors

Ask: *How can we find out about the favorite colors of all the children in our class?* Give each child a square piece of paper to color with his or her favorite color. When children have finished coloring their squares, call on them to sit in groups according to their favorite color. Once all of the children have been grouped according to favorite colors, have them count the number in each group.

Ask: *How can we show this information on paper?* Discuss the option of using a graph; remind children of other graphs they have made, such as the Birthday Graph, the Age Change Graph, or the Favorite Part of School Graph.

Together, decide how to place their color squares on the posterboard to create a graph. (The bars for each color can be either horizontal or vertical.) Then, model how to

NOTE You can extend the activity by choosing other favorites to graph, such as favorite numbers or favorite games.

appropriately label the columns and rows. (One will show the colors; the other will show the number of children who chose that color as their favorite.) Explain that this is called a **bar graph** and elicit children's ideas about how it got its name. As a class, decide on a title for the graph.

Enlist the class in counting the number of children with each favorite color on the graph. Use questions and modeling to guide children to make comparisons and analyze the information on the graph. For example, *Why do we use a title and labels when we create a graph? What does this graph tell us? Which color is the most popular in our class? Which color is the least popular? Can we put them in order from most to least popular? How many more people chose red than green? How did you figure that out? If another class graphed their favorite colors, do you think their graph would look the same as ours? Why or why not?*

▶ **Measuring with Objects** (Revisit Activity 3•7, p. 152)

Place a collection of objects in the Math Center along with connecting cubes or other uniform-length objects to measure them with. Encourage children to record their findings using pictures and numbers.

B **Teaching Options**

LITERACY CONNECTION

▶ **Graphing Hat Colors**

Read *Caps for Sale* by Esphyr Slobodkina (HarperTrophy, 1987) and have the class create a bar graph that shows the number of hats of each color in the story.

SOCIAL STUDIES CONNECTION

▶ **Learning Color Names in Different Languages**

Children who know another language can teach the class the names of colors in that language.

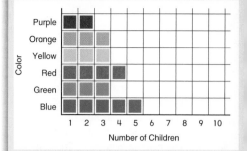

Ongoing Assessment:

Informing Instruction

Watch for children who are not able to use information from the graph to answer questions. You might want to work with these children to create concrete graphs using connecting cubes. (See below.)

NOTE You may wish to have children make real-object graphs with connecting cubes. Put about 30 connecting cubes of 3 or 4 different colors in a paper bag. Invite children to take turns randomly picking a cube from the bag. As each cube is taken from the bag, children should connect it to other cubes of the same color. Talk with children about the resulting real-object graph.

Count by 10s

ACTIVITY 3·15

Objective To introduce skip counting by 10s.

CCSS

Mathematical Practices
SMP1, SMP2, SMP3, SMP4, SMP5, SMP6, **SMP7, SMP8**

Content Standards
K.CC.1, K.OA.1, K.OA.2, K.OA.5

☑ Whole Group
☐ Small Group
☐ Partners
☐ Center

Planning Tip Refer to the Number of the Day Routine (p. 8) for the Growing Number Line and the Concrete Number Count containers with objects representing the number of days in school.

Key Concepts and Skills
• Count orally by 1s and 10s. [Number and Numeration Goal 1]
• Begin to recognize patterns of 10 when counting. [Patterns, Functions, and Algebra Goal 1]

Terms to Use 1s, 10s, skip counting, counting by 10s

Materials Home Link Master (*Math Masters,* p. 31); Growing Number Line; Concrete Number Counts containers; additional straws or sticks (optional)

 A **Core Activities**

▶ Counting by 10s

Have children sit in a circle. Call on one child to stand up and extend his or her fingers one by one as the class counts to 10. Continue with a few more children, counting the total number of fingers by 1s. After the class has counted 40 or 50 fingers, stop counting and have children remain standing with their fingers extended. Point out that all of the children are holding up 10 fingers and ask whether anyone knows a quicker way to count all of the fingers. After children have had a chance to share, model how to count the fingers by 10s. Call on a few more children to stand and hold up their 10 fingers. Count all of the fingers by 10s again.

Have all of the children sit down, then ask: *How many children do we need in order to have 40 fingers in the middle of the circle? 50? 70?* Lead children in a choral count by 10s as you call one child at a time to the center (each holding up 10 fingers).

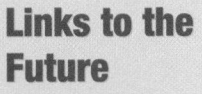

Links to the Future

Patterned counting enhances children's understanding of the number system. Children will learn about counting by 5s in Activity 5-8 and counting by 2s in Activity 6-10. They will learn to skip count on calculators in Activity 6-14.

Refer to your Growing Number Line and the Concrete Number Count containers. If you are already marking the 10s (10, 20, 30, ...) on the number line, point this out to children. Mention that they can use the number line as a reference as they count by 10s. If you have not been marking the 10s, go back and circle them now. (Continue to do so as the Growing Number Line is extended.) Show children the Concrete Number Count container and ask whether counting by 10s might help them count how many objects they have collected so far. Model how to count the bundles by 10s, and then count up by 1s for the remaining objects.

Practice choral counting by 10s frequently. To help solidify what it means to count by 10s, encourage children to flash their fingers as they say each 10.

 Home Link 3·15 *(Math Masters,* p. 31)
Children count the total number of fingers (and toes) in their families.

▶ **Solving Pocket Problems** (Revisit Activity 3·8, p. 156)
Pose a few pocket problems. You can use the colored dice from the Train Games activity (page 166) to decide how many counters to add or remove from the pocket.

B Teaching Options

(MUSIC CONNECTION)

▶ **Counting to Rhythms and Music**
Choral count by 10s to a rhythmic pattern or to the tune of a familiar song.

(LITERACY CONNECTION)

▶ **Reading a Book about Counting by 10s**
Read *One Hundred Is a Family* by Pam Munoz Ryan (Hyperion, 1994).

NOTE If time permits, use additional sticks or straws to make a few more bundles of 10 and practice counting those with the class. Add a few additional sticks or straws so children can practice counting on by 1s after counting the bundles by 10s.

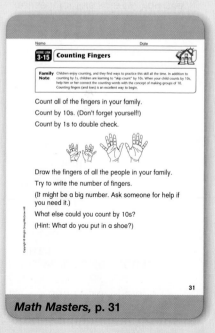

Math Masters, p. 31

ACTIVITY 3·16

Teen Frame Game

CCSS Mathematical Practices
SMP1, SMP2, SMP3,
SMP6, SMP7, **SMP8**
Content Standards
K.CC.4a, K.CC.4b, K.CC.6,
K.NBT.1

◎ **Objective** To introduce a game that provides practice with teen numbers and builds number sense.

☐ Whole Group
☑ Small Group
☑ Partners
☑ Center

Key Concepts and Skills

• Count up to 20 objects. [Number and Numeration Goal 2]

• Recognize teen numbers. [Number and Numeration Goal 3]

• Represent teen numbers as "10 and some more." [Number and Numeration Goal 5];

• Compare numbers and sets. [Number and Numeration Goal 6]

Terms to Use count, teen, ten, more, less, same, equal

Materials Game Masters (*Math Masters,* pp. 137–139), laminated or mounted on cardstock; large paper clips; pencils; counters for the gameboard; scoring counters

Planning Tip If you made an 11–20 Spinner (*Math Masters,* p. 139) for the *Teen Tangle* game extension in Activity 2-10, you can reuse it for this activity. You may want to create additional spinners so that more groups can play at one time. Cut the ten strips (*Math Masters,* p. 138) into individual strips (enough for each player) or have children do this.

A Core Activities

▶ **Playing *Teen Frame*** (*Math Masters,* pp. 137–139)

Remind children of the Teen Partner activity (Activity 2-12, page 112). Spin the 11–20 Spinner and have children work in pairs to show the number: one child holds up all 10 fingers and the other child holds up the additional number of fingers needed to make the number. Once children are comfortable with this activity, introduce the teen frame.

Have children look closely at the *Teen Frame* gameboard (*Math Masters,* page 137) and describe it. Make sure everyone realizes that there are 10 spaces in each row. (Have children cover each space with one finger so they can see the connection with the Teen Partner activity.) Ask children to guess how many spaces there are altogether and then count them. Show the 11–20 Spinner and explain that the numbers on it can be shown on the *Teen Frame* gameboard. Model how to spin the spinner (Activity 2-4, page 94),

NOTE While playing *Teen Frame,* encourage children to use the terms *more than, less than,* or *same* (or *equal*) when they compare counters to determine winners. If there are more than 2 players, have children order the counters from the smallest to the largest group.

read the number, and cover that number of spaces on the *Teen Frame* gameboard with counters.

Once children are familiar with the teen frame, teach them the *Teen Frame* game. Give each player a copy of the *Teen Frame* gameboard. In pairs or small groups, players take turns spinning a number and then putting that number of counters on their teen frames. After each round, players compare their *Teen Frame* boards. The player who has the most counters wins the round and takes a scoring counter. Children then clear their boards and spin again. (You can vary the game so the person who has the fewest counters wins the round.)

If children realize that they can just add single counters (1s) to the 10 counters in one row, they are ready to use a ten strip. (See the Extra Practice activity below.)

▶ Choosing from a Probability Tray (Revisit Activity 3•11, p. 162)

Place two or three colors of counters (fewer than 15) on a tray. Have children describe the likelihood (using terms such as *certain* or *likely*) of picking a particular color with their eyes closed. Vary the number of counters of each color and repeat.

B Teaching Options

EXTRA PRACTICE

▶ Using a 10 Die (*Math Masters,* pp. 137 and 138)

Vary *Teen Frame* by creating a "10 die" (a cube labeled "10" on all sides). Children roll the 10 die and a regular dot die, say the total, and record it on a *Teen Frame* gameboard. Children can use a ten strip (*Math Masters,* page 138) to represent the 10.

ART CONNECTION

▶ Creating Number Art

Children can use various materials to represent teen numbers on paper. Bind the pages into a book titled *Teen Numbers* to keep in the Math Center or class library.

Ongoing Assessment:
Recognizing Student Achievement

Use **Teen Frame** to assess children's ability to count and compare teen numbers. Children are making adequate progress with counting if they can count the correct number of objects to place on the Teen Frame.

[Number and Numeration Goal 2]

They are making adequate progress with comparing numbers if they can tell who had the highest number in each round.

[Number and Numeration Goal 6]

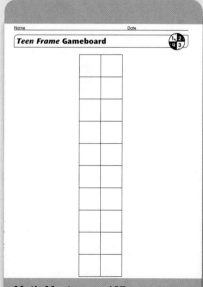

Math Masters, p. 137

Fun with Games

CCSS Mathematical Practices
SMP1, SMP2, SMP6, SMP7, SMP8
Content Standards
K.OA.1, K.OA.2, K.OA.3, K.OA.4, K.OA.5

Objective To develop problem-solving strategies and promote mathematical skills and thinking through games.

Terms to Use rules, strategy

Materials

Games from Home
☐ games children bring in

Multicultural Games
☐ Project Masters (*Math Masters,* pp. 68–73)
☐ Mancala game
☐ counters or movers for various games

Kid-Made Games
☐ Project Masters (*Math Masters,* pp. 74–76)
☐ index cards; playing cards
☐ counters or movers; dice; spinners (or materials to make them)
☐ paper; cardboard; markers; stickers

Addition and Subtraction Facts Games
☐ Project Masters (*Math Masters,* pp. 76A and 76B)
☐ Teaching Aid Master (*Math Masters,* p. 103)
☐ Teaching Aid Masters (*Math Masters,* pp. 105 and 106), or *My First Math Book,* Activity Sheets 1 and 2
☐ small plate; pennies or counters; dominoes (optional)

NOTE Games provide a strong bridge between home and school. This project encourages children to share games from home with their classmates. In addition, children should share games from school with their families. Playing mathematics games at home gives parents natural opportunities to help children apply the mathematics they are learning in school.

Introduction

Incorporating games into your curriculum has many benefits. Games add fun, enhance skill development, provide an incentive to learn specific skills, and encourage new thinking. Games offer rich opportunities for children to reinforce and strengthen their developing mathematics skills. While playing games, children learn to apply rules consistently, follow sequences, match actions and symbols, learn the logic of strategies, and apply their growing understanding of numbers. Many games integrate literacy skills, such as using symbols, tracking and sequencing, reading, and communicating. Children make social studies and art connections as they learn games from other countries and make their own games. Games also enhance children's social skills as they learn teamwork and gain experience resolving conflicts.

NOTE For additional information about the use of games in *Everyday Mathematics,* see Section 2.2: Games in the *Teacher's Reference Manual.* See Section 14.3.3 for information about using games for fact practice.

Choose and develop the games ideas presented in this project to fit your classroom and teaching style. You may choose to integrate games into your ongoing schedule of activities, or you might set aside a period of time to focus more intensively on games. Consider creating a games area in the classroom where games can be played and stored. In addition to the games that are outlined here, you can find countless other game suggestions in books, on the Internet, and in stores and catalogs. Inventing your own games is strongly encouraged!

Activity Options

▶ Games from Home   ✔ Whole Group   ✔ Small Group   ✔ Partners   ✔ Center

Encourage children to bring in favorite games from home (labeled with the child's name) to play during free time, center time, or a designated "games time." Popular games, such as checkers and Go Fish may be familiar to many children. Invite children to share their games during group time. The class can discuss what they know about the game and how to play it. Help children identify mathematics skills or ideas that are necessary or helpful in playing the game. Have another discussion after children have played the game.

As children play games at school, you may want to engage the class in discussing and resolving issues such as the following:

- Can unfinished games be left out to be played later? Where should they be stored?
- How many children can play a game at one time? Can others watch? How should we decide who's next? (Many classrooms create sign-up sheets to track turns.)
- How many games should be available at one time?
- If conflicts occur while playing a game, how should they be resolved?

NOTE When many children have played a particular game at home, you may need to negotiate a set of "school rules" to avoid conflict.

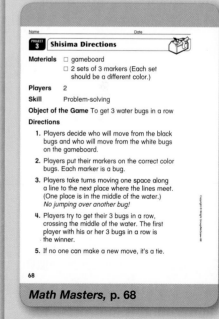

Math Masters, p. 68

▶ Multicultural Games

☑ **Small Group** ☑ **Partners** ☑ **Center**

(*Math Masters*, pp. 68-73)

Introduce games from other countries and cultures to the class. Many of these games have been played for hundreds of years and are the basis for familiar modern games. Children may be interested to learn that often the same game is played in many countries with slight variations (for example, "three-in-a-row" games such as Tic-Tac-Toe, and "distributing games," such as Mancala). Some of these games are described below.

Three-in-a-Row Games Children all over the world play versions of a game whose object is to align three marks or objects in a row. Three-in-a-row games require little equipment and can be played anywhere. These simple games are for two players. Winning involves more than just chance.

Tic-Tac-Toe is played throughout the United States. Many children are familiar with it. Review how to play, or have children teach each other.

Shisima is a three-in-a-row game from Kenya. Shisima (Shi-SEE-Mah) is a body of water in the Tiriki language. The markers are water bugs. The winner is the first to get all three water bugs in a row. To play, you need copies of *Math Masters*, pages 68 and 69 and three markers for each player.

Nine Holes is played all over the world and has many different names. The version on *Math Masters*, pages 70 and 71 originated in England. In addition to the gameboard, each player needs three markers.

🔵 **Literature Link** Here are just a few of the many books that describe games from around the world:
Math Games and Activities from Around the World and *More Math Games and Activities from Around the World* by Claudia Zaslavsky (Chicago Review Press, 1998; 2003); *The Multicultural Game Book* by Louise Orlando (Scholastic, 1993); *Great Big Book of Children's Games* by Debra Wise (McGraw-Hill, 2003).

Name _____ Date _____

PROJECT 3 **Nine Holes Directions**

Materials ☐ gameboard
☐ 2 sets of 3 markers (Each set should be a different color.)

Players 2

Skill Problem-solving

Object of the Game To get 3 markers in a row on the 9 intersections on the gameboard.

Directions

1. Players place their 3 markers on their circles next to the gameboard.

2. Players take turns placing one marker on any intersection (where the lines meet) on the board.

3. If no one has 3 markers in a row after placing all 3 of their markers, players try again from where they are on the board. They take turns moving one marker at a time from one intersection to an open intersection next to it.

4. The game is tied if no one can get 3 in a row.

70

Math Masters, p. 70

Name _____ Date _____

PROJECT 3 **Owari Directions**

Materials ☐ gameboard   **Players** 2
☐ 2 cups   **Skill** Problem-solving
☐ 16 beans or   **Object of the Game** To collect
small counters   the most beans

Directions

1. Players face each other and put the gameboard between them. They place 2 beans in each square. Each player takes a cup to store his or her beans.

2. Players take turns picking up the beans from any square on their side and placing 1 bean in each square around the board until the beans from the chosen square are gone.

3. If a player's last bean lands on the other player's side in a square with 1 bean, the player whose turn it is takes both beans and puts them in his or her cup.

4. Play continues until there are no beans left on one side of the board.

5. The winner is the player with the most beans.

72

Math Masters, p. 72

Distributing Games These games involve the movement of game pieces around a board according to rules. Like three-in-a-row games, many of these have multiple variations and can be played with simple materials.

Mancala has been played throughout the world for thousands of years. It has many variations, but the basic game is suitable for Kindergartners. It is usually played on a gameboard with cups. The game can be purchased or made.

Owari (Oh-WAHR-ee) is a game of sowing seeds from Ghana. It is a simple version of Mancala that can be made in class. You will need *Math Masters,* pages 72 and 73, and 16 small counters, such as beads or beans.

▶ Kid-Made Games

☑ **Center**   ☑ **Small Groups**   ☑ **Partners**

(*Math Masters,* pp. 74-76)

Create a center with materials for making games. Use questions such as the following to help individuals or groups of children get started: *What is a game? Can we make games? What do we need to think about? What materials do we need? What kind of games do you like to play?* Encourage children to use numbers or other math ideas in their games, even though these games need not be exclusively about mathematics. Record children's ideas and help them create a list of steps for making their games. For children who seem stuck, provide copies of Project Master page 76 to make a simple board game. Making a game *with* children can spark their ideas. The following are just two examples:

Tug of War Two children can play Tug of War using *Math Masters,* pages 74 and 75, a die, and a playing piece such as a penny. You can make a larger version using the master as a model.

Concentration Give each child in your class two blank cards and assign each of them a number. Children write their assigned numbers on one card, and represent their numbers with drawings or stickers on the second card. Combine the card pairs into a deck to play Concentration. (You may want to divide the card pairs into several decks, depending on the size of your class.)

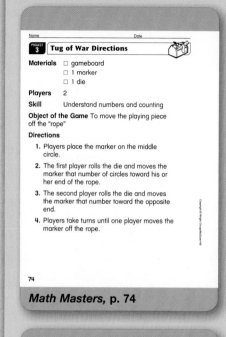

Math Masters, p. 74

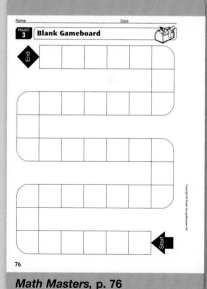

Math Masters, p. 76

▶ Addition and Subtraction Facts Games

☑ **Center** ☑ **Small Groups** ☑ **Partners**

(*Math Masters,* pp. 76A and 76B; *Math Masters,* pp. 105 and 106 or *My First Math Book,* Activity Sheets 1 and 2; *Math Masters,* p. 103)

Throughout the grades, *Everyday Mathematics* includes many engaging and motivating fact-practice games to lessen the need for tedious drills. Most fact games can be modified to target specific facts. The games described in this section provide opportunities for kindergarten children to practice addition and subtraction facts within 5 and to reinforce combinations of numbers with sums to 10. Introduce these games as children are ready for them, which may not be until later in the year—after they have had time to understand the concepts of addition and subtraction and to explore and practice various strategies for solving simple addition and subtraction problems.

Top-It Facts Games In Activity 4-2, children will learn the standard version of *Top-It.* (You may remember the game as War.) The more advanced variations, *Addition* and *Subtraction Top-It,* described below, target addition and subtraction facts and number comparisons. Because the versions require different number cards, create and label decks for each game. You can use the appropriate number cards on *Math Masters,* page 105 (laminated or copied on cardstock) or the number cards from *My First Math Book,* Activity Sheets 1 and 2.

Addition Top-It provides practice with addition facts. To practice sums within 5 (as well as 3 + 3 = 6), create a deck that includes 4 each of number cards 0–3. Game directions can be found on *Math Masters,* page 76A.

Subtraction Top-It is similar to *Addition Top-It* but requires a deck with 4 each of number cards 0–5 to practice differences for facts within 5. Game directions can be found on *Math Masters,* page 76A.

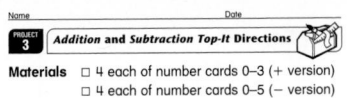

Name _____ Date _____

PROJECT 3 *Addition and Subtraction Top-It Directions*

Materials □ 4 each of number cards 0–3 (+ version)
□ 4 each of number cards 0–5 (− version)

Players 2 to 4

Skill Practice + and − facts within 5

Object of the Games To collect the most cards

Directions: *Addition Top-It*

1. Place the shuffled deck face down. Each player turns over 2 cards and says the sum of the numbers. The player with the largest sum wins the round and takes all the cards.

2. In case of a tie, each tied player turns over 2 more cards and says the sum. The player with the largest sum takes all the cards.

3. The game ends when there are not enough cards left for each player to have another turn. The player with the most cards wins.

Directions: *Subtraction Top-It*

Play like *Addition Top-It,* but use 0–5 number cards and have each player subtract the smaller number from the larger number in his/her own pair of cards. The player with the largest difference wins the round and takes the cards.

Math Masters, p. 76A

NOTE You can modify *Addition* and *Subtraction Top-It* by using more or fewer number cards to target different facts. Another variation is to use dominoes instead of cards and have children add or subtract the dots on each side of the domino.

Complements of 10 Games These games help children learn combinations of numbers with sums to 10. These are useful facts to learn because they can serve as anchors for learning other facts and because they are important later for multidigit subtraction.

Penny Plate is played with partners. Each pair will need a small plate and 10 pennies. Game directions can be found on *Math Masters,* page 76B.

For an easier version of this game, have children use a ten frame (*Math Masters,* page 103) instead of a plate. Player 1 will place a number of pennies on the ten frame. Player 2 then decides how many more pennies are needed to fill the empty spaces on the ten frame. Players check their answers and keep track of their score, just as in *Penny Plate.*

Go Fish for Ten is a challenging version of the familiar card game, Go Fish, that reinforces sums of 10. Give each small group a deck with 4 cards each of numbers 0–10. (This game works best with 3 or 4 players.) Deal 4 cards to each player and place the remaining cards in the center. On their turns, players "fish" for combinations that add up to 10. So if a player has a 7 in her hand, she will ask another player for a 3 to make a sum of 10. If the player she asks does not have a 3, the first player must "go fish" from the pile in the center. Play then passes to the next player. As players get pairs of cards that add up to 10, they place them faceup in front of them. Play ends when there are no more cards in the center and no more combinations of 10 that can be made. The winner is the player with the most pairs of cards that add up to 10.

NOTE To match children's interests or a class theme, you or the children may want to create a context for the ten-frame version of *Penny Plate* using counters. For example, they might imagine that the ten-frame spaces are 10 garages (5 on each side of the block) and they need to put one car in each garage. Or, the spaces could be lily pads and the counters could be frogs. Children may wish to decorate ten frames to match their game contexts.

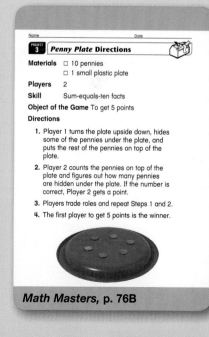

Math Masters, p. 76B

Section 4

Overview

Section 4 has a number of main areas of focus:

- To introduce addition and subtraction symbols and terminology through number stories and concrete experiences,
- To introduce calculators,
- To introduce attribute blocks,
- To introduce *"What's My Rule?" Fishing* game activities,
- To continue patterning activities using pattern blocks and the Pattern-Block Template,
- To continue to explore 2-dimensional shapes and symmetry,
- To reinforce and extend counting, numeral recognition, and number-writing skills,
- To reinforce number sequencing and number comparison skills, and
- To continue graphing, measuring, estimation, and probability activities.

Maintaining Ongoing Daily Routines

Doing the Routines

In addition to Section 4 activities, continue to do the following Ongoing Daily Routines:

- Number of the Day
- Attendance
- Job Chart
- Monthly Calendar
- Daily Schedule
- Weather Observation
- Recording Daily Temperature
- Survey

Adjusting the Routines

Each Ongoing Daily Routine can be adjusted periodically according to children's progress and interests. Ongoing Daily Routines are powerful tools for practicing and reinforcing the skills that are introduced in the activities. If you haven't already done so, use the following routines to introduce new ideas and ask different questions as you complete Section 4 and later sections:

- **Job Chart** You might want to have a child help you rotate the job cards to help children better understand the system of rotation.
- **Weather Observation and Recording Daily Temperature** Use these routines to explore basic concepts and language related to probability and chance. *Is it likely to snow today? Are you sure it rained yesterday? Which type of weather (or temperature) are we most likely to have tomorrow?*

Using Routines for Ongoing Assessment

All of the Ongoing Daily Routines offer opportunities for ongoing assessment of a variety of skills and concepts. You might want to use the following routines for ongoing assessment during Section 4:

- **Job Chart** Do children recognize the pattern of movement on the job chart? Can they predict when they (or someone else) will have a particular job?
- **Daily Schedule** Can children correctly order the events of the day? Do they use time-of-day and day-of-the-week terminology as they set up and read the daily schedule?

Learning in Perspective

Core Activities

Activity	Objective	Revisit Activity	Page
4·1	**Number Line Mathematics** To develop addition and subtraction strategies using a walk-on number line.	**Exploring Pattern Blocks** (Activity 1-2, p. 48)	188
4·2	***Top-It* Card Games** To introduce a game that reinforces number recognition and number comparisons.	**Skip Counting by 10s** (Activities 1-12 and 3-15, pp. 68 and 170)	190
4·3	**The Pattern-Block Template** To introduce the Pattern-Block Template.	**Solving Pocket Problems** (Activity 3-8, p. 156)	192
4·4	**The Addition Symbol (+)** To introduce addition terminology and symbols using number stories and counters. 🔗 **Links to the Future** Children will be introduced to the subtraction symbol in Activity 4-11.	**Creating Pattern Strips** (Activity 4-3, p. 192)	194
4·5	**Follow My Pattern** To provide practice with creating, extending, and describing patterns.	**Estimating Objects in a Collection** (Activity 2-13, p. 114)	196
4·6	**Interrupted Counts** To introduce interrupted counting.	**Graphing Dice Rolls** (Activity 3-3, p. 142; *Math Masters,* p. 26 or 27) 🔗 **Links to the Future** Children will graph sums of dice throws in Activity 4-8.	198
4·7	**Meet the Calculator** To introduce calculators and to provide practice with reading and entering numbers.	**Playing *Teen Frame*** (Activity 3-16, p. 172; *Math Masters,* pp. 137 and 138)	200
4·8	**Roll and Record with Two Dice** To provide experiences with addition, graphing outcomes, and probability.	**Feeling Shapes** (Activity 2-2, p. 90)	204
4·9	**Body and Rope Shapes** To deepen children's understanding of shapes through a cooperative movement activity.	**Making Symmetrical Snowflakes** (Activity 2-16, p. 122; *Math Masters,* p. 35)	206

Core Activities, *continued*

Activity	Objective	Revisit Activity	Page
4·10	**Shape Comparisons** To solidify children's understanding of shapes.	**Sorting Names** (Activity 1-6, p. 56) **Links to the Past** Children have sorted various collections in previous activities.	208
4·11	**The Subtraction Symbol (–)** To introduce subtraction terminology and symbols using number stories and counters. **Links to the Future** In Activity 6-9, children will explore comparison situations.	**Practicing Number Writing** (Activity 2-7, p. 100) **Links to the Past** Children made number books in Activity 3-1.	210
4·12	**Slate Activities** To provide practice with number writing and other numeration skills.	**Measuring with Objects** (Activity 3-7, p. 152) **Links to the Future** Children will do many measurement activities in Section 5.	212
4·13	**Introduction to Attribute Blocks** To introduce attribute blocks. **Links to the Future** Children will use attribute blocks throughout Kindergarten.	**Counting On from Different Numbers** (Activity 4-6, p. 198)	214
4·14	***"What's My Rule?" Fishing* Game** To introduce a game that helps children think about sorting rules. **Links to the Future** In Section 8, children will use rules to generate one number from another in "function machines."	**Playing *I Spy* with Shapes** (Activity 4-10, p. 208)	216
4·15	**Number Stories: Stage 2** To develop understanding of mathematical symbols and language in the context of addition and subtraction number stories. **Links to the Future** In Activity 7-3, children will focus on writing number sentences to model their number stories.	**Counting by 10s** (Activities 2-6 and 3-15, pp. 98 and 170)	218
4·16	**Two-Digit Numbers** To provide practice with reading and representing 2-digit numbers.	**Describing Probability** (Activity 3-11, p. 162)	220

Section Opener

Ongoing Learning and Practice

Practice through Games

Games are an essential component of practice in the *Everyday Mathematics* program. Games offer skills practice and promote strategic thinking. These games are introduced in this section:

Activity	Game	Skill Practiced
4◆1	*Go Forward, Back Up*	**Moving along a number line using + and – symbols** [Number and Numeration Goal 2; Operations and Computation Goals 1 and 2]
4◆2	*Top-It* *Addition Top-It*	**Reading and comparing numbers** [Number and Numeration Goals 3 and 6]; **Adding numbers and comparing sums** [Number and Numeration Goal 6; Operations and Computation Goal 1]
4◆5	*Pattern Cover Up*	**Determining missing elements in a pattern** [Patterns, Functions, and Algebra Goal 1]
4◆14	*"What's My Rule?" Fishing*	**Figuring out sorting rules** [Patterns, Functions, and Algebra Goal 1]
4◆14	*Who Am I Thinking Of?*	**Using attributes to identify a "mystery" person** [Patterns, Functions, and Algebra Goal 1]

Home-School Connection

Home Links provide homework and home communication. The following activities contain Home Links: 4-2, 4-5, 4-13.

Home Connection Handbook provides more ideas to communicate effectively with parents. ▶

◀ *Mathematics at Home* Books 1–4 provide additional ideas for enjoyable mathematics activities that families can do together, as well as lists of children's books related to topics in each strand area. Families can do activities from *Mathematics at Home* Book 2 during Section 4.

Balanced Assessment

Use the **Assessment Management Spreadsheets** to collect, review, and share information about children's progress.

Ongoing Assessment

 Recognizing Student Achievement

Opportunities to assess children's progress toward Kindergarten Goals:

Activity	Content Assessed
4✦2	Compare pairs of numbers 0–20 to determine the smaller and larger number. [Number and Numeration Goal 6]
4✦5	Create, extend, and describe 2- and 3-part patterns. [Patterns, Functions, and Algebra Goal 1]
4✦6	Counting by 1s to at least 30 and counting backward. [Number and Numeration Goal 1]
4✦13	Recognizing and naming shapes. [Geometry Goal 1] Using rules to sort a collection of objects. [Patterns, Functions, and Algebra Goal 1]

Informing Instruction

To anticipate common trouble spots and highlight problem-solving strategies:

Activity 4✦7
Enter 2-digit numbers on a calculator

Activity 4✦10
Identify shapes when orientation is changed

Activity 4✦12
Use clues to figure out numbers

Activity 4✦16
Read and represent 2-digit numbers

Periodic Assessment

Mid-Year assessment tasks will be completed in Sections 4 and 5.

Portfolio Opportunities

◆ Pattern strips, **Activities 4-3** and **4-4**
◆ Dice-Throw Grid, **Activity 4-8**

Assessment Handbook

◆ Kindergarten Goals, pp. 27–33
◆ Section 4 Assessment Overview, pp. 56–57
◆ Assessment Overviews by Strand, pp. 66–75
◆ Mid-Year Periodic Assessment Tasks, pp. 42–44
◆ Individual Profile of Progress and Class Checklist (Mid-Year), pp. 87–90
◆ Individual Profile of Progress and Class Checklist (Sections 3–4), pp. 79–80
◆ Cumulative Individual Profile of Progress (Sections 1–4), pp. 97–98

Differentiated Instruction

Teaching Options

Use optional Part B activities as time permits to meet individual and class needs and to integrate mathematics throughout the Kindergarten classroom and schedule.

ELL SUPPORT

4•9 Reviewing basic shapes

4•15 Acting out number stories

READINESS

4•7 Practicing 2-digit number recognition

4•12 Learning number-writing songs and rhymes

CONNECTIONS

Literacy

4•4 Reading "The Gingerbread Boy"

4•6 Saying an interrupted alphabet

4•10 Reading *Grandfather Tang's Story*

4•13 Reading *3 Little Firefighters*

Science

4•7 Investigating the solar cell

Art

4•3 Creating Pattern-Block Template creatures

4•8 Drawing a 10-part bug

Movement

4•13 Playing Simon Says

Outdoors

4•1 Playing Hopscotch

ENRICHMENT

4•1 Playing number line games

4•2 Playing *Addition Top-It*

4•5 Playing *Pattern Cover Up*

4•11 Solving subtraction pocket problems

ENRICHMENT Continued

4•14 Playing *Who Am I Thinking Of?*

4•16 Building numbers with 10s and 1s

EXTRA PRACTICE

4•2 Playing number card games

4•4 Playing the *Growing Train Game*

4•6 Playing oral counting games

4•9 Creating shape outlines

4•10 Using geoboards and tangrams

4•11 Playing the *Disappearing Train Game*

4•12 Practicing with spinners and dice

4•14 Playing *"What's My Rule?" Fishing* with attribute blocks

4•15 Playing the *Growing and Disappearing Train Game*

4•16 Playing Bingo

CENTERS

Dramatic Play

4•7 Playing with calculators

4•12 Playing with slates

TECHNOLOGY

4•16 Reading calculator numbers

HALF-DAY AND FULL-DAY PROGRAMS ◆ CROSS-CURRICULAR INTEGRATION ◆ CENTERS-BASED LEARNING

Language Support

Everyday Mathematics provides activity-specific suggestions to help *all* young children develop the language necessary to acquire, process, and express mathematical ideas. Activities that provide additional support for non-native English speakers are marked by **ELL SUPPORT** and **ELL**.

Connecting Math and Literacy

Activity 4•10 *Grandfather Tang's Story* by Ann Tompert (Dragonfly Books, 1997)

See pages 195 and 215 for more literature suggestions.

Using the Projects

Use Class Celebration (Project 4, page 222) during or after Section 4 to reinforce skills and concepts related to counting, measuring, using shapes and patterns, and solving problems. If you have a class holiday party, the ideas in Project 4 will help you integrate mathematics into planning and hosting the event.

Adjusting the Activity

AUDITORY ◆ KINESTHETIC ◆ TACTILE ◆ VISUAL

Activity 4•1 Using only counting-on or counting-back prompts

Activity 4•2 Using counters or dot cards for *Top-It* and using smaller numbers

Activity 4•8 Using a large number grid to record and graph sums

Activity 4•10 Classifying shapes

Activity 4•12 Using higher numbers in slate activities

Activity 4•16 Reading higher 2- and 3-digit numbers

Language & Vocabulary

Use these terms informally.

1s, 10s	number line
add	number sentence
all together	
angle	number story
attribute	parallelogram
calculator	pattern
chance	plus
circle	plus sign
clear	probability
continue	rectangle
corner	repeat
count back	rotate
count on	shape
digits	side
display	sorting rule
edge	square
equal	subtract
extend	sum
hexagon	symbol
higher	take away
join	template
less	thick
likely	thin
lower	trapezoid
minus	triangle
minus sign	turn
more	

Planning Tips

Pacing Pacing depends on a number of factors, such as children's individual needs and how long your school has been using *Everyday Mathematics*. Use the optional Part B activities throughout Section 4 if you have extended mathematics instructional time. See page 184 for a list of these activities.

◄————— **MOST CLASSROOMS** —————►

DECEMBER	JANUARY

Teaching Resources

Resources for the Kindergarten Classroom provides additional teaching ideas, including suggestions for bringing mathematics into thematic instruction, as well as using games, literature, technology, and rhymes to support mathematics learning. ►

Minute Math provides brief activities for transition times and for spare moments throughout the day. During Section 4, use activities in Part 2, pages 67–196.

NCTM Standards

Content Standards: 1 Number and Operations, 2 Algebra, 3 Geometry, 4 Measurement, 5 Data Analysis and Probability
Process Standards: 6 Problem Solving, 7 Reasoning and Proof, 8 Communication, 9 Connection, 10 Representation

Section 4 Activities	4◆1	4◆2	4◆3	4◆4	4◆5	4◆6	4◆7	4◆8	4◆9	4◆10	4◆11	4◆12	4◆13	4◆14	4◆15	4◆16
NCTM Standards	1, 6, 8	1, 10	2, 3	1, 6, 8, 10	2, 8	1	1	1, 5, 8	3, 6	3, 8	1, 6, 10	1	2	2, 6	1, 6–10	1, 10

Professional Development

Teacher's Reference Manual Links

Activity	Topic	Section	Activity	Topic	Section
4◆7	Calculators	3.1.1	4◆14	Functions	15.1.4
4◆12	Number and Numeration Tools	3.2.1			

Materials

Activity	Masters	Materials	
4•1		• large walk-on 0–20 number line	
4•2	Home Link Master, p. 32	• card decks made from two sets of Small Number Cards 0–20	
4•3		• Pattern-Block Templates* • pattern blocks* • pencils	• long strips of paper (sentence strips work well) • markers or crayons
4•4	Teaching Aid Master, p. 109	• construction paper or slates*	• craft sticks* • counters*
4•5	Home Link Master, p. 33	• pattern blocks*	
4•6		• stop sign or red circle (optional)	
4•7		• solar-powered calculators • a large sign labeled with the symbol	[ON/C] or [AC] (depending on your calculator's clear mechanism)
4•8	Teaching Master, p. 34	• dice* • pencils	
4•9		• rope or string with the ends tied together (about 20 feet per group)	• shape collages from Activity 2-1 (optional)
4•10		• construction paper shapes (triangles, squares, and rectangles) that differ in size (triangles should	have different-sized angles) • rope or string (2 long pieces, each with ends tied together)

* Indicates items in the Kindergarten manipulative kit.

Activity	Masters	Materials	
4•11	Teaching Aid Master, p. 109	• construction paper or slates*	• craft sticks* • counters*
4•12		• Large Number Cards • slates*	• writing tools for slates
4•13	Home Link Master, p. 36	• attribute blocks*	
4•14			
4•15			
4•16		• Large Number Cards • straws* or sticks* (singles and bundles of ten)	
Mid-Year Assessment	Assessment Handbook, pp. 42–44	• number line* or Class Number Grid • estimation and reference jar • rubber bands* • straws or craft sticks* • number cards 0–20 • collection of objects	• pattern blocks*; attribute blocks* • tray • measuring tools* • drawing of something symmetrical • *Minute Math*

Technology

Assessment Management Spreadsheets, Section 4: See the *iTGA*.

Number Line Mathematics

◎ **Objective** To develop addition and subtraction strategies using a walk-on number line.

CCSS **Mathematical Practices**
SMP1, SMP2, SMP5,
SMP6, **SMP7**
Content Standards
K.OA.1, K.G.2, K.G.4, K.G.6

☑ Whole Group
☑ Small Group
☐ Partners
☐ Center

Key Concepts and Skills
• Use a number line to explore addition and subtraction concepts and strategies.
[Operations and Computation Goal 1]

Terms to Use number line, count on, count back

Materials large walk-on 0–20 number line

Planning Tip If you do not have a walk-on number line, you can create one by writing each numeral on a file folder (or other stiff paper) and taping them together.

A Core Activities

▶ Counting Steps on the Number Line

Show children the walk-on number line. Invite them to look for other number lines and discuss similarities and differences. Have a child stand on the 0 on the walk-on number line. Ask the class where they think the child will end up if he or she takes five steps, using one step for each number. Check their guesses by having the child on the number line take five steps while the other children count each step out loud.

Next, with the child still standing on the 5, ask the class how many steps it will take to get back to 2. Discuss their predictions and strategies. Have the child on the number line take steps to the number 2, while the other children count the steps. Repeat several times, varying the information you present and the

Adjusting the Activity

If children seem confused, use counting-on prompts initially and move to counting-back prompts in a separate session. Be sure children are counting steps *between* numbers. Some children may benefit from keeping track of each step with their fingers.

AUDITORY ◆ KINESTHETIC ◆ TACTILE ◆ VISUAL

range between starting and stopping numbers. Sometimes have children guess the stopping number; other times have them figure out how many steps between numbers. *For example:*

- Where will you end up if you start on 0 and take 2 steps forward?

- If you start on 4, how many steps will it take to get to 8?

- If you are on 7 and take 5 steps back, where will you end up?

Model finger "hops" on your Growing Number Line. Explain the connection between finger hops and children's steps on the walk-on number line. Try to leave the walk-on number line where children can use it frequently. Encourage children to use it to help them solve addition and subtraction problems.

▶ Exploring Pattern Blocks (Revisit Activity 1·2, p. 48)

Set out pattern blocks in the Math Center for free explorations. The Pattern-Block Template will be introduced in Activity 4-3. Also remember to use *Minute Math* during spare moments in the day.

B Teaching Options

ENRICHMENT

▶ Playing Number Line Games (*Math Masters,* p. 124)

In a center, place a number line, a set of number cards, and an object to move along the line. Children draw two cards and figure out how many steps there are between the numbers. Children also can play *Go Forward, Back Up* using a number die and a "+ and −" die to move along a number line (*Math Masters,* page 124).

MATHEMATICS OUTDOORS

▶ Playing Hopscotch

Encourage children to play Hopscotch and count the hops between numbers.

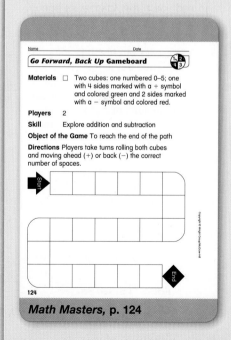

NOTE This activity is a concrete introduction to the addition and subtraction strategies of "counting on" and "counting back." It also helps children think of a number line as a problem-solving tool.

Math Masters, p. 124

ACTIVITY
4·2

Top-It Card Games

◎ **Objective** To introduce a game that reinforces number recognition and number comparisons.

CCSS **Mathematical Practices**
SMP2, SMP3, **SMP5,**
SMP6, **SMP7,** SMP8
Content Standards
K.CC.1, K.CC.6, K.CC.7

☐ Whole Group   ✔ Partners
✔ Small Group   ✔ Center

Key Concepts and Skills
• Read numbers. [Number and Numeration Goal 3]
• Compare numbers. [Number and Numeration Goal 6]

Terms to Use more, less, higher, lower

Materials Home Link Master (*Math Masters,* p. 32); card decks made from two sets of Small Number Cards 0–20 (*Math Masters,* pp. 105–107) or the cardstock number cards in the *My First Math Books.*

Planning Tip Use two copies of *Math Masters,* pages 105–107, cut and laminated or mounted on cardstock to prepare each card deck. (Alternately, combine sets of the cardstock number cards in the *My First Math Books.*) You may want to combine some of the decks you made for Activity 3-9. Each pair of children will need a deck of cards, so you may want to teach the game in small groups.

A Core Activities

▶ **Playing *Top-It*** (*Math Masters,* pp. 105–107)

Show children the card decks and explain that each deck has two of each of the numbers 0–20. Pick two cards from a deck. Have children say the numbers and tell you which number is more and which is less. Ask children to share how they knew which number was higher. (If children don't share them, model strategies such as checking the number line or counting out loud.) Repeat this warm-up activity a few times before teaching how to play *Top It.* (You may remember the game as War.)

Give each pair of children a shuffled card deck. Direct them to divide the deck so that each child has the same number of cards. Have them place their stacks facedown on the table or desk, turn over the top card, and read the numbers. The player with the larger number takes both cards. If players have the same number, they turn over and compare the next card on their stacks until someone wins the round and takes all the cards.

Adjusting the Activity

Provide counters or cards with dots and numerals for children who may still need concrete or visual supports to compare numbers. Some children may also benefit from using only numbers 0–10 at first.

AUDITORY ♦ KINESTHETIC ♦ TACTILE ♦ VISUAL

The winner is the player with the most cards when play stops. Below are variations of *Top-It* that you can introduce as children are ready.

▷ *Opposite Top-It* (or *Bottom-It*) The smaller number takes the cards.

▷ *Top-It with a Spinner* Prepare a spinner with sections labeled "Larger" and "Smaller." Players spin before each round to decide which number takes the cards.

▷ *Top-It Using Higher Numbers* Use decks with numbers above 20.

 Children can play a computer version of *Top-It* using *Everyday Mathematics EM Games.*

 Home Link 4·2 (*Math Masters*, p. 32)
Children teach a family member how to play *Top-It*.

▶ **Skip Counting by 10s** (Revisit Activities 1·12 and 3·15, pp. 68 and 170)
Play *Give the Next Number,* but have children count by 10s rather than 1s. (Be sure all of the "10s" are highlighted on your Growing Number Line for reference, as needed.)

ENRICHMENT

▶ **Playing *Addition Top-It*** (*Center Activity Cards*, 16)
Children add the numbers on two overturned cards; the higher sum wins. (Begin with 0–5 cards and gradually increase numbers.) Dots on the cards can help with addition.

See Project 3, Fun with Games, for other addition and subtraction games.

EXTRA PRACTICE

▶ **Playing Number Card Games**
In addition to the *Top-It* variations, provide card games such as Go Fish. Also encourage children to play the card games from Activity 3-9, page 158.

Math Masters, p. 32

 Ongoing Assessment:
Recognizing Student Achievement

Use *Top-It* to assess children's ability to identify the smaller and larger number in a pair. Children are making adequate progress if they can do this for the numbers 0–20. Some children may be able to compare larger numbers.

[Number and Numeration Goal 6]

ACTIVITY
4·3

The Pattern-Block Template

CCSS **Mathematical Practices**
SMP1, SMP2, SMP3,
SMP5, SMP6, SMP7, **SMP8**
Content Standards
K.OA.1, K.OA.2, K.OA.5, **K.G.2,
K.G.5, K.G.6**

◎ **Objective** To introduce the Pattern-Block Template.

☑ Whole Group
☑ Small Group
☑ Partners
☑ Center

Key Concepts and Skills

• Use the names of pattern-block shapes. [Geometry Goal 1]

• Use the Pattern-Block Template to combine simple shapes to form larger shapes and pictures.
[Geometry Goal 1]

• Use the Pattern-Block Template to record patterns. [Patterns, Functions, and Algebra Goal 1]

Terms to Use template, circle, triangle, square, parallelogram, trapezoid, hexagon, pattern

Materials Pattern-Block Templates; pattern blocks; pencils; long strips of paper (sentence strips work well); markers or crayons

Planning Tip You might want to introduce the template on one day, and then have children create their pattern strips in a later session or in a center over the course of several days.

A Core Activities

▶ Exploring the Pattern-Block Template

Introducing the Template Show children the Pattern-Block Template and ask what they notice about it. Then, ask: *What do you think it might be for?* Distribute a handful of pattern blocks and a template to individuals or pairs of children. Invite children to put the blocks on top of the corresponding shapes on the template. After children have seen the relationship between the template and the blocks, demonstrate how to make a shape both by tracing around the block and by using the template. Emphasize the following techniques as you use the template. Practice first (to be a good coach).

● Hold the template firmly with one hand.

● Keep your pencil against the sides of the shape.

● Move your pencil around the entire shape.

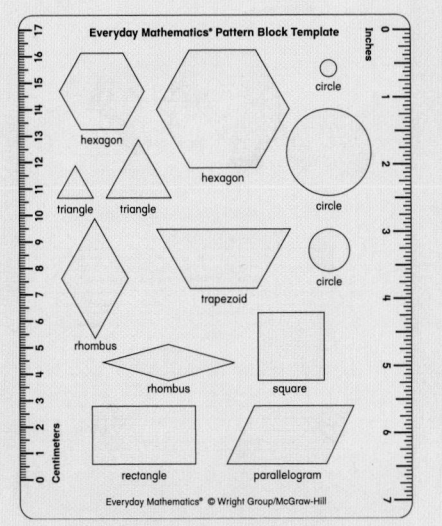

Everyday Mathematics® Pattern Block Template

circle
hexagon
hexagon
triangle triangle
circle
trapezoid
circle
rhombus
rhombus square
rectangle parallelogram

Everyday Mathematics® © Wright Group/McGraw-Hill

Give children a chance to practice using the template to trace shapes. Then, provide pattern blocks for children to use to create pictures, designs, and larger shapes; model how to use the template to record their creations.

Creating Pattern Strips After children are comfortable using the template, have them make pattern strips. Direct children to create a pattern with the pattern blocks and then use the template to copy their pattern on a strip of paper. Have them color in their shapes using the color that matches the actual color of the pattern block (for example, yellow for hexagons). Demonstrate and offer assistance with lining up and orienting the template shapes on the paper. (This will be difficult for some children.) Save children's pattern strips to use in a Teaching Option in Activity 4-5, page 197.

Keep several templates in the Math and Art Center. Encourage children to use the templates to create or record patterns, pictures, designs, and larger shapes.

> NOTE Children are often interested in the pattern block shape names. Label some of the shapes when you display children's patterns and designs.

▶ Solving Pocket Problems (Revisit Activity 3•8, p. 156)

Use your pocket and counters to pose a few pocket problems. Focus on addition problems in preparation for the next activity which introduces the "+" symbol.

B Teaching Options

ART CONNECTION

▶ Creating Pattern-Block Template Creatures (*Center Activity Cards,* 17)

Children can design and make creatures, such as animals, people, robots, monsters, aliens, or imaginary characters using the template. Encourage children to use symmetry in creating their pictures. Have children label their pictures and share them with the class.

The Addition Symbol (+)

CCSS Mathematical Practices
SMP1, **SMP2,** SMP3,
SMP4, SMP5, SMP6, **SMP7**
Content Standards
K.OA.1, K.OA.2, K.G.2, K.G.5,
K.G.6

ACTIVITY 4·4

Objective To introduce addition terminology and symbols using number stories and counters.

✔ Whole Group
✔ Small Group
☐ Partners
✔ Center

Key Concepts and Skills

• Model and solve addition number stories using manipulatives. [Operations and Computation Goal 1]

• Make up addition number stories. [Operations and Computation Goal 1]

• Recognize "joining" situations as addition. [Operations and Computation Goal 2]

• Learn about the + symbol. [Patterns, Functions, and Algebra Goal 2]

Terms to Use add, join, all together, addition, symbol, plus sign

Materials Teaching Aid Master (*Math Masters,* p. 109); construction paper or slates; craft sticks; counters

Planning Tip Cut out and laminate the addition symbol (+) from *Math Masters,* page 109. You will use the subtraction symbol (−) in Activity 4-11.

 Core Activities

▶ Joining Objects Using the Addition Symbol (*Math Masters,* p. 109)

Give each child a sheet of paper or a slate, a craft stick, and about 10 counters. Show children how to put their craft stick in the middle of their paper or slate. Then have them place 5 counters on one side of the stick and 2 on the other side. Have them remove the craft stick, slide the counters all together, and then figure out the total number of counters. Tell a number story about combining the two groups. For example, *I had 5 shells. Then my mom gave me 2 more. Now I have 7 shells all together.* Repeat with different numbers of counters on each side of the paper or slate and different stories. The stories need not refer to the objects that represent them—a counter can be a cookie, a person, or a dinosaur!

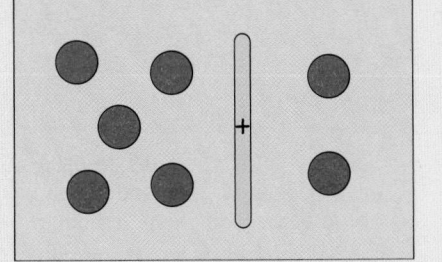

Invite children to make up and share joining (addition) number stories. As the class continues to tell and model number stories with the counters, ask children what the stories have in common. Listen for comments such as: "We are putting things together," "The numbers get bigger," and "We are adding things."

Show children the large addition symbol (+) from *Math Masters,* page 109. Discuss what it means and how it is used. Children may also call it the "plus symbol" or "plus sign." Have children write the symbol on their craft stick. Tell a few more addition number stories and have the children model them with their counters and craft sticks. Describe the action for each story as follows: *3 plus 2 more is 5.* As children gain experience modeling the actions for their number stories, you might write a corresponding number model on the board using the "+" symbol (for example, 3 + 2). Leave the materials in the Math Center for children to use independently.

▶ Creating Pattern Strips (Revisit Activity 4•3, p. 192)

Portfolio Ideas

Give children time to use the pattern blocks and Pattern-Block Templates to create pattern strips. This can be done in a center or as a whole group activity.

B Teaching Options

EXTRA PRACTICE

▶ Playing the *Growing Train Game*

Children can play the *Growing Train Game.* (See Activity 3-13, page 166 for directions.) To reinforce its meaning, you may want to add a "+" symbol to each side of the green die.

LITERACY CONNECTION

▶ Reading "The Gingerbread Boy"

Read a version of this story and encourage children to keep track of how many people join at each step. Ask: *How many are chasing him altogether?*

NOTE Continue to emphasize the action of joining, or putting objects together, in conjunction with the "+" symbol to help children focus on its meaning.

ACTIVITY
4·5

Follow My Pattern

Objective To provide practice with creating, extending, and describing patterns.

CCSS

Mathematical Practices
SMP1, SMP2, **SMP3,**
SMP4, SMP5, **SMP6,** SMP7

☑ Whole Group
☑ Small Group
☑ Partners
☑ Center

Key Concepts and Skills
• Create and describe patterns with pattern blocks. [Patterns, Functions, and Algebra Goal 1]
• Continue pattern-block patterns. [Patterns, Functions, and Algebra Goal 1]

Terms to Use patterns, extend, continue, repeat

Materials Home Link Master (*Math Masters,* p. 33); pattern blocks

Planning Tip Conduct the partners activity in small groups or a center if you don't have enough pattern blocks for the whole class to use at the same time.

A Core Activities

▶ Creating and Extending Pattern-Block Patterns

Have children watch as you begin a pattern with pattern blocks. Once you have placed enough blocks to establish the pattern, call on a child to add the next block to your pattern. Repeat with several children. To support English language learners, discuss the meaning of the word *extend*. After several blocks have been added, ask for a volunteer to describe your pattern (for example, "yellow hexagon, green triangle; yellow hexagon, green triangle; …" or "one triangle, two squares; one triangle, two squares; …"). Reinforce shape identification and labeling by having children use the names of the pattern-block shapes when they describe the patterns.

Have children continue the activity with a partner. Each partner creates a pattern with pattern blocks. After a few minutes, partners change places and describe and continue each other's patterns. Encourage children to make increasingly complex patterns for their partners to extend.

NOTE It is not necessary—and is potentially distracting—for the teacher or children to label patterns as ABAB, ABCABC, and so on at this point.

NOTE Children can explore both growing and repeating patterns during this activity. (See page 96 for more information.)

 Home Link 4-5 (*Math Masters*, p. 33)

Children create patterns at home.

▶ **Estimating Objects in a Collection** (Revisit Activity 2•13, p. 114)

Put a collection of 30 or more edible items (such as raisins or chocolate chips) in your estimation jar. (Also use a reference jar containing a known number of the same item.) After children make estimates and do a class count to check their estimates, encourage them to find a way to evenly distribute the items for snacking. (See Estimating Pennies in Activity 3-2, page 141, for suggestions about collecting and organizing children's estimates.)

B Teaching Options

ENRICHMENT

▶ **Playing *Pattern Cover Up*** (*Center Activity Cards*, 18)

Children use a small piece of paper to cover a block in the middle of a pattern sequence. Their partners try to figure out the hidden block. Children can use the pattern strips they created in Activity 4-3, page 193, or they can create patterns with pattern blocks and remove or cover a block. To increase difficulty, players can cover or remove more than one block.

 Ongoing Assessment:

Recognizing Student Achievement

Use the partner activity in **Follow My Pattern** to assess children's ability to create, extend, and describe patterns. Children are making adequate progress if they are able to create, extend, and describe 2- and 3-part patterns. Some children may be able to work with more complex patterns.

[Patterns, Functions, and Algebra Goal 1]

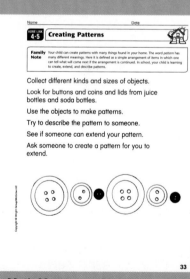

Math Masters, p. 33

Interrupted Counts

ACTIVITY
4·6

 Objective To introduce interrupted counting.

CCSS Mathematical Practices
SMP1, SMP2, **SMP4, SMP5,** SMP6
Content Standards
K.CC.1, K.CC.2, K.CC.4a, K.CC.4b

☑ Whole Group
☑ Small Group
☐ Partners
☐ Center

Key Concepts and Skills
• Count by 1s through at least 50 using different starting points. [Number and Numeration Goal 1]

Materials stop sign or red circle (optional)

> **Planning Tip** Create a stop sign (or use a red circle) for oral counting activities throughout the year. If you prefer, you can establish hand signals to stop and start the counts.

 **A** **Core Activities**

▶ Counting from Different Numbers

Review with children the different types of counting they have practiced so far: counting forward and backward by 1s and counting by 10s. Ask children what number they usually start with when they count. Explain that today they are going to practice counting by 1s from a number other than 0 or 1 and that you are going to interrupt their counting. To support English language learners, ask for volunteers to explain what it means to interrupt their parents or teacher. Encourage children to look for things in the room that can help them as they count, such as the calendar, the Growing Number Line, or another number line.

> **NOTE** In addition to extending counting practice to higher numbers, this activity provides practice with the important concept of counting on.

Call out a number and point to one child or a small group of children to begin counting from that number. After a few numbers have been counted, use your stop sign or hand signal to stop the counting. Point to another group or child to continue the count from wherever the previous counter(s) left off, or from a new number that you designate. Repeat the process, stopping and starting at different numbers, until all have had a turn.

Children should also practice counting backward from different starting numbers.

▶ Graphing Dice Rolls

(Revisit Activity 3•3, p. 142; *Math Masters*, p. 26 or 27)

Set out the dice and Roll and Record sheets in the Math Center. Encourage children to work on a dice roll graph independently or to play *Dice Race* (from the Teaching Options on page 143) with a friend. Provide dice and record sheets with different numbers for children who are ready. Children will do a Roll and Record activity with two dice in Activity 4-8.

Also remember to use *Minute Math* during spare moments in the day.

 **Teaching Options**

(EXTRA PRACTICE)

▶ Playing Oral Counting Games

Play some of the oral counting games from previous activities using higher numbers. See Activity 1-12 (page 68) for *Give the Next Number*, and Activity 2-6 (page 98) for *Count and Sit* and *Follow the Leader*. At this point, most children will be comfortable with numbers through at least 30. Begin venturing into higher numbers with your oral counting activities, keeping in mind that children's comfort level with higher numbers will vary greatly and that repeated exposure over time is the best way to extend their range.

(LITERACY CONNECTION)

▶ Saying an Interrupted Alphabet

Have children start and stop at different letters as they say the alphabet.

 Ongoing Assessment:
Recognizing Student Achievement

Use **Interrupted Counts** to assess how high children can count by 1s. Children are making adequate progress if they can count through at least 30. Many children will be able to count much higher. Also monitor whether children can count backward by 1s from different numbers.

[Number and Numeration Goal 1]

Meet the Calculator

CCSS Mathematical Practices
SMP1, SMP2, SMP4, **SMP5**
Content Standards
K.CC.4a, K.CC.4b, K.CC.6,
K.OA.1, K.NBT.1

ACTIVITY 4·7

◎ **Objectives** To introduce calculators and to provide practice with reading and entering numbers.

☑ Whole Group
☑ Small Group
☐ Partners
☐ Center

Key Concepts and Skills
• Read and display numbers on a calculator. [Number and Numeration Goal 3]

Terms to use calculator, display, clear or all clear

Materials solar-powered calculators; a large sign labeled with the symbol [ON/C] or [AC] (depending on your calculator's clear mechanism)

Planning Tip You can use any calculator to complete the activities in *Kindergarten Everyday Mathematics*. For demonstration purposes, key sequences for the TI-108 and the Casio SL-450 calculators are provided. Check your calculator users' manual and adjust the instruction accordingly.

Each child or pair of children should have a calculator for this activity, so you may need to conduct the activity with small groups.

A Core Activities

▶ Exploring Calculators

Pass out the calculators and allow children some time to play with them. Do this before each calculator lesson.

When the free-play time is over, ask children what they know or noticed about the calculators. Probe with questions such as: *Have you ever seen anyone use a calculator? Where? What did they use it for? Do the numbers on the calculator look different from numbers you have seen elsewhere? How?* After children have shared their ideas and observations, explain that the calculator is a fast and fun way to work with numbers. Mention that they will learn some different ways to use calculators.

All calculators have a key that clears the display. On most calculators, this is the On/Clear key ([ON/C]) or the All Clear key ([AC]). Go through the following steps to help children learn to use these keys.

ON/C ———

AC ———

ON/C

AC

1. Point to your display sign and have children find the key marked ⌨ON/C or Ⓐ Ⓒ.
The C in ON/C stands for "Clear." Explain that the AC stands for "All Clear." Ask:
Can you think of anything else that you clear? (Clear the table, the chalkboard ...)
What do you see when you press ⌨ON/C *or* Ⓐ Ⓒ*?* (0) *Where do you see the number?* Tell
children that the window where they see the number is called the display window,
and the other window is the solar cell that powers the calculator. (See the Science
Connection for more discussion of the solar cell.)

2. Next, pose some questions for children to answer using their calculator displays.
Remind them to press ⌨ON/C or Ⓐ Ⓒ to clear their displays before each question. Discuss
each answer with the class as you proceed. (To support English language learners,
you may need to discuss the meanings of some of the words in your questions.) For
example, you might ask:

   ● *How many ears does a cat have?* (2)

   Press ⌨ON/C or Ⓐ Ⓒ to clear the display.

   ● *How many legs are on your chair?* (4)

   Clear the display.

   ● *How many toes do you have on one foot?* (5)

   Clear the display.

It is important for children to learn to
clear their calculators by pressing
⌨ON/C or Ⓐ Ⓒ at the beginning of each
new calculator problem. Make and
use the appropriate sign to help
children find the key on their
calculators.

- *How many legs does a spider have?* (8)

Clear the display.

- *How many trunks does an elephant have?* (1)

Clear the display.

- *How many wheels does a tricycle have?* (3)

Clear the display.

- *How many wings does a dog have?* (0)

Clear the display.

- *How many legs does an ant have?* (6)

Clear the display.

- *How many days are in a week?* (7)

Clear the display.

- *What's the number that comes after nine?* (10)

3. After children have a chance to consider the last question, ask: *Does anyone see a 10 key? How can we display the number ten?* This should lead to a discussion about pressing two keys to display 10 and other 2-digit numbers. Have children work with a partner to make and read 2-digit numbers on the calculator. (One child can enter a number and the partner can read it. Or, one child can say a number and the partner can enter it.) Tell children to only use numbers they are able to read.

After the activity, set several calculators in the Math Center for continued exploration.

▶ **Playing *Teen Frame*** (Revisit Activitiy 3∙16, p. 172; *Math Masters,* pp. 137 and 138)

Have children play *Teen Frame*, this time recording "10 + _____" number models to represent their numbers for each round. (For example, if they spin a "14," they would write "10 + 4 = 14.") Children can write their number models on slates, paper, or laminated copies of *Math Masters,* page 137.

NOTE If time permits, invite children to pose questions that can be answered with numbers. (They have to know the right answers to their questions!)

Ongoing Assessment:
Informing Instruction

Watch for children who are not entering the digits in the right order. Remind them to enter the digit on the left first, and encourage them to check the display after each entry. Some children will benefit from referring to a number line or other printed number as they enter digits.

READINESS

▶ Practicing 2-Digit Number Recognition

Provide practice with reading 2-digit numbers by randomly pointing to a number on the Growing Number Line and asking children to say the number. You can also cover up a number and ask children to figure out what the covered number is and how to write it (for example, what digits to use and in what order). Repeat for several numbers. This activity may help children enter 2-digit numbers on their calculators.

MATHEMATICS IN THE DRAMATIC PLAY CENTER

▶ Playing with Calculators

Place some calculators in the Dramatic Play Center and watch how children use them. Some children might incorporate them into "office," "bank," or "store" play, especially if you place real or pretend money in the center.

SCIENCE CONNECTION

▶ Investigating the Solar Cell

Ask children to cover the calculators' solar cells with their hands or fingers and see what happens. (The 0 on each calculator should disappear—and then quickly reappear when children uncover the solar cells.) See if children can figure out the connection between light and the appearance of the number on their calculators.

ACTIVITY 4·8

Roll and Record with Two Dice

◎ **Objective** To provide experiences with addition, graphing outcomes, and probability.

CCSS **Mathematical Practices**
SMP2, **SMP3, SMP4,** SMP5, SMP6, SMP7
Content Standards
K.CC.4a, K.CC.4b, **K.OA.1, K.OA.2, K.OA.3, K.OA.5,** K.G.2, K.G.4

☑ Whole Group   ☑ Partners
☑ Small Group   ☑ Center

Key Concepts and Skills
• Develop and use strategies to find the sum of two dice rolls. [Operations and Computation Goal 1]
• Create a graph of dice rolls. [Data and Chance Goal 1]
• Compare the probability of various outcomes from rolling two dice. [Data and Chance Goal 3]

Terms to Use add, sum, probability, likely, chance

Materials Teaching Master (*Math Masters,* p. 34); dice; pencils

---

A **Core Activities**

▶ Graphing Sums of Dice (*Math Masters,* p. 34)

Remind children of the graph they made in Activity 3-3, page 142. Tell them that today they will do a similar activity with two dice. Give each pair of children two dice and demonstrate how to use the Dice-Throw Grid (*Math Masters,* page 34). Have them roll their dice, find the sum, and report their totals to you while you record the totals on the master. Ask children to share how they figured out their sums. Model common strategies, such as counting dots, adding on, and memorizing combinations. Ask: *Why doesn't the grid have columns for "0" or "1"?*

NOTE Children's strategies will evolve over the course of the year and in later grades. Fluently adding and subtracting within 5 is a Kindergarten goal that will be emphasized toward the end of the year, but many children will begin to show fluency with these (and other) basic addition facts through repetition in the context of activities like this one.

Planning Tip This activity may span several days. You might introduce it to the whole group or to small groups, then have children work on their individual graphs in the Math Center over several days. Compile the results as a whole group after everyone has had a chance to do at least one graph.

Later, put out dice and Dice-Throw Grids in the Math Center for children to continue addition practice. You may also want to make copies of the grids for children to use at home.

Adjusting the Activity

Enlarge *Math Masters,* page 34 to fill an 11" × 17" sheet of paper for children who may have difficulty writing or tracking results on the smaller grid. As in Activity 3-3, children can fill in or mark the grid spaces, or they can write the number in each space.

AUDITORY ◆ KINESTHETIC ◆ TACTILE ◆ VISUAL

Give each child a copy of the Dice-Throw Grid and their own pair of dice. Children should work independently to roll and record the sums of dice throws on their own graph. A graph is finished when one column is filled. (If children want to continue rolling and recording, have them mark the "winning" number [the one that fills the column first] so you can compile the class results.)

When every child has finished at least one graph, record each child's winning number on a new copy of the Dice-Throw Grid. (You may need to tape two masters together.) Encourage children to share their ideas about why the middle numbers came up most often. Probe with questions such as: *How many ways are there to get 2? Are there more ways to get 8?* In the course of discussion, help children realize that a middle number (such as 7) can be made in more ways than the highest and lowest numbers, so the middle numbers are more likely outcomes. Incorporate probability language (*likely, chance*) into the discussion.

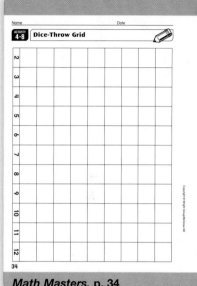

Math Masters, p. 34

▶ Feeling Shapes (Revisit Activity 2•2, p. 90)

Put a few pattern blocks or attribute blocks into your "Feely Box" (or Bag) and have children try to identify the shapes by feel.

B Teaching Options

ART CONNECTION

▶ Drawing a 10-Part Bug

Players try to be the first to draw a 10-part bug (body, head, 6 legs, and 2 antennae). To begin, each player rolls a pair of dice to determine his or her assigned number. Next, players take turns rolling the dice. If their number comes up, they draw a bug part. The first to complete a bug wins. Discuss whether everyone has the same chance of finishing first. For a shorter game, make a creature with fewer parts.

Body and Rope Shapes

CCSS Mathematical Practices
SMP1, SMP2, SMP3,
SMP4, SMP6, SMP7
Content Standards
K.G.2, K.G.4, K.G.5

Objective To deepen children's understanding of shapes through a cooperative movement activity.

☑ Whole Group
☑ Small Group
☐ Partners
☐ Center

Key Concepts and Skills
• Make circles, squares, rectangles, and triangles using bodies and ropes. [Geometry Goal 1]
• Identify and describe attributes of shapes. [Geometry Goal 1]

Terms to Use circle, square, rectangle, triangle, side, corner, shape

Materials rope or string with the ends tied together (about 20 feet per group); shape collages from Activity 2•1 (optional)

Planning Tip This activity can be done outdoors if you need more space. You may want to extend this activity over several days by working on just one or two shapes per day.

Making Shapes

Draw or post a large circle, square, rectangle, and triangle for reference. You can use the shape collages from Activity 2-1 if you saved them. Ask: *What are some differences among the shapes? What is the same?* Explain that children will work together to make shapes with their bodies. Before they try each shape, discuss how many children they should use to form the shape. Select the designated number of children to start making the shape with their bodies while the rest of the class serves in an "advisory" capacity. Children may want or need to add more children to join the shape-making group as they work and problem solve. To promote further problem solving, prompt them to change the size of the shape. To involve more children, have two groups of children work simultaneously to create the same shape. This activity is rich with opportunities for children to discuss and solve problems cooperatively. As much as possible, let children work out difficulties through discussion and trial and error.

NOTE You may also want to invite children to make body and rope shapes for a hexagon and trapezoid.

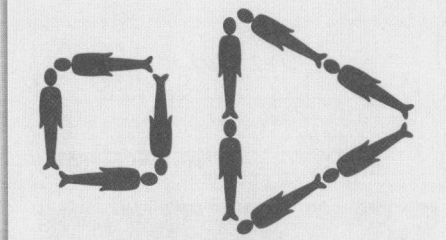

Body Shapes

Next, have children work together to create the shapes with the long loop of rope. (You may want to work in small groups at this point.) Afterward, discuss the experience with them. Prompt with questions such as:

- *What number of children did you use to make a triangle? A square or a rectangle?* (Note that these numbers may vary, depending on the size of the shapes children make. Encourage discussion about discoveries they have made, such as needing the same number of children on opposite sides for rectangles.)

- *What makes the shape change?* (Changing the number of corners or sides and/or the lengths of the sides.)

- *How was using the rope different than using your body? How was it the same? Did using rope work better than using bodies for certain shapes?*

▶ Making Symmetrical Snowflakes

(Revisit Activity 2◆16, p. 122; *Math Masters*, p. 35)

Model how to fold and cut out the snowflake on the master. Children can make more interesting snowflakes by folding a sheet of paper in half or quarters and making small cuts along the edges. Encourage them to analyze the symmetry of their snowflakes.

EXTRA PRACTICE
▶ Creating Shape Outlines

Provide yarn, string, ribbon, or shoelaces to make circles, squares, rectangles, and triangles in a center. Encourage making other shapes such as hexagons and octagons.

ELL SUPPORT
▶ Reviewing Basic Shapes

Call out a shape name and have children use large arm motions to draw the shape in the air as they say the name of the shape out loud.

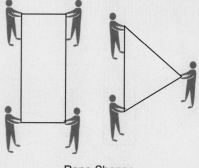

Rope Shapes

NOTE If you live in a snowy climate, you might want to save the Symmetrical Snowflakes activity until the first snowfall.

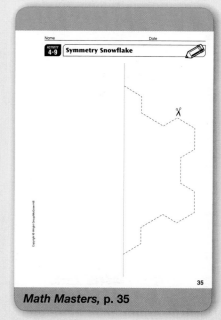

Math Masters, p. 35

ACTIVITY
4·10

Shape Comparisons

 **Objective** To solidify children's understanding of shapes.

CCSS **Mathematical Practices**
SMP1, SMP3, SMP6, SMP7, **SMP8**
Content Standards
K.MD.3, **K.G.2, K.G.4**

☑ Whole Group
☑ Small Group
☐ Partners
☐ Center

Key Concepts and Skills

• Compare shapes. [Geometry Goal 1]

• Explore variations of size and angle measures of shapes. [Geometry Goal 1]

• Realize that shapes remain the same even if their position is changed. [Geometry Goal 1]

Terms to Use shape, side, corner, angle, edge, turn, rotate

Materials construction paper shapes (triangles, squares, and rectangles) that differ in size (triangles should have different-sized angles); rope or string (2 long pieces, each with ends tied together)

A **Core Activities**

▶ Comparing Shapes

Remind children of the previous activity in which they made shapes with their bodies and the rope. Ask three children to use their bodies or the rope to make a triangle. Have another group of three children see if they can make a different triangle. Encourage the rest of the class to help think about how the second triangle could be different (length of sides, size of angles). Throughout this activity, informally model and encourage children to use the words **side, corner,** and perhaps **angle.**

Take one of the paper triangles you made and rotate it while children watch. Ask: *Is this still a triangle? Why or why not?* Then place two of the paper triangles (with different angles and lengths of sides) on the floor and ask: *Are both of these triangles? Why or*

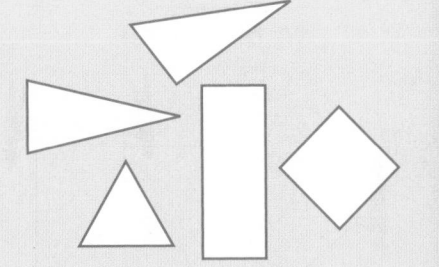

why not? How are they the same? (Be sure children recognize that the number of sides and corners are the same.) *How are they different?* Allow plenty of time for discussion.

One at a time, take the paper rectangle and square and rotate them while children watch. Ask: *Is this still a rectangle? A square? Why or why not?* Next, hold up one square and one rectangle together. Ask: *Are they exactly the same? How are they different? Is there anything similar about them?* Again, allow time for discussion. Display the shapes at different orientations to emphasize that the orientation of a shape does *not* change the properties of the shape itself.

▶ Sorting Names (Revisit Activity 1+6, p. 56)

Write each child's first name on an index card, and encourage children to find different ways to sort the cards (by first letter, last letter, number of letters, and so on). Also remember to use *Minute Math* during spare moments in the day.

B Teaching Options

EXTRA PRACTICE

▶ Using Geoboards and Tangrams (*Center Activity Cards*, 19)

Invite children to use geoboards and rubber bands to make the same shape in a variety of ways. Have them discuss their results and discoveries. If you have tangrams, encourage children to explore and manipulate them in the Math Center.

LITERACY CONNECTION

▶ Reading *Grandfather Tang's Story*

Read *Grandfather Tang's Story* by Ann Tompert (Dragonfly Books, 1997). Discuss how the positions of the shapes change to make the different pictures. If possible, encourage children to use tangrams in conjunction with the book.

Adjusting the Activity

Some children might enjoy thinking about the following questions: *Are all squares rectangles?* (Yes.) *Are all rectangles squares?* (No, a square is a special kind of rectangle.) Focus on children's observations and ideas, rather than on correct answers.

AUDITORY ♦ KINESTHETIC ♦ TACTILE ♦ VISUAL

Ongoing Assessment:
Informing Instruction

Watch for children who cannot identify shapes when the shape's orientation is changed. To help those children, provide opportunities to work with concrete objects, such as pattern or attribute blocks or jigsaw puzzles. Discuss how the shape stays the same even when children change the orientation. You might also provide pre-cut shapes for creating shape art. Children will manipulate the shapes to make their pictures.

The Subtraction Symbol (−)

CCSS Mathematical Practices
SMP1, SMP2, SMP4,
SMP6, SMP7
Content Standards
K.CC.3, **K.OA.1, K.OA.2**

Objective To introduce subtraction terminology and symbols using number stories and counters.

✔ Whole Group
✔ Small Group
☐ Partners
✔ Center

Key Concepts and Skills
• Model and solve subtraction number stories using manipulatives. [Operations and Computation Goal 1]
• Make up subtraction number stories. [Operations and Computation Goal 1]
• Recognize "take away" situations as subtraction. [Operations and Computation Goal 2]
• Learn about the − symbol. [Patterns, Functions, and Algebra Goal 2]

Terms to Use take away, subtract, subtraction, symbol, minus sign

Materials Teaching Aid Master (*Math Masters*, p. 109); construction paper or slates; craft sticks; counters

Planning Tip Cut out and laminate the subtraction symbol (−) from *Math Masters*, page 109.

A Core Activities

▶ Removing Objects Using the Subtraction Symbol (*Math Masters*, p. 109)

Give each child a sheet of paper or a slate, a craft stick, and about 10 counters. As you tell a take-away (subtraction) story, have the children model the action with their counters. For example, have children put 7 counters on their paper or slate. Say: *Kim had 7 new books at school. She took 3 home today. How many of her books are left at school?* Then have children use their sticks to sweep 3 counters off to the side and count how many remain. Repeat with more take-away stories, inviting children to make up and share stories, too. As the class continues to tell and model number stories with the counters, ask the children what the stories have in common. (For example, "The number

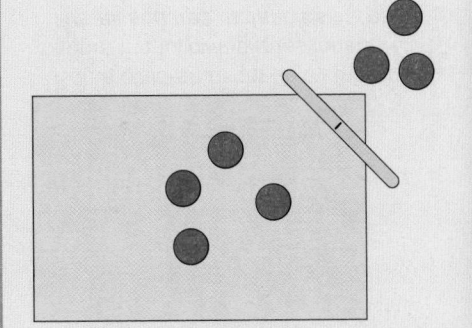

gets smaller," "We are taking things away," or "We subtract things.") Explain that these are called take-away or subtraction stories.

Show children the large subtraction symbol (−) from *Math Masters,* page 109. Discuss what it means and how it is used. Children may also call it the "minus symbol" or "minus sign." Have them write the symbol on their craft sticks. Tell a few more take-away stories and have children model them with their counters and craft sticks. Each time, describe the action with words (for example, *7 take away 3 leaves 4*). As children gain experience modeling the actions for their number stories, you might write a corresponding number model using the "−" symbol (7 − 3, for example).

Leave the materials in the Math Center for children to use independently.

▶ **Practicing Number Writing** (Revisit Activity 2•7, p. 100)

Call out numbers and have children "write" them in the air with large arm motions. Begin with single-digit numbers, and then call out 2-digit numbers.

B Teaching Options

ENRICHMENT

▶ **Solving Subtraction Pocket Problems**

Pose take-away pocket problems. (See Activity 3-8, page 156.) You might want to put the materials in the Math Center and encourage children to make up pocket problems for each other. Some children may be interested in recording their problems with pictures and/or number sentences.

EXTRA PRACTICE

▶ **Playing the *Disappearing Train Game***

Children can play the *Disappearing Train Game.* (See Activity 3-13, page 166 for directions.) You may want to add a "−" symbol to each side of the red die to reinforce its meaning.

NOTE In the course of the discussion, children (or you) may mention the "+" symbol they learned about in Activity 4-4. Capitalize on the opportunity to compare "joining" and "taking away" actions and to emphasize the need for different symbols for each action.

Links to the Future

These take-away or change situations provide exposure to one use for subtraction. Another use for subtraction—comparison situations—will be explored in Activity 6-9. (See "Operations and Number Models," *Teacher's Reference Manual,* Chapter 9.)

Slate Activities

ACTIVITY 4·12

🎯 **Objective** To provide practice with number writing and other numeration skills.

CCSS **Mathematical Practices**
SMP2, **SMP3**, SMP5, **SMP6**
Content Standards
K.CC.3, K.CC.4a, K.CC.4b,
K.MD.1

☑ Whole Group
☑ Small Group
☑ Partners
☐ Center

Key Concepts and Skills
• Practice one-to-one counting. [Number and Numeration Goal 2]
• Recognize and write numbers. [Number and Numeration Goal 3]
• Compare and order numbers. [Number and Numeration Goal 6]

Materials Large Number Cards (*Math Masters*, pp. 92–102); slates; writing tools for slates

Planning Tip If you do not have slates, the activities can be done on paper instead. Children love using colored pencils or crayons! See the *Teacher's Reference Manual* Chapter 3 for a discussion of slates.

A Core Activities

▶ **Using Slates** (*Math Masters*, pp. 92–102)

Have children sit in a circle so you can readily see what they write on their slates. Before beginning any of the activities, provide some exploration time for children to write on and erase their slates. Also discuss procedures and rules for using slates. Then select from the activities listed below.

▷ Clap a certain number of times. Children write how many claps they heard.

▷ Hold up a certain number of fingers. Children write that number on their slates.

▷ Say a number and have children write it.

▷ Show a number card and have children write the number that comes after or before the displayed number.

▷ Do Multisensory Counts (Activity 1-3, page 50), and have children write the number they hear.

 **Adjusting the Activity**

Use numbers in the range that children are practicing. Repeat the activities throughout the year, using higher numbers as children are ready. Children can also do slate activities with a partner, taking turns giving the directions and writing on the slate while you circulate to observe and assist. Pair children who are comfortable with a similar range of numbers.

AUDITORY ◆ KINESTHETIC ◆ TACTILE ◆ VISUAL

▷ Give clues about a mystery number, such as: *A teen number with a 4 in it,* or *The number of days we've been in school.* Have children write down what they think the number is.

▶ Measuring with Objects (Revisit Activity 3•7, p. 152)

Place objects in the Math Center along with connecting cubes or other uniform-length objects to measure with. Encourage children to use pictures and numbers to record their findings. Keep materials available as long as interest continues.

B Teaching Options

READINESS

▶ Learning Number-Writing Songs and Rhymes

See *Resources for the Kindergarten Classroom* for number-writing songs and rhymes that may be helpful to some children.

EXTRA PRACTICE

▶ Practicing with Spinners and Dice

Children can practice writing numbers on slates by rolling dice or spinning spinners and recording the numbers they generate.

MATHEMATICS IN THE DRAMATIC PLAY CENTER

▶ Playing with Slates (*Center Activity Cards,* 20)

Put some slates in your Dramatic Play Center and encourage children to use them as they play school, store, office, or other activities that might involve number writing.

Ongoing Assessment:
Informing Instruction

Watch for children who do not respond to prompts with the correct number. Note which types of prompts (for example, ordering numbers or one-to-one counting) are difficult for them, and provide extra practice in these areas. Because children's fine motor skills vary so dramatically, do not focus on assessing number formation at this time.

Introduction to Attribute Blocks

CCSS
Mathematical Practices
SMP1, SMP5, **SMP6, SMP7**
Content Standards
K.CC.1, K.CC.2, **K.MD.1, K.MD.3,
K.G.2**

**ACTIVITY
4·13**

◎ **Objective** To introduce attribute blocks.

☑ Whole Group
☑ Small Group
☐ Partners
☑ Center

Key Concepts and Skills
• Identify circles, squares, triangles, and rectangles. [Geometry Goal 1]
• Explore attribute blocks. [Patterns, Functions, and Algebra Goal 1]
• Sort blocks according to different attributes. [Patterns, Functions, and Algebra Goal 1]

Terms to Use thick, thin, attribute

Materials Home Link Master (*Math Masters,* p. 36); attribute blocks

A Core Activities

▶ Exploring Attribute Blocks

Have children sit in a circle. Spread the attribute blocks in the center where everyone can easily see them. Ask children what they notice about the blocks. After they share their observations, ask how the blocks might be sorted. Have children sort the blocks by one of the attributes that were mentioned. With the blocks sorted into groups, ask children why

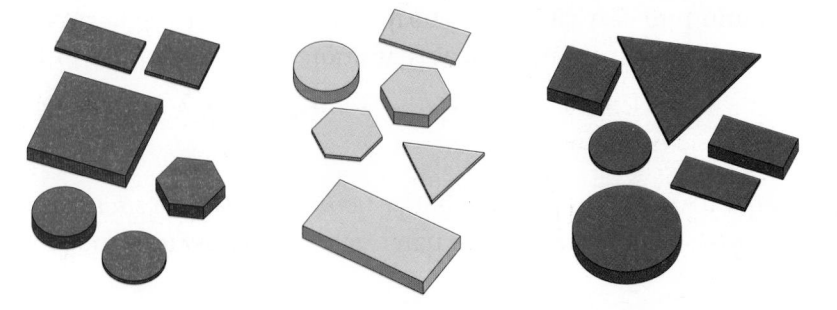

★ Ongoing Assessment:
Recognizing Student Achievement

Use **Introduction to Attribute Blocks** to assess children's ability to recognize and name basic shapes and to use rules to sort a collection of objects. Children are making adequate progress with shape identification if they are able to correctly identify circles, squares, triangles, and rectangles as they work with attribute blocks.

[Geometry Goal 1]

Children are making adequate progress with sorting if they are able to sort a collection of attribute blocks according to an attribute such as color, shape, or size.

[Patterns, Functions, and Algebra Goal 1]

each group of blocks belongs together. Ask for other ways to sort, and have the class help you re-sort accordingly. Continue until all new ways of sorting are explored. Discuss the attributes children have used to sort—for example, color, size, and shape.

Divide the class into small groups and give each group a handful of same-colored blocks. Have each group find another criterion (besides color) by which to sort their blocks into sub-groups. Once the blocks have been sorted, ask children how they sorted their blocks. Encourage children to describe their groupings using more than one attribute (for example, "red and thick" or "red triangles"). Then describe a block from their collection in great detail and ask children to find it. (For example, say: *Find a large, red, thin triangle;* or: *Look for a small, blue, thick circle.*) If time permits, call on a few children to describe a block for others to find. Place the blocks in the Math Center for children to continue to sort and explore.

Home Link 4-13 (*Math Masters*, p. 36)

Children practice using attributes as they conduct a treasure hunt.

▶ Counting On from Different Numbers (Revisit Activity 4•6, p. 198)

Using your stop sign or hand signals, practice interrupted counts at least through 50.

MOVEMENT CONNECTION

▶ Playing Simon Says

Play Simon Says using more than one attribute. For example, say: *Simon says children wearing red and having long sleeve shirts take one giant step.*

LITERACY CONNECTION

▶ Reading *3 Little Firefighters*

Discuss how buttons are sorted in this story by Stuart J. Murphy (HarperCollins, 2003).

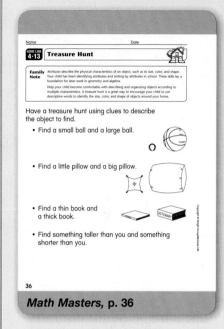

Math Masters, p. 36

"What's My Rule?" Fishing Game

CCSS Mathematical Practices
SMP1, **SMP3**, SMP6, SMP7, **SMP8**
Content Standards
K.G.2, K.G.4

Objective To introduce a game that helps children think about sorting rules.

☑ Whole Group
☐ Small Group
☐ Partners
☐ Center

Key Concepts and Skills
• Figure out and apply sorting rules. [Patterns, Functions, and Algebra Goal 1]

Terms to Use attribute, sorting rule

Materials none

A Core Activities

▶ Fishing for Children

Tell the class that they are going to pretend to be fish, and you are going to pretend to be a fisherperson. Explain that you will only catch one kind of fish at a time, such as fish with red shirts or fish with slip-on shoes. Children will watch you fish and try to guess what kind of fish you are looking for.

Begin fishing by using an obvious attribute (such as a color on some of the children's clothes). As you catch children, have them stand at the front of the group so others can clearly see them. Ask: *What sort of fish am I fishing for?* or: *What's my fishing rule?* Continue to catch children according to your sorting rule until someone guesses it correctly. To clarify, ask: *What is the same about the children I caught?* (They are all wearing red.) *What is the same about the children who are not in my net?* (They are not wearing red.) Play again using a different attribute. Over time, use more subtle rules. When they seem ready, let children take turns choosing the rule and being the fisherperson.

Fishing for red

Links to the Future

Expect the majority of children to be able to identify and invent sorting rules. In later *Kindergarten Everyday Mathematics* activities, children will describe and apply rules to generate one number from another. This exposure to rules will help prepare them to understand how rules are used in algebraic functions. See "Patterns, Sequences, Functions, and Algebra," *Teacher's Reference Manual,* Chapter 15.

▶ Playing *I Spy* with Shapes (Revisit Activity 4•10, p. 208)

Focus on shapes of various sizes and orientations. For example, give clues such as *I spy a large circle,* or *I spy a triangle sitting on one of its corners.*

(ENRICHMENT)

▶ Playing *Who Am I Thinking Of?*

Write one child's name on a piece of paper, but do not show it to the children. Children ask "yes" or "no" questions to try to figure out who you are thinking of. To begin, have all children stand up. Children sit down when they are in the "no" group. For example, if someone asks, "Is it a girl?" and you answer *yes,* the girls remain standing and the boys sit down. If children then ask "Does she have blue on?" and your answer is *no,* then all the girls wearing blue sit down. Continue until the person you identified is the only one standing.

(EXTRA PRACTICE)

▶ Playing *"What's My Rule?" Fishing* with Attribute Blocks

"Fish" for attribute blocks and have children guess what rule you are using.

Number Stories: Stage 2

Objective To develop understanding of mathematical symbols and language in the context of addition and subtraction number stories.

CCSS Mathematical Practices
SMP1, SMP2, SMP3, SMP4, SMP5, SMP6, **SMP7,** SMP8
Content Standards
K.CC.1, **K.OA.1, K.OA.2**

☑ Whole Group
☑ Small Group
☐ Partners
☐ Center

Key Concepts and Skills

- Use concrete materials and pictures to represent and solve addition and subtraction stories. [Operations and Computation Goal 1]
- Identify addition and subtraction stories. [Operations and Computation Goal 2]
- Use the +, −, and = symbols in the context of addition and subtraction number stories. [Patterns, Functions, and Algebra Goal 2]

Terms to Use joining, take away, number story, add, subtract, addition, subtraction, plus, minus, equal, symbol, number sentence

Materials counters; chart paper or chalkboard

A Core Activities

▶ Relating Symbols to Number Stories

By now, children have had many experiences telling and solving number stories and have been introduced to the addition and subtraction symbols. In this second stage of number story development, you will help children become aware of whether they are telling an addition or subtraction story and relate the "+," "−," and "=" symbols to their stories. Incorporate these ideas casually over time.

Invite a child to tell either a "joining" or a "take-away" number story, such as those they worked with in Activity 4-4, page 194 and Activity 4-11, page 210. Quickly write the story with words on the board or on a piece of chart paper. Call on other children to say the answer to the number story and share their strategies for solving it. Try to elicit a

NOTE See Activity 2-14 on page 118, to review the introduction of number stories and for a complete list and description of the stages of number story development.

variety of strategies, such as using fingers, a number line, and counting on or back in their heads. Provide counters for children who would like to use them. Next, ask the class whether they think the story was an addition story or a subtraction story. Encourage children to share reasons for their responses. If needed, prompt with questions such as: *Did we end up with more or fewer than we started with? Was anything put together? Was anything taken away? Did we add or subtract anything?*

Reread the story. Ask if anyone can think of a shorter way to write it. Remind children of the "+" and "−" symbols. Together write a number sentence to model the number story $(3 + 2 = 5$, for example). Point to the addition or subtraction symbol and ask if anyone knows what the symbol means. (Add or take away objects.) Point to the equal symbol. Elicit ideas from the class before explaining that it means "the same as" or "is equal to." Repeat with several more number stories.

▶ **Counting by 10s** (Revisit Activities 2•6 and 3•15, pp. 98 and 170)

Play *Count and Sit* to practice counting by 10s. Also remember to use *Minute Math* during spare moments in the day.

B **Teaching Options**

EXTRA PRACTICE

▶ **Playing the *Growing and Disappearing Train Game***

If you haven't already done so, add "+" and "−" symbols to the appropriate sides of the die that children use for the *Growing and Disappearing Train Game*. (See Activity 3-13, page 166.) Encourage children to make up number stories that correspond to each move they make with their counters.

ELL SUPPORT

▶ **Acting Out Number Stories**

Invite children to act out number stories as you (or other children) tell them.

Links to the Future

Expect the majority of children to record their number stories with pictures. Some may also want to try adding symbols or number sentences to their drawings, but this is not the main objective at this point. In Activity 7-3 children will focus on writing number sentences to model their number stories.

Two-Digit Numbers

◎ **Objective** To provide practice with reading and representing 2-digit numbers.

CCSS Mathematical Practices
SMP1, **SMP2,** SMP3,
SMP6, **SMP7,** SMP8
Content Standards
K.CC.3

☑ Whole Group
☑ Small Group
☐ Partners
☐ Center

Key Concepts and Skills

- Read 2-digit numbers. [Number and Numeration Goal 3]
- Represent 2-digit numbers with manipulatives. [Number and Numeration Goal 3]
- Represent 2-digit numbers as groups of tens and ones. [Number and Numeration Goal 5]

Terms to Use digits, 10s, 1s

Materials Large Number Cards (0–9) (*Math Masters,* pp. 92–97); straws or sticks (singles and bundles of 10)

Planning Tip Use the Large Number Cards (*Math Masters,* pages 92–97) that you have used in previous activities.

A Core Activities

▶ Reading 2-Digit Numbers (*Math Masters,* pp. 92–97)

By now children have been exposed to 2-digit numbers on the Growing Number Line, the calendar, and in other contexts. Many children need more practice with reading these larger numbers. Select some of the following activities to provide additional experiences with reading 2-digit numbers and to begin to develop children's understanding of place value.

▷ Point to 2-digit numbers on the calendar or Growing Number Line. Ask children to read the number. You can also blindfold a child and have the child point to a number to be read by the group.

▷ Focus children on a section of the Growing Number Line (the 20s, for example). Ask: *How are these numbers the same? How are they different?*

Remind children that words, just like numbers, have to be read from left to right.

▷ Show a group of sticks or straws (singles and bundles of 10). Have children count them by 10s and 1s, and then find the number on the Growing Number Line or tell you how to write the number.

▷ Use two Number Cards (0–9) to create numbers for children to read. Reverse the digits and compare the numbers. Challenge them to arrange the digits to create either the highest or lowest number. (This may be tricky at first. Children will do more work with comparing 2-digit numbers in Activity 7-13.) Children can also do this as partners, with each person selecting one number card.

▶ Describing Probability (Revisit Activity 3•11, p. 162)

Put an assortment of attribute blocks on a "probability tray." Vary the assortment and discuss the probability of choosing a block with a particular attribute, such as a red block. Encourage children to use terms such as *impossible* or *very likely*.

B Teaching Options

ENRICHMENT

▶ Building Numbers with 10s and 1s

Put straws, sticks, or base-10 blocks in the Math Center for making groups of 10s and 1s. Children can select two number cards to make a number, and then build it with 10s and 1s. Or, they can build a number and have a partner say the number.

EXTRA PRACTICE

▶ Playing Bingo

Children can play Bingo to practice reading 2-digit numbers.

TECHNOLOGY

▶ Reading Calculator Numbers

Children can enter and read 2-digit numbers on their calculators.

Adjusting the Activity

Use numbers in the range that children are practicing. Repeat the activities throughout the year, using higher numbers as children are ready. Most of the activities can also be used for working with 3-digit or larger numbers.

AUDITORY ♦ KINESTHETIC ♦ TACTILE ♦ VISUAL

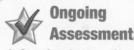
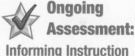

Ongoing Assessment:
Informing Instruction

Watch for children who are having difficulty reading or representing 2-digit numbers. Some children may become confused beyond a particular number. Others may have more global difficulties, such as reversing numbers or attending to only one of the numbers. Tailor the practice or assistance you provide accordingly.

Class Celebration

CCSS
Mathematical Practices
SMP1, SMP4, SMP5, SMP6, SMP7

◎ **Objective** To engage children in applying mathematics skills as they collaborate to prepare a classroom celebration.

Terms to Use measure, recipe, pattern, shape words

Materials

Classroom Setup
☐ food items
☐ paper goods
☐ utensils

Decorations
☐ long sheets of paper
☐ posterboard
☐ construction paper
☐ sponges; paint

Cooking
☐ Project Masters (*Math Masters,* pp. 77 and 78) (optional)
☐ measuring cups and spoons
☐ large bowls
☐ cooking ingredients

Introduction

Planning and carrying out a classroom celebration offers numerous opportunities for children to apply their developing mathematics skills, which include counting, measuring, using shapes and patterns, and solving problems. Celebration plans also can incorporate other curriculum areas; a few examples are: making decorations (art), writing invitations (language arts), choosing a theme (social studies or science), and providing entertainment (music, drama, or movement). Planning also allows children to cooperate and develop social skills in an enjoyable and meaningful way. Classroom celebrations are a great way to involve parents or other classes.

Begin by choosing a reason or event to celebrate. Some ideas include: holidays, the beginning or ending of a season, author studies, or the culmination of a unit or theme. Next, brainstorm a list of tasks for preparing the celebration. The tasks can be grouped into categories, such as cooking, decorating, writing invitations, setting up the classroom, and so on. Form committees to take responsibility for each type of task. Use a familiar system, such as voting or taking a survey of interests to place children on committees. When planning and preparing for your class celebration, consider using the following activities, which feature opportunities to apply and practice mathematics skills.

Activity Options

▶ Classroom Setup
✔ **Whole Group** ✔ **Small Group**

Collecting materials and setting up the classroom for the party will involve lots of counting and one-to-one correspondence. You can involve children in the following tasks:

▷ Figure out how many people are coming. Keep a growing tally chart to record attendees as they respond to your invitation. Or, children can use a calculator or counters to add the anticipated number of guests from each child's family. The Setup Committee might think of another way to track the number of expected guests.

▷ Use the number of guests to figure out how many chairs, tables, paper goods, and food items are needed for the party. (A simple diagram might be useful for figuring out how many tables are needed.) Later, children can count to check that the numbers of items are correct.

▷ Have children set tables. They will practice one-to-one correspondence as they place the correct number of place settings. They might arrange the plates or placemats in patterns.

▷ The Setup Committee may need to measure to decide where to place tables, what size tablecloths are needed, and so on. They might create a map or diagram to show how to organize the classroom and tables in order to fit the guests.

Literature Link *Spaghetti and Meatballs for All* by Marilyn Burns (Scholastic, 1997) is a humorous mathematical story about setting up for a big gathering. Some of the concepts are too advanced for most Kindergartners, but children will still enjoy the book and relate the events in the book to their party preparation tasks.

▶ Decorations

☑ **Whole Group** ☑ **Small Group**

Children can design decorations for the party. They may want to make items that are related to the theme of the celebration. This is a great time to incorporate concepts of patterning and using shapes. Consider some of the following suggestions for the Decorations Committee:

▷ Make colorful tablecloths by cutting sponges into different shapes, dipping them into paint or ink pads, and stamping them onto long sheets of paper, perhaps in patterns. The same technique can be used to make placemats, hats, or nametags from construction paper.

▷ Create invitations and posters announcing the date and time of the celebration. Use patterns and/or shapes to decorate the posters and invitations.

▷ Create patterned paper chains of varying lengths to decorate the room.

> **NOTE** Encourage children to incorporate repeating patterns and growing patterns in their decorations.

Math Masters, p. 77

▶ Cooking (Math Masters, pp. 77–78)

☑ **Whole Group** ☑ **Small Group**

Cooking involves counting and measurement. It provides opportunities to talk about different types of measuring tools, weight and volume of ingredients, and comparisons. You can use the drawings of measuring cups and spoons on *Math Masters*, pages 77 and 78 to create pictorial recipes for children to follow. The following recipes do not require an oven or stove and can be made in large quantities in the classroom. In addition, you probably have your own favorite recipes to prepare. For more ideas, see the Literature Link on page 225 for some child-friendly cookbooks.

> **NOTE** Find out if any children have food allergies before deciding on food for the celebration.

Sherbet Salad

2 small packages of orange-flavored gelatin dissolved in $1\frac{1}{4}$ cup boiling water (let an adult handle this)

1 pint orange sherbet

1 cup mandarin oranges

1 small can crushed pineapple, drained

1 container whipped topping

Mix ingredients together, chill to set, and serve.

Fruit Salad

2 cups fruit (bananas, strawberries, and apple), cut into bite-sized pieces

14 oz can of pineapple chunks in water or juice

$\frac{1}{4}$ cup orange juice

1 container whipped topping (optional)

Mix ingredients together and serve. Top with whipped topping if desired.

Fish in the Pond

2 celery stalks

$\frac{1}{4}$ cup cream cheese or other cheese spread

8 fish-shaped crackers

Trim and wash celery and fill with cheese. Top with crackers and serve. Substitute raisins for crackers to make Ants on a Log. (You can substitute peanut butter for cream cheese if no one in class has an allergy to peanuts.)

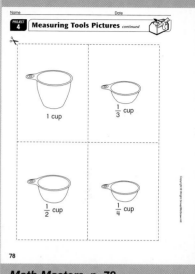

Math Masters, p. 78

Home Link Suggestions

Encourage parents to involve their children in cooking for a family celebration at home. Children can bring in a favorite recipe to add to a class cookbook. You might photocopy and distribute the class cookbook to all of the children's families.

Literature Link The following books feature cooking and celebrations:
Bread, Bread, Bread by Ann Morris (HarperCollins, 1989);
Sun Bread by Elisa Kleven (Dutton Children's Books, 2001).

These books include child-friendly recipes, as well as information about celebrations around the world:
The Kids' Multicultural Cookbook by Deanna F. Cook (Ideals Publications, 1995);
Pretend Soup and *Honest Pretzels* by Molly Katzen (Ten Speed Press, 1994; 1999);
Kids Around the World: Celebrate by Lynda Jones (John Wiley & Sons, 1999);
Kids Around the World: Cook and *Kids Around the World: Create* by Arlette Braman (John Wiley & Sons, 1999);
Children Just Like Me: Celebrations by Anabel Kindersley (DK Publishing, 1997).

Section 5

Overview

Section 5 has a number of main areas of focus:

- ◆ To introduce the need for standard measurement tools and units through continued measuring activities,
- ◆ To reinforce the use of multiple attributes to identify, describe, and sort objects,
- ◆ To reinforce the meanings of addition and subtraction and the use of symbols to write number models for addition and subtraction number stories,
- ◆ To develop awareness of equivalent names for numbers,
- ◆ To introduce the concept of making exchanges,
- ◆ To introduce the Class Number Grid,
- ◆ To introduce skip counting by 5s and tally marks,
- ◆ To reinforce and extend counting, estimation, and other numeration skills, and
- ◆ To continue patterning and graphing activities.

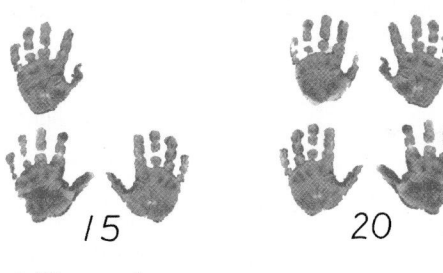

Maintaining Ongoing Daily Routines

Doing the Routines

In addition to Section 5 activities, continue to do the following Ongoing Daily Routines:

- Number of the Day
- Attendance
- Job Chart
- Monthly Calendar
- Daily Schedule
- Weather Observation
- Recording Daily Temperature
- Survey

Adjusting the Routines

Each Ongoing Daily Routine can be adjusted periodically according to children's progress and interest. If you haven't already done so, you can use the following routines to introduce new ideas and ask different questions during and after Section 5:

- **Number of the Day** Engage children in a countdown to the 100th day of school. In addition, remember to use the Growing Number Line frequently for counting, number recognition, and number games such as *Monster Squeeze*. You might ask children to count to or from a given number (by 1s, 5s, or 10s) or tell what comes before and after a given number.

- **Monthly Calendar** Ask questions to further develop children's familiarity with the calendar. *How many Wednesdays are in this month? Which day did the month start on? Point to the second Monday of the month.* Also incorporate these types of clues as the class dismantles the monthly calendar.

Using Routines for Ongoing Assessment

All of the Ongoing Daily Routines offer opportunities for ongoing assessment of a variety of skills and concepts. You might want to use the following routines for ongoing assessment during Section 5:

- **Number of the Day** Can children read the numbers on the Growing Number Line or tell you how to write the next number? Can they count to the number of the day by 1s? By 10s? By 5s?

- **Monthly Calendar** Can children read the numbers on the calendar or put them on the calendar in order? Do they know the correct day? Can they find a date if they are given the day of the week or similar clues?

Learning in Perspective

Core Activities

Activity	Objective	Revisit Activity	Page
5·1	**Order of Daily Events** To increase awareness of the passage of time and order of events.	**Playing the *Growing and Disappearing Train Game*** (Activities 3-13 and 4-15, Extra Practice, pp. 166 and 219)	**236**
5·2	**Patterns with Craft Sticks** To reinforce patterning skills, including creating, extending, and describing visual patterns.	**Looking Ahead to the 100th Day** (Project 5, p. 268) **Links to the Future** Project 5 provides many ideas for integrating mathematics in a 100th day of school celebration.	**238**
5·3	***Find the Block* Game** To introduce a game that involves using multiple attributes to identify and describe objects.	**Using Slates to Practice Writing 2-Digit Numbers** (Activities 4-12 and 4-16, pp. 212 and 220)	**240**
5·4	***Guess My Number* Game** To develop awareness of equivalent names for numbers using a guessing game. **Links to the Future** Finding equivalent names for numbers is a focus in Sections 7 and 8.	**Using Pan Balances** (Activities 3-4 and 3-12, pp. 144 and 164) **Links to the Past** Children were introduced to the pan balance in Section 3.	**242**
5·5	**Count with Calculators** To introduce counting forward and backward on the calculator.	**Playing *Monster Squeeze*** (Activity 3-6, p. 150)	**244**
5·6	**Measurement with Children's Feet** To develop and extend measurement skills by using children's feet to measure objects.	**Playing *Top-It*** (Activity 4-2, p. 190; *Math Masters,* p. 108)	**246**
5·7	**How Big Is a Foot?** To promote discussion and recognition of the need for standard measurement units.	**Counting by 10s** (Activity 3-15, p. 170)	**248**
5·8	**Count by 5s** To introduce skip counting by 5s. **Links to the Future** In Activity 6-10, children will learn to count by 2s.	**Graphing Sums of Dice Throws** (Activity 4-8, p. 204; *My First Math Book,* p. 3 or *Math Masters,* p. 34)	**250**

Core Activities, *continued*

Activity	Objective	Revisit Activity	Page
5·9	**Introduction of Tally Marks** To introduce or review tally marks as a way to count and record groups of 5.	**Making Equivalent Names for Numbers** (Activity 5-4, p. 242)	252
5·10	***The Raft Game*** To reinforce counting by 5s and introduce exchanges through a game. 〜 **Links to the Future** Children will make exchanges with coins beginning in Section 6 and in later grades. They will learn about place-value exchanges in Sections 7 and 8 and in later grades.	**Estimating Beans** (Activities 2-13 and 3-2, pp. 114 and 140; *My First Math Book*, p. 4) 〜 **Links to the Past** In Activity 2-13, children were introduced to estimation. They have had opportunities to practice estimation in every section.	254
5·11	**Standard and Nonstandard Feet** To reinforce the need for using standard units of measurement. 〜 **Links to the Past** Children explored nonstandard measurement in Activities 3-7, 5-6, and 5-7.	**Counting by 1s** (Activity 2-6, p. 98)	256
5·12	**Tools for Measuring Length** To provide experiences with a variety of measuring tools. 〜 **Links to the Future** In Grades 1 and 2, children will measure with standard linear measuring tools.	**Playing *Domino Concentration*** (Activity 3-5, p. 148) 〜 **Links to the Past** In Activity 3-5, children played *Domino Concentration* with double-6 dominoes and 0–12 number cards. They may now be ready for more challenging variations.	258
5·13	**Pet Bar Graph** To help children make and interpret a graph about pets.	**Following Craft Stick Patterns** (Activities 4-5 and 5-2, pp. 196 and 238)	260
5·14	***Attribute Spinner Game*** To introduce a game to help children focus on multiple attributes of attribute blocks.	**Tallying Class Data** (Activity 5-9, p. 252; *Math Masters*, p. 43)	262
5·15	**Introduction to the Number Grid** To introduce the Class Number Grid as a mathematical tool.	**Writing Number Models for Number Stories** (Activity 4-15, p. 218)	264
5·16	***Number-Grid Search* Game** To develop understanding of number sequence and patterns on the Class Number Grid using a game.	**Playing the *Matching Coin Game*** (Activity 2-8, p. 104) 〜 **Links to the Future** Children will be formally introduced to pennies, nickels, and dimes in Section 6.	266

Section Opener

Ongoing Learning and Practice

Practice through Games

Games are an essential component of practice in the *Everyday Mathematics* program. Games offer skills practice and promote strategic thinking. These games are introduced in this section:

Activity	Game	Skill Practiced
5♦3	*Find the Block*	Using attributes to find and describe objects [Patterns, Functions, and Algebra Goal 1]
5♦4	*Guess My Number*	Using addition and subtraction, place value, and other numeration clues to guess numbers [Number and Numeration Goals 3 and 5; Operations and Computation Goal 1]
5♦10	*The Raft Game* *Penny-Nickel Exchange*	Making exchanges for equivalent numbers [Number and Numeration Goals 3 and 5] Identifying coins and their values, and exchanging coins of equal value [Number and Numeration Goal 5; Measurement and Reference Frames Goal 2]
5♦14	*Attribute Spinner Game*	Using multiple attributes to identify objects [Patterns, Functions, and Algebra Goal 1]
5♦16	*Number-Grid Search* *Number-Grid Game*	Using number patterns to locate numbers and navigating spaces on a number grid [Number and Numeration Goals 2 and 3; Patterns, Functions, and Algebra Goal 1]

Home-School Connection

Home Links provide homework and home communication. The following activities contain Home Links: 5-2, 5-4, 5-7, 5-9.

Home Connection Handbook provides more ideas to communicate effectively with parents. ▶

◀ *Mathematics at Home* Books 1–4 provide additional ideas for enjoyable mathematics activities that families can do together, as well as lists of children's books related to topics in each strand area. Families can do activities from *Mathematics at Home* Book 3 during Section 5.

Balanced Assessment

Use the **Assessment Management Spreadsheets** to collect, review, and share information about children's progress.

Ongoing Assessment

 ### Recognizing Student Achievement

Opportunities to assess children's progress toward Kindergarten Goals:

Activity	Content Assessed
5•1	Sequence events and describe time periods of the day. [Measurement and Reference Frames Goal 4]
5•3	Read and write numbers to 30. [Number and Numeration Goal 3]
5•10	Make reasonable estimates. [Number and Numeration Goal 2]
5•13	Answer questions based on a bar graph. [Data and Chance Goal 2]

Informing Instruction

To anticipate common trouble spots and highlight problem-solving strategies:

Activity 5•11
Use proper measuring techniques

Activity 5•14
Work with multiple attributes

Activity 5•15
Locate numbers on a number grid

Periodic Assessment

Mid-Year assessment tasks will be completed in Section 5.

Portfolio Opportunities

◆ Daily Event timelines, **Activity 5-1**

Assessment Handbook

◆ Kindergarten Goals, pp. 27–33

◆ Section 5 Assessment Overview, pp. 58–59

◆ Assessment Overviews by Strand, pp. 66–75

◆ Mid-Year Periodic Assessment Tasks, pp. 42–44

◆ Individual Profile of Progress and Class Checklist (Mid-Year), pp. 87–90

◆ Individual Profile of Progress and Class Checklist (Sections 5–6), pp. 81–82

◆ Cumulative Individual Profile of Progress (Sections 5–8), pp. 99–102

Differentiated Instruction

Teaching Options

Use optional Part B activities as time permits to meet individual and class needs and to integrate mathematics throughout the Kindergarten classroom and schedule.

ELL SUPPORT

5•4	Creating a number tree
5•9	Telling the "Sleepy Snake" story

READINESS

5•10	Playing a beans and planks game
5•14	Describing blocks and other objects with multiple attributes

CONNECTIONS

Literacy

5•1	Comparing schedules
5•2	Finding patterns in a book
5•3	Reading *I Spy* books
5•5	Reading about a "Quack-U-Lator"
5•7	Reading about animal feet
5•8	Reading about counting by 5s
5•11	Reading *Inch by Inch*
5•12	Reading *Building a House*
5•15	Reading *How the Stars Fell into the Sky*

Science

5•7	Comparing feet
5•13	Researching pets

Art

5•2	Making toothpick patterns
5•8	Making a handprint display

Outdoors

5•11	Measuring outside

Social Studies

5•1	Making life timelines

ENRICHMENT

5•8	Listening and counting with nickels	5•14	Making attribute trains
5•10	Playing *Penny-Nickel Exchange*	5•16	Playing the *Number-Grid Game*

EXTRA PRACTICE

5•3	Playing *I Spy*	5•12	Measuring long chains
5•4	Playing a missing number game	5•15	Using write on/wipe off number grids
5•6	Measuring with paces	5•16	Playing a mini *Number-Grid Search* game
5•9	Counting with tally cards		

CENTERS

Block Center

5•6	Measuring block buildings

Writing Center

5•13	Writing pet stories

TECHNOLOGY

5•2	Working with patterns on the computer

HALF-DAY AND FULL-DAY PROGRAMS ◆ CROSS-CURRICULAR INTEGRATION ◆ CENTERS-BASED LEARNING

Language Support

Everyday Mathematics provides activity-specific suggestions to help *all* young children develop the language necessary to acquire, process, and express mathematical ideas. Activities that provide additional support for non-native English speakers are marked by **ELL SUPPORT** and **ELL**.

Connecting Math and Literacy

Activity 5◆1	*Jesse Bear, What Will You Wear?* by Nancy White Carlstrom (Aladdin, 1996)
Activity 5◆3	*I Spy* books by Jean Marzollo and Walter Wick (Cartwheel)
Activity 5◆5	*Little Quack* by Lauren Thompson (Simon & Schuster, 2003)
Activity 5◆7	*How Big Is a Foot?* by Rolf Myller (Dell Yearling, 1991)
Activity 5◆8	*Counting by: Fives* by Esther Sarfatti (Rourke, 2007)
Activity 5◆11	*Inch by Inch* by Leo Lionni (HarperTrophy, 1995)

See pages 239, 243, 249, 259, 260, and 265 for more literature suggestions.

Using the Projects

Use The 100th Day of School (Project 5, page 268) during or after Section 5 to reinforce skills and concepts related to counting, estimating, and problem solving.

Adjusting the Activity

AUDITORY ◆ KINESTHETIC ◆ TACTILE ◆ VISUAL

Activity 5◆1 Following step-by-step directions for sequencing **ELL**

Activity 5◆14 Using fewer attributes to identify an object in a game

Language & Vocabulary

Use these terms informally with children.

12-inch rulers	morning
add	next
after	nonstandard
afternoon	number grid
all clear	order
attributes	pattern
bar graph	plus
before	right
clear	row
column	scale
digit	second
equal/equals	skip count
evening	small
exchange	standard
fewer	standard foot
first	subtract
foot	take away
heel to toe	tally marks
large	thick
last	thin
left	third
measure	time
medium	total
minus	trade
more	unit

Planning Tips

Pacing Pacing depends on a number of factors, such as children's individual needs and how long your school has been using *Everyday Mathematics*. Use the optional Part B activities throughout Section 5 if you have extended mathematics instructional time. See page 232 for a list of these activities.

← MOST CLASSROOMS →
JANUARY	FEBRUARY

NOTE Children will use *My First Math Book* for the first time in Activity 5-2. Allow time for children to look through their books and explain how they use the books.

Teaching Resources

Resources for the Kindergarten Classroom provides additional teaching ideas, including suggestions for bringing mathematics into thematic instruction, as well as using games, literature, technology, and rhymes to support mathematics learning. ▶

Minute Math provides brief activities for transition times and for spare moments throughout the day. During Section 5, use the activities in Part 2, pages 67–196.

NCTM Standards

Content Standards: 1 Number and Operations, **2** Algebra, **3** Geometry, **4** Measurement, **5** Data Analysis and Probability
Process Standards: 6 Problem Solving, **7** Reasoning and Proof, **8** Communication, **9** Connection, **10** Representation

Section 5 Activities	5•1	5•2	5•3	5•4	5•5	5•6	5•7	5•8	5•9	5•10	5•11	5•12	5•13	5•14	5•15	5•16
NCTM Standards	1, 4, 9	2, 8	2	1, 8	1, 2, 10	4	4	1, 2	1, 5, 10	1, 10	4	1, 4, 6	5, 8	2	1, 2, 8	1, 2

Professional Development

Teacher's Reference Manual Links		
Activity	**Topic**	**Section**
5•8	Plain and Fancy Counting and Sequences	8.2.2 and 15.1.3

Materials

Activity	Masters	Materials	
5·1		• large sheets of construction paper	• crayons or markers
5·2	*My First Math Book*, p. 1 Home Link Master, p. 37	• craft sticks*	
5·3		• set of attribute blocks*	
5·4	Home Link Master, p. 38	• paper or slate*	• chart paper
5·5		• solar-powered calculators	• large display signs or transparencies with [ON/C] or [AC], [+], [−], and [=]
5·6	*My First Math Book*, p. 2	• stiff paper (file folders work well) • markers or crayons	• scissors
5·7	Home Link Master, p. 40 Teaching Master, p. 39	• children's foot cutouts from Activity 5-6 • *How Big Is a Foot?* by Rolf Myller (Dell Yearling, 1991)	• tape or string • scissors • 12-inch ruler*
5·8		• Growing Number Line or other number line*	
5·9	Home Link Master, p. 42 Teaching Master, p. 41 (optional)	• tape or glue (optional)	• chart paper
5·10		• craft sticks* • beans • glue • dice*	• small plastic animals, such as bear counters

Activity	Masters	Materials	
5·11	*My First Math Book*, p. 5	• standard cutout feet from Activity 5-7 (*Math Masters*, p. 39)	• children's cutout feet from Activity 5-6
5·12	*My First Math Book*, p. 6	• a variety of standard measuring devices, such as rulers*, metersticks* or	yardsticks, tape measures*, and carpenter's measures
5·13	*My First Math Book*, p. 7	• posterboard • index cards or paper (pre-cut to fit the graph)	• drawing materials • tape or glue • book about pets (optional)
5·14	Game Masters, pp. 118 and 119	• set of attribute blocks* • cardstock	• glue • paper clips • sharp pencils
5·15		• Class Number Grid • wipe-off marker	• stick-on notes
5·16		• Class Number Grid • stick-on notes	• blindfold (optional)
Mid-Year Assessment	*Assessment Handbook*, pp. 42–44	• number line* or Class Number Grid • estimation and reference jar • rubber bands* • straws or craft sticks* • number cards 0–20 • collection of objects	• pattern blocks*; attribute blocks* • tray • measuring tools* • drawing of something symmetrical • *Minute Math*

Technology

Assessment Management Spreadsheets, Section 5: See the *iTGA*.

---

* Indicates items in the Kindergarten manipulative kit.

Order of Daily Events

CCSS Mathematical Practices
SMP1, **SMP2,** SMP4,
SMP6, SMP7, SMP8

Content Standards
**K.CC.4a, K.CC.4b, K.CC.4c,
K.CC.5,** K.OA.1, K.OA.4

ACTIVITY 5·1

@ **Objective** To increase awareness of the passage of time and order of events.

☑ Whole Group
☑ Small Group
☐ Partners
☐ Center

Key Concepts and Skills
- Use ordinal numbers to describe a sequence of events. [Number and Numeration Goal 2]
- Sequence daily events and describe when events occur. [Measurement and Reference Frames Goal 4]

Terms to Use morning, afternoon, evening, before, after, first, second, third, next, last, order, time

Materials large sheets of construction paper; crayons or markers

Planning Tip You may want to fold the paper into thirds before the activity.

A Core Activities

▶ Sequencing Daily Events

Encourage children to think of different activities that occur during the day, both in and out of school (eating breakfast, eating dinner, going to bed, waking up, going to gym, having a snack, and so on). List children's ideas in no particular order. Read a few items, suggesting a mixed-up sequence (for example, *So, you put on your pajamas, then you come to school, then you go home and eat breakfast*). When children object, ask them to give their reasons. (The activities are in the wrong order!) Discuss the correct order of events. For example, ask: *What do you do first thing in the morning? What do you do after you get dressed? What's next? What do you do before dinner?* As children sequence the list, rewrite the activities in the correct order. Put numbers next to the items and state their ordinal positions—first, second, third, and so on. (You may need to mention that everyone does not do everything in the same order.)

NOTE You can refer to your Daily Schedule Routine as an example of correctly ordered events. You might also have a discussion about how the schedule of home days differs from that of school days.

Give each child a sheet of paper and help him or her fold it into thirds (if you haven't pre-folded). Tell children to pick three activities and draw them in the order they occur during the day. In the left section, children should draw something they do early in the day; in the middle section, something they do in the middle of the day; and in the right section, something they do late in the day. Children can label their pictures with the time of day (for example, morning, afternoon, evening; or before school, during school, after school). Children can write or dictate brief captions for their pictures. Display the timelines or allow children to show them to the group while you read their captions aloud.

▶ Playing the *Growing and Disappearing Train Game*

(Revisit Activities 3•13 and 4•15, Mathematics Extension, pp. 166 and 219)

Place materials in the Math Center to play the *Growing and Disappearing Train Game*. Add a minus sign to the red die and a plus sign to the green die, if you haven't already done so. Leave the game out for several days or as long as interest continues.

B Teaching Options

SOCIAL STUDIES CONNECTION

▶ Making Life Timelines

Children can create timelines of their lives by sequencing photos or drawings of events that occurred at different ages—perhaps a picture from each year.

LITERACY CONNECTION

▶ Comparing Schedules

Read *Jesse Bear, What Will You Wear?* by Nancy White Carlstrom (Aladdin, 1996). Discuss how the events in Jesse Bear's day compare with children's schedules.

Adjusting the Activity   ELL

Provide additional structure by numbering the sections of the paper 1, 2, and 3 and giving step-by-step directions such as:

Draw the first thing you do each day in the box labeled 1.

Draw one thing that happens in the middle of the day in the box labeled 2.

Draw the last thing you do each day in the box labeled 3.

Children who are ready can include additional events on their timelines.

AUDITORY ◆ KINESTHETIC ◆ TACTILE ◆ VISUAL

Ongoing Assessment:
Recognizing Student Achievement

Use **Order of Daily Events** to assess children's ability to sequence events and describe time periods of the day. Children are making adequate progress if they can order events correctly and use appropriate language to describe when the events occur.

[Measurement and Reference Frames Goal 4]

ACTIVITY 5·2

Patterns with Craft Sticks

CCSS
Mathematical Practices
SMP1, SMP2, SMP3,
SMP6, **SMP7**

Objective To reinforce patterning skills, including creating, extending, and describing visual patterns.

✔ Whole Group
✔ Small Group
☐ Partners
✔ Center

Key Concepts and Skills
- Copy and extend a visual pattern that is not color based. [Patterns, Functions, and Algebra Goal 1]
- Create and describe a visual pattern that is not color based. [Patterns, Functions, and Algebra Goal 1]

Materials *My First Math Book,* p. 1; Home Link Master (*Math Masters,* p. 37); craft sticks

---

NOTE This is the first time children will use their *My First Math Books.* Allow time for children to look through their books, and explain how they will use the books.

A Core Activities

▶ Making Craft-Stick Patterns (*My First Math Book,* p. 1)

Begin to make a pattern with craft sticks, arranging them for children to see. Ask: *Can you tell me what comes next?* Encourage children to describe the pattern (for example, cross, line; cross, line; and so on). Give each child a handful of craft sticks. Have them use the sticks to copy and extend the pattern. Next, choose a child to make a new pattern using the craft sticks. Call on another child to describe the pattern, and have the rest of the class copy and extend it with their sticks. Prompt children to vary the types of patterns they initiate.

Place a supply of craft sticks in the Math Center for children to use to make patterns. Encourage them to try patterns with more than two parts. Have children record at least one craft-stick pattern on page 1 of their math books during the whole group activity or later in the Math Center.

Craft-Stick Patterns

1. Draw your craft-stick pattern here.

   Answers vary.

2. Draw another craft-stick pattern.

   Answers vary.

Use with Activity 5·2.   1

My First Math Book, p. 1

▶ Looking Ahead to the 100th Day (See Project 5, p. 268)

As the 100th day of school approaches, talk with children about the upcoming celebration of this event. Introduce the idea of making collections of 100 items at home in preparation for the big day, and help children think of a variety of things that would make good "100 collections." Encourage children to begin collecting and counting at home. Use or modify Home Link Master page 37 to explain the project to families. Also see Project 5, page 268, for other suggestions for celebrating the 100th day of school.

 Home Link 5·2 (*Math Masters*, p. 37)

Children begin working on 100th day projects.

 **B** Teaching Options

ART CONNECTION

▶ Making Toothpick Patterns (*Center Activity Cards*, 21)

Have children use toothpicks to create a patterned border around a drawing.

LITERACY CONNECTION

▶ Finding Patterns in a Picture Book

Read *Pattern Fish* or *Pattern Bugs* by Trudy Harris (Lerner, 2000 and Lerner, 2001). Encourage children to share and discuss the patterns they notice in the pictures.

TECHNOLOGY

▶ Working with Patterns on the Computer

Many computer games for young children feature activities that encourage children to create or extend visual or auditory patterns. See *Resources for the Kindergarten Classroom* for software suggestions.

 **Links to the Future**

Describing and extending craft-stick patterns helps children develop their abilities to recognize, describe, and consistently apply rules, which prepares them to understand functions in later grades.

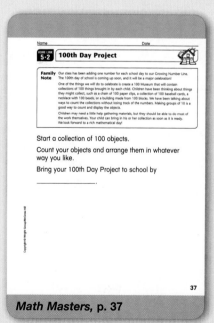

Math Masters, p. 37

Find the Block Game

ACTIVITY 5·3

Objective To introduce a game that involves using multiple attributes to identify and describe objects.

☑ Whole Group
☑ Small Group
☐ Partners
☐ Center

Key Concepts and Skills
• Use multiple attributes to find and describe objects. [Patterns, Functions, and Algebra Goal 1]
• Apply sorting rules. [Patterns, Functions, and Algebra Goal 1]

Terms to Use attributes, color and shape names, large, medium, small, thick, thin

Materials set of attribute blocks

A Core Activities

▶ Playing *Find the Block*

Show children the attribute blocks. Hold up a block and ask children to describe it. Prompt children until they mention all attributes of the block. Repeat with several other blocks. Remind children that the ways of describing the block (shape, color, size, and thickness) are called **attributes.** Distribute all the attribute blocks. (Some children may have more blocks than others. As the activity progresses, children should exchange blocks so everyone will have a chance to work with different blocks and with a larger number of blocks.)

Tell the class you are going to choose a mystery block. (To support English language learners, discuss the meaning of the word *mystery* in this context.) Give directions based on attribute clues to help children figure out the mystery block. *For example:*

• All children with a *large* block stand and hold up their blocks.

• All children with a *large, blue* block remain standing. (All others sit.)

- All children with a *large, blue circle* remain standing.
- All children with a *large, blue, thin circle* remain standing.

At this point only one child should be standing (unless you have multiple sets of blocks). Have the child repeat the block description (*a large, blue, thin circle*). Play the game several times, each time choosing a different mystery block. Children can give the clues after they become familiar with the game.

▶ Using Slates to Practice Writing 2-Digit Numbers

(Revisit Activities 4•12 and 4•16, pp. 212 and 220)

Lead the class in slate activities that provide practice with number writing. Focus on 2-digit numbers with prompts such as: *Write 42. Write the number that comes before it. Write the number that comes after it. Write the number you get if you switch the digits. Read that number.*

B) Teaching Options

(EXTRA PRACTICE)

▶ Playing *I Spy*

Have children use number clues, in conjunction with color, shape, and/or size clues, to identify mystery objects. For example, "I spy four things that are brown" (chairs at the table); or "I spy three things that are large rectangles" (windows). Children can choose mystery objects and give clues too.

(LITERACY CONNECTION)

▶ Reading *I Spy* Books

Read one or more *I Spy* books by Jean Marzollo and Walter Wick (Cartwheel). Leave them out so that children can use the clues in the text to find objects in the pictures.

Ongoing Assessment:

Recognizing Student Achievement

Use the slate activities to assess children's ability to read and write 2-digit numbers. Children are making adequate progress if they read numbers to 30 and use the correct digits in the correct order to write numbers to at least 30. Many children will be able to read and write numbers well beyond 30.

[Number and Numeration Goal 3]

ACTIVITY 5·4

Guess My Number Game

CCSS

Mathematical Practices
SMP1, **SMP2,** SMP3,
SMP5, SMP6
Content Standards
K.OA.5, K.MD.1, K.MD.2

 **Objective** To develop awareness of equivalent names for numbers using a guessing game.

☑ Whole Group
☑ Small Group
☐ Partners
☐ Center

Key Concepts and Skills
• Think about the combinations of digits used to write numbers. [Number and Numeration Goal 3]
• Recognize and find equivalent names for numbers. [Number and Numeration Goal 5]
• Use addition and subtraction clues to develop strategies and fluency. [Operations and Computation Goal 1]

Terms to Use digit

Materials Home Link Master (*Math Masters*, p. 38); paper or slate; chart paper

---

 **Links to the Future**

In this activity children are exposed to the idea that there are multiple ways to describe the same number. Finding equivalent names for numbers is a focus in Sections 7 and 8.

 **A Core Activities**

▶ Playing *Guess My Number*

Write a number on a piece of paper or a slate, but do not let children see the number. Invite the class to guess the number, based on one or more clues you give. Use different types of clues, such as those that involve simple addition and subtraction, place value, or other information. *For example:*

• The number that is 2 less than 5

• The number between 7 and 9

• A number in the teens with a 6 in it

• A number with a 2 and a 4 as the digits

• Another number with a 2 and a 4 as the digits

• The number of legs on a chair

NOTE Give lots of +/−1 and +/−0 clues to develop strategies and fluency for these addition and subtraction facts. *For example:* the number that equals 3 + 1, the number that equals 4 − 0. Discuss children's strategies for these types of problems.

When someone guesses correctly, show the number and have children read it aloud. Ask: *Are there other clues that could describe this number?* Write the number on chart paper along with the clues children suggest. Invite children to add to the list as they think of other clues. Repeat the game often, using higher numbers as children are ready. Allow children to think of numbers and give the clues.

Home Link 5·4 (*Math Masters*, p. 38)
Children play a number guessing game at home.

▶ Using Pan Balances (Revisit Activities 3·4 and 3·12, pp. 144 and 164)

Set out pan balances, clay, and objects for weighing. Add objects over the course of several days. Encourage children to record their findings with drawings. They can use the writing and drawing pages in their math books, if desired.

Also remember to use *Minute Math* during spare moments in the day.

 B **Teaching Options**

EXTRA PRACTICE

▶ Playing a Missing Number Game (*Center Activity Cards*, 22)

Partners arrange a set of number cards in numerical order. One child removes a card while the other isn't looking. The second child then looks at the cards to figure out the missing number. Increase difficulty by using cards with higher numbers.

ELL SUPPORT

▶ Creating a Number Tree

Read *Chicka Chicka 1, 2, 3* by Bill Martin Jr. and Michael Sampson (Simon & Schuster, 2004). Create a class number tree. Each branch can represent a number (such as 5). Over time, children can add leaves to the branch with equivalent names for that number (such as "3 + 2" or "the number before 6").

243   **Activity 5·4** *Guess My Number* Game

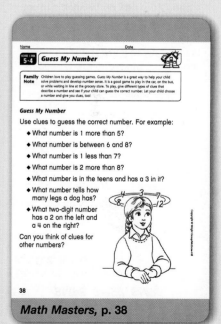

Math Masters, p. 38

Count with Calculators

 Objective To introduce counting forward and backward on the calculator.

CCSS Mathematical Practices
SMP1, SMP2, SMP3,
SMP5, SMP7, **SMP8**
Content Standards
K.CC.2, K.CC.7

☑ Whole Group
☑ Small Group
☑ Partners
☑ Center

Key Concepts and Skills
• Use calculators to count up and back. [Number and Numeration Goal 1]
• Identify +, −, =, and ON/C or AC keys on the calculator. [Patterns, Functions, and Algebra Goal 2]

Terms to Use clear, all clear, plus, add, minus, take away, subtract, equals

Materials solar-powered calculators; large display signs or transparencies with [ON/C] or [AC], [+], [−], and [=]

Planning Tip Make display signs for the [+], [−], and [=] signs that are similar to those you made for the [ON/C] or [AC] key in Activity 4-7. Each child or pair of children should have a calculator for this activity, so you may need to conduct it with small groups.

A Core Activities

▶ Counting Forward and Backward with a Calculator

Distribute calculators and allow time for free exploration. As a review, pose a few questions and have children display the answers on their calculators. For example, ask: *How many wheels are on a bicycle? How many fingers are on one hand?* Remind children to use ⟨ON/C⟩ or ⟨AC⟩ before each new question.

Explain that there are different ways to count with calculators. One way is to press each number key in order, clearing between each one. Lead children in pressing, then clearing, each number on their calculators as they slowly count aloud together. When they get to 10, ask if anyone remembers how to enter it. If necessary, refresh their memories about the procedure for entering two-digit numbers.

Next, introduce a faster way to count, using the calculator to supply the next counting number. Show the large [+] sign and ask children to find this key on their calculators.

Key sequences for counting forward by adding:
1. Press ⟨ON/C⟩ or ⟨AC⟩ to clear.
2. Press ⟨1⟩ to display 1.
3. Press ⟨+⟩ ⟨1⟩.
4. Press ⟨=⟩. What number do you see now? (2)
5. Keep pressing ⟨+⟩ ⟨1⟩ ⟨=⟩ to continue counting forward.

Lead the class in counting up by adding, using the key sequence instructions in the margin. After they've counted through at least 10, ask why they think using the [+] sign works for counting by 1s. (*Counting by 1s is like adding one more each time.*)

Finally, have children do a choral count backward from 10 to 0. Show the [−] sign display and ask children to find the key on their calculators. Remind the class that this is called a minus (or take-away) sign. Model the key sequence for counting back, explaining that they can count backward on their calculators if they take away, or subtract, 1 each time. You might point out that this is the opposite of the way they counted forward. (Children who go past 0 will get negative numbers. You might mention the thermometer as a familiar example of the use of numbers below 0.)

Leave calculators in the Math Center and encourage children to count as high as they can on the calculators. Periodically have them stop and read the number on the display. Also have children use different starting numbers for counting up and back.

▶ **Playing *Monster Squeeze*** (Revisit Activity 3•6, p. 150)

Play a few rounds of *Monster Squeeze*. Allow children to choose the number and move the monsters in response to the guesses. If children seem ready, play a few rounds of mental *Monster Squeeze*—using clues only, no monsters.

B Teaching Options

LITERACY CONNECTION

▶ **Reading about a "Quack-U-Lator"**

Read *Little Quack* by Lauren Thompson (Simon & Schuster, 2003). Children can follow along with the book's Quack-U-Lator problems using their calculators.

Key sequences for counting backward by subtracting:

1. Press [ON/C] or (AC) to clear.
2. Press [1] [0] to display 10.
3. Press [−] [1].
4. Press [=]. What number do you see now? (9)
5. Keep pressing [−] [1] [=] to continue counting backward.

NOTE The term *equals* may still be unfamiliar to many children. Use it casually in conjunction with synonyms such as "that makes" and "is the same as" to connect to everyday language.

NOTE Children will learn how to use the "repeat" function on a calculator in Activity 6-14.

ACTIVITY 5·6

Measurement with Children's Feet

CCSS Mathematical Practices
SMP2, SMP3, **SMP5, SMP6,** SMP7
Content Standards
K.MD.1, K.CC.7

⊙ **Objective** To develop and extend measurement skills by using children's feet to measure objects.

✔ Whole Group
✔ Small Group
✔ Partners
✔ Center

Key Concepts and Skills
- Measure with nonstandard "feet." [Measurement and Reference Frames Goal 1]
- Practice measuring techniques. [Measurement and Reference Frames Goal 1]

Terms to Use measure, foot, heel to toe

Materials *My First Math Book*, p. 2; stiff paper (file folders work well); markers or crayons; scissors

---

Planning Tip You might want to do the first part of the activity (discussion and making foot cutouts) in one session or at a center. Then use the cutouts to measure in a separate session.

 **A Core Activities**

▶ Measuring with Feet (*My First Math Book*, p. 2)

Tell children that long ago people used parts of their bodies to measure (hand spans, finger widths, feet, outstretched arms). Demonstrate how to measure the edge of a rug or the side of the room by walking along it, placing feet heel to toe. Model how to count to the closest number of feet. Then call on a few children to walk slowly (heel to toe) along the rug or the side of the room while the rest of the children count the number of steps (feet).

Discuss with children how they might measure a vertical length, such as the height of a table. If it doesn't come up, propose that they make a cutout foot for measuring. Show children how to trace one of their feet on stiff paper, cut it out, and label it with their name. Provide assistance as needed.

Have children use their cutout feet to measure objects in the room. Demonstrate how to keep track of the end of the toe and put the heel in front of it, just as they did with their own feet. This is known as "marking off." Working with a partner might help

NOTE If your class did Project 2, children may have already tried measuring with various body parts.

them mark off and keep track of the counts as they measure. (Pair children who understand the concept of marking off with those who are having difficulty with it.) Have children measure a table and another object that they choose. They should record their findings on page 2 in their math books.

Save the cutout feet and encourage children to use them for further measuring. The cutout feet will be used again in Activities 5-7 and 5-11.

▶ **Playing *Top-It*** (Revisit Activity 4•2, p. 190; *Math Masters*, p. 108)

Place card decks in the Math Center and encourage children to play *Top-It*. Consider introducing some of the *Top-It* variations, such as using decks with numbers above 20 or playing *Addition Top-It* with smaller number cards. Choose variations according to individual children's current skill levels. You can use blank number cards (*Math Masters*, page 108) to customize decks.

One child marks off the end of the toe with his finger while the other child moves the foot cutout so the heel is right in front of the first child's finger.

B **Teaching Options**

EXTRA PRACTICE

▶ **Measuring with Paces**

Explain and demonstrate that a natural walking step (a pace) is often used to make an approximate measure of the distance between two places. Have children pace off the distance to the playground, bathroom, or coatroom. Record the results and discuss why different children get different measures.

MATHEMATICS IN THE BLOCK CENTER

▶ **Measuring Block Buildings**

Encourage children to use their feet cutouts to measure their block buildings. Help them record their measurements ("5 Cindy feet," for example). They can use the writing and drawing pages in their math books to record their measurements.

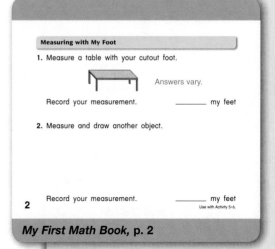

My First Math Book, p. 2

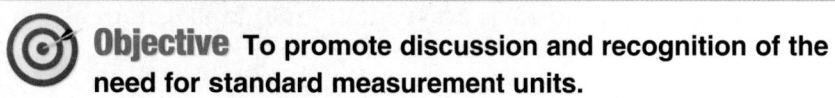

How Big Is a Foot?

CCSS Mathematical Practices
SMP3, **SMP5**, SMP6, **SMP7**, SMP8
Content Standards
K.MD.1, K.MD.2, K.CC.1

ACTIVITY 5·7

◎ **Objective** To promote discussion and recognition of the need for standard measurement units.

☑ Whole Group
☐ Small Group
☐ Partners
☐ Center

Key Concepts and Skills
• Measure with standard and nonstandard units. [Measurement and Reference Frames Goal 1]
• Understand the need for standard measurement units. [Measurement and Reference Frames Goal 1]

Terms to Use standard foot, unit

Materials Home Link Master (*Math Masters*, p. 40); Teaching Master (*Math Masters*, p. 39); children's foot cutouts from Activity 5•6; *How Big Is a Foot?* by Rolf Myller (Dell Yearling, 1991); tape or string; scissors; 12-inch ruler

Planning Tip Save the standard foot cutouts and children's individual foot cutouts to use for other measuring activities. Both will be used again in Activity 5-11.

A Core Activities

▶ **Reading and Discussing *How Big Is a Foot?*** (*Math Masters*, p. 39)

Read (or re-tell) *How Big Is a Foot?* Discuss why the bed in the story didn't turn out to be the right size. You might want children to act out the story.

Show the class a 12-inch ruler and explain that it is the standard measure of length in the United States. Compare it to the standard (12-inch) foot on *Math Masters*, page 39. Have each child cut the foot from a copy of the master. Give children their own cutout foot from Activity 5-6 so they can compare it to the standard foot.

Have the class work together to make two bed outlines, each 6 units by 4 units. For the first outline, use one child's cutout foot to mark off the length, and then use tape or string to mark the outline of the bed. For the second, use the standard foot. (Since each child has a standard foot, you might mark the outline of this bed by laying the standard

How Big Is a Foot? **Story Summary** The king decides to have a bed made for the queen's birthday. He marks off the dimensions of the bed with his feet and gives them to the head carpenter, who gives them to his apprentice. When the bed is delivered, it is too small. The apprentice must figure out why this has happened. (The king's feet are longer than the apprentice's feet!)

foot cutouts end to end.) Discuss the reasons for the different-sized beds. Allow children to try lying in them.

Home Link 5·7 (Math Masters, p. 40)
Children make and use different-sized cutout feet to measure objects.

▶ Counting by 10s (Revisit Activity 3·15, p. 170)
Practice counting by 10s through at least 110. You can use a counting game, such as *Count and Sit,* or incorporate a loud/soft pattern to maintain interest and enthusiasm.

Also remember to use *Minute Math* during spare moments in the day.

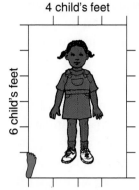

4 child's feet

6 child's feet

If desired, children can make additional bed outlines using other children's cutout feet.

B Teaching Options

SCIENCE CONNECTION

▶ Comparing Feet
Tape down a paper cutout of a paw print that measures 8 inches in length. Explain that this is about the size of a grizzly bear paw. Children can compare their cutout feet to the paw print and sort the feet into three piles: longer, shorter, and about the same length. Research other animal paw prints and repeat this activity if interest is high.

LITERACY CONNECTION

▶ Reading about Animal Feet
Read *Whose Tracks Are These?* by Jim Nail (Roberts Rinehart, 1996), and discuss the relationship between the size of animals and the size of their tracks.

6 standard feet

4 standard feet

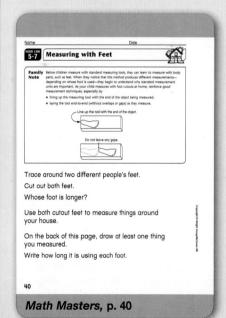

Name   Date

5·7 Measuring with Feet

Family Note Before children measure with standard measuring tools, they can learn to measure with body parts, such as feet. When they notice that this method produces different measurements—depending on whose foot is used—they begin to understand why standard measurement units are important. As your child measures with foot cutouts at home, reinforce good measurement techniques, especially by
• lining up the measuring tool with the end of the object being measured,
• laying the tool end-to-end (without overlaps or gaps) as they measure.

Line up the tool with the end of the object

Do not leave any gaps.

Trace around two different people's feet.

Cut out both feet.

Whose foot is longer?

Use both cutout feet to measure things around your house.

On the back of this page, draw at least one thing you measured.

Write how long it is using each foot.

40

Math Masters, p. 40

Count by 5s

ACTIVITY 5·8

◎ **Objective** To introduce skip counting by 5s.

CCSS Mathematical Practices
SMP1, SMP2, **SMP4,**
SMP5, SMP7, SMP8
Content Standards
K.CC.4a, K.CC.4b, K.OA.1, K.OA.2,
K.OA.3, K.OA.5

☑ Whole Group
☐ Small Group
☐ Partners
☐ Center

Key Concepts and Skills
• Skip count by 5s. [Number and Numeration Goal 1]
• Use fingers to represent groups of 5. [Number and Numeration Goal 3]
• Find patterns in counts by 5. [Patterns, Functions, and Algebra Goal 1]

Terms to Use skip count, pattern

Materials Growing Number Line or other number line

A Core Activities

▶ Counting by 5s

Have children hold up both hands with their fingers spread. Invite children to join you in counting all the fingers in the room. Touch each hand as you skip count by 5s. (Children put their hands down as they are touched and counted.) Write on the board the total number of fingers. Discuss whether you would have gotten the same number of fingers if you had counted by 1s. Ask children whether it is faster to count by 1s or by 5s. Together, think of other things that can be counted by 5s, such as toes or tally marks. Lead another choral count by 5s, creating a rhythm and having children flash 5 fingers on one hand as they count.

Direct children's attention to the Growing Number Line and mark the multiples of 5 if you have not already done so. Beginning with 0, use your finger to hop 5 spaces, then circle, underline, or add a sticker to the 5. Hop 5 more spaces and mark the 10. Continue for several more intervals of 5. Ask whether anyone notices a pattern and discuss

NOTE The finger count will probably extend beyond 200. Children enjoy hearing number patterns and big numbers, and some may make it all the way with you!

children's observations. Together, mark the rest of the 5s on the number line. (Continue to mark 5s as you add to the Growing Number Line.)

Practice choral counting by 5s frequently. Encourage children to use the number line as a reference if needed. To help solidify what it means to count by 5s, encourage children to "flash" the fingers on one hand as they say each 5.

▶ Graphing Sums of Dice Throws

(Revisit Activity 4•8, p. 204; *My First Math Book*, p. 3 or *Math Masters*, p. 34)

Have children work on Dice-Throw Grids using 2 dice. They can use the grid on page 3 of their math books or *Math Masters,* page 34. To develop fluency with simple addition facts, encourage children to try to recall some of the combinations before checking by counting.

 **Teaching Options**

ENRICHMENT

▶ Listening and Counting with Nickels (*Center Activity Cards*, 23)

Drop nickels in a can as children count by 5s. (You can do this activity again after nickels are introduced formally in Activity 6-2.)

ART CONNECTION

▶ Making a Handprint Display

Children can make traced or painted handprints and add labels *5, 10, 15, 20, ...*

LITERACY CONNECTION

▶ Reading about Counting by 5s

Read *Counting by: Fives* by Esther Sarfatti (Rourke, 2007) or *Hands Down: Counting by Fives* by Michael Dahl (Picture Window Books, 2004). Help children count the pictures by 1s and by 5s.

Links to the Future

Skip counting is a numeration skill, but it is also an example of a growing pattern—a number sequence in which the next number in the list is created by applying a rule (such as "plus 5") to the previous number. Recognizing that skip counting involves repeated application of a rule helps prepare children to understand mathematical functions later. See Chapter 15 of the *Teacher's Reference Manual* for more information about growing patterns, number sequences, and functions.

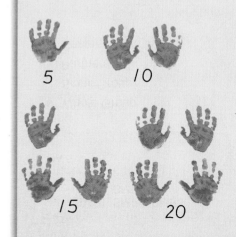

5   10

15   20

Introduction of Tally Marks

CCSS Mathematical Practices
SMP1, **SMP2**, SMP3,
SMP4, SMP6
Content Standards
K.OA.5

ACTIVITY 5·9

◎ **Objective** To introduce or review tally marks as a way to count and record groups of 5.

☑ Whole Group
☐ Small Group
☐ Partners
☐ Center

Key Concepts and Skills

• Count tally marks by 5s. [Number and Numeration Goal 1]

• Use tally marks to represent numbers. [Number and Numeration Goal 5]

• Use tally marks to record classroom data. [Data and Chance Goal 1]

Terms to Use tally marks

Materials Home Link Master (*Math Masters,* p. 42); Teaching Master (*Math Masters,* p. 41; optional); tape or glue (optional); chart paper

Planning Tip Prior to the activity, prepare a transportation tally chart that will show how children came to school. You can use the pictures from *Math Masters,* page 41, and tape them along the left side of a chart. Or have children help you draw the following pictures on the chart: a car, bus, bicycle, and child walking.

 **A** **Core Activities**

▶ Introducing and Using Tally Marks (*Math Masters,* p. 41)

Lead the class in rote counting by 5s to 110. Mention how quickly they can count to a high number this way! Draw a group of tally marks (about 12) on the board. Tell children that these are **tally marks.** Explain and demonstrate how tally marks work, emphasizing that after you draw 4 "up and down" tally marks you always do the fifth tally as a diagonal across the first 4. Count aloud from 1 to 5 as you draw several sets of 5 tally marks on the board. Have children draw tally marks in the air with their fingers as you draw them on the board. Count the tally marks together by 5s.

Show children the transportation tally chart you prepared and ask: *How did you get to school today?* As each child answers the question, make a tally mark beside the appropriate picture. When everyone has responded, model how to count the tally marks

NOTE If your class is already familiar with tally marks, just begin the activity with a brief review. If they haven't used tally marks, you might want to tell the "Sleepy Snake" story in the Teaching Options section as part of your introduction.

by counting the tally groups by 5s and then counting on by 1s for the rest of the tallies. Discuss the totals for each category. Also discuss other possible uses for tallying.

Home Link 5·9 (*Math Masters*, p. 42)

Children tally car colors in their neighborhoods.

▶ Making Equivalent Names for Numbers (Revisit Activity 5·4, p. 242)

Have children think of equivalent names for the day-of-the-month number on the calendar. Record their suggestions. (Prompt them to show the date with tally marks, too!) Repeat this exercise frequently when you do your class calendar routine.

B Teaching Options

EXTRA PRACTICE

▶ Counting with Tally Cards

Prepare cards with tally marks. Children count the tally marks and write the number. You might also encourage children to practice making and counting tally marks on the writing and drawing pages in their math books. Children can work with a partner; one child draws tally marks and the other child counts them.

ELL SUPPORT

▶ Telling the "Sleepy Snake" Story

Tell the "Sleepy Snake" story and have each child act it out using 5 craft sticks.

Once upon a time there were 5 snakes. One by one, 4 snakes crawled up on a flat rock and stretched out right beside each other to take a nap. When the fifth snake crawled onto the rock, there was no room left, so he stretched himself across the other 4 and went to sleep!

Count by 5s the number of snakes (craft sticks) in your classroom!

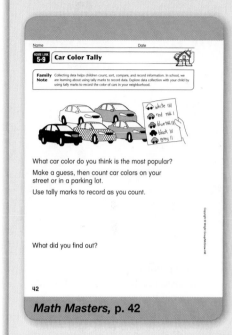

Math Masters, p. 42

NOTE Using tally marks supports counting by 5s by encouraging children to think of groups of 5. Incorporate tally marks into your survey and weather routines. Also use tally marks for classroom voting, tracking points in games, and other occasions that arise.

The Raft Game

Objective To reinforce counting by 5s and introduce exchanges through a game.

☑ Whole Group   ☑ Partners
☑ Small Group   ☑ Center

Key Concepts and Skills
• Use objects to represent numbers and make exchanges. [Number and Numeration Goal 3]
• Explore equivalent names for numbers. [Number and Numeration Goal 5]

Terms to Use exchange, trade, equal

Materials craft sticks; beans; glue; dice; small plastic animals, such as bear counters

Planning Tip A few days before introducing the game, have children make planks and rafts. They glue (or draw) 5 beans on each craft stick to make planks, then glue 5 planks together to make rafts (see diagram). You will need at least 10 planks, 3 rafts, a handful of beans, and a plastic animal for each pair of children who will play at the same time.

A   Core Activities

▶ Playing *The Raft Game*

Place a die, several planks, two or more rafts, a few bear counters, and a pile of beans where children can see them. With a child as your partner, demonstrate and discuss the rules for playing the game.

▷ Players take turns rolling the die and counting out that number of beans.

▷ When a player collects 5 beans, he or she trades them for one plank.

▷ When a player collects 5 planks, he or she trades them for a raft. When someone gets a raft, they can place a bear counter (or other animal) on it and "float" it across a pretend river. Children may collect as many rafts as time (and materials) allow.

Exchange Table
5 beans = 1 plank
5 planks = 1 raft
1 counter per raft

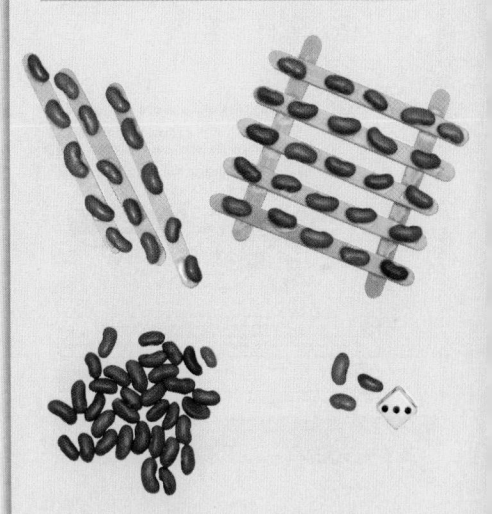

Help children understand why you can exchange 5 beans for a plank and 5 planks for a raft. If necessary, point out that it is an equal exchange. To support

English language learners, discuss and model the meanings of the words *plank, raft, trade,* and *equal exchange.*

After you introduce the game to the whole group or small groups, provide supplies for children to play in the Math Center.

▶ Estimating Beans

(Revisit Activities 2•13 and 3•2, pp. 114 and 140; *My First Math Book,* p. 4)

Place 30 to 50 beans in your estimation jar. (Also prepare a reference jar with 10 beans.) Have children record their estimates on page 4 of their math books. After everyone has made an estimate, have children group the beans in piles of 5 and then count them by 5s. Each child should then circle whether their estimate was "way too low," "way too high," or "pretty close" on their math book page. You might track and record with tally marks how many estimates were in each category.

Also remember to use *Minute Math* during spare moments in the day.

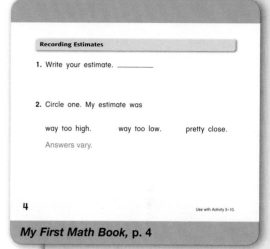

My First Math Book, p. 4

B   Teaching Options

READINESS

▶ Playing a Beans and Planks Game

For children who are not yet ready to play *The Raft Game,* simplify the game. Have partners exchange 5 beans for 1 plank and collect as many planks as time allows.

ENRICHMENT

▶ Playing *Penny-Nickel Exchange*

Children who are already familiar with money may enjoy rolling a die, collecting pennies, and exchanging 5 pennies for a nickel. If desired, they can go further and exchange 5 nickels for a quarter. Help children relate this game to *The Raft Game.* (Activities 6-1 and 6-2 introduce pennies and nickels and their values.)

Ongoing Assessment:

Recognizing Student Achievement

Use **Estimating Beans** to assess children's estimation skills. Children are making adequate progress if they do not make a wild guess or attempt to do an exact count. Some children may be able to make a relatively close estimate.

[Number and Numeration Goal 2]

ACTIVITY 5·11

Standard and Nonstandard Feet

CCSS Mathematical Practices
SMP3, **SMP4**, SMP5,
SMP6, SMP7, SMP8
Content Standards
K.MD.1, K.MD.2, K.CC.1

◎ **Objective** To reinforce the need for using standard units of measurement.

☑ Whole Group
☑ Small Group
☑ Partners
☐ Center

Key Concepts and Skills

• Practice measuring with standard and nonstandard units of measurement.
[Measurement and Reference Frames Goal 1]

• Compare and discuss measurements using standard and nonstandard units.
[Measurement and Reference Frames Goal 1]

• Understand the need for standard units of measurement. [Measurement and Reference Frames Goal 1]

Terms to Use standard, nonstandard, 12-inch rulers

Materials *My First Math Book*, p. 5; standard cutout feet from Activity 5·7 (*Math Masters*, p. 39); children's cutout feet from Activity 5·6

A Core Activities

▶ **Measuring and Comparing** (*My First Math Book*, p. 5)

Hold up a standard cutout foot and one of the children's cutout feet. Ask: *What will happen if we measure the chalkboard with each foot?* In the course of discussion, review the book *How Big Is a Foot?* and the beds children made in Activity 5-7. Remind children that the standard foot is used for measuring in the United States. (Compare it to a 12-inch ruler to reinforce this point.) Explain that when the standard foot is used, all measurements of the same object should be the same.

Have children measure the chalkboard using a child's cutout foot and a standard cutout foot. Review proper measuring techniques as they work.

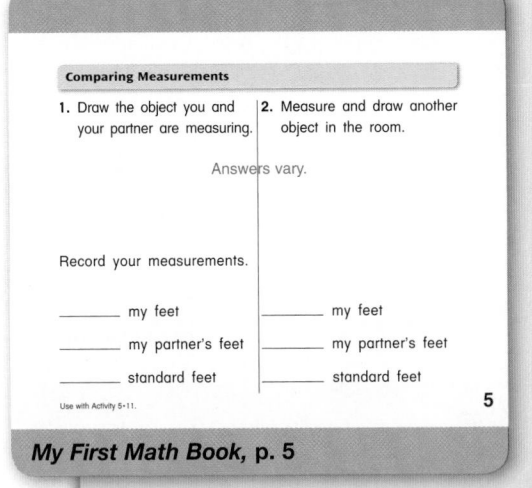

My First Math Book, p. 5

If the measure includes a portion of a foot at the end, discuss which number of feet best describes the length of the object. Emphasize that the measure is not exact. Record the results on the board as "about __ child's feet" and "about __ standard feet." Discuss why the measurements are different and why this might be a problem. If children seem uncertain about the need for a standard unit, measure the board again using a standard foot and a different child's foot (noticeably bigger or smaller). Point out that the number of standard feet stayed the same, but the number of child's feet changed.

Have each child measure a classroom object with his or her own nonstandard foot, and then work with a partner to measure the same object with the standard foot. Children record the results in their math books and then repeat for another object.

▶ **Counting by 1s** (Revisit Activity 2•6, p. 98)

When you add to the Growing Number Line, lead the class in a choral count to the Number of the Day. You might incorporate movements or a loud/soft pattern to keep it fun and interesting. Repeat at least once per week for counting practice.

B Teaching Options

MATHEMATICS OUTDOORS

▶ **Measuring Outside**

Children can take their cutout feet outside to measure various things, such as the length of the slide, the height of the monkey bars, or the distance they can jump. They can record their measurements on the writing and drawing pages in their math books.

LITERACY CONNECTION

▶ **Reading** *Inch by Inch*

Read *Inch by Inch* by Leo Lionni (HarperTrophy, 1995). Discuss whether the inchworm in the story represents a standard or a nonstandard measurement unit.

NOTE The most common measurement errors children make are not lining up the 0 end of the measurement tool with the end of the object being measured and being careless about marking off. You may want to have children lay their standard foot cutouts end to end to show what one is really doing when one measures heel to toe or marks off with a measuring tool.

Ongoing Assessment:

Informing Instruction

Watch for children who do not measure heel to toe. For children who are having difficulty, provide additional foot cutouts so they can lay them end to end. You can also model other ways for children to mark off, such as using tape or chalk to make a mark. Children will continue to practice proper measuring techniques in later grades.

Tools for Measuring Length

CCSS

Mathematical Practices
SMP1, SMP2, **SMP5**, SMP6, SMP8

(◎) **Objective** To provide experiences with a variety of measuring tools.

☑ Whole Group
☑ Small Group
☐ Partners
☑ Center

Key Concepts and Skills
• Read numbers on measuring tools. [Number and Numeration Goal 3]
• Practice linear measuring techniques with various tools. [Measurement and Reference Frames Goal 1]
• Choose tools to fit measuring tasks. [Measurement and Reference Frames Goal 1]

Terms to Use measuring tools, scale

Materials *My First Math Book,* p. 6; a variety of standard measuring devices, such as rulers, metersticks or yardsticks, tape measures, and carpenter's measures

A Core Activities

▶ Measuring with Different Tools (*My First Math Book,* p. 6)

Ask children to think about the things they have used to measure with and to compare the lengths of objects (paper strips, cubes, body parts, cutout feet, and so on). Tell children these are all useful ways to measure, but explain that there are standard tools used just for measuring. Show the measuring tools you collected and ask children what they know or notice about them. Children may note that many of the measuring tools have two sets of numbers. Briefly explain why there are two scales; then focus their attention on the foot/inch scale. To support English language learners explain that the word *scale* has several meanings. Explain the meaning in this context.

Review good measuring techniques. Show children how to line up the beginning or zero end of the scale with the item being measured and how to find the foot marks. (While children should focus primarily on the foot markings, some may be curious about the

NOTE Remind the class that just as carpenters, doctors, and other adults respect and care for the tools they use, children should learn to do the same. Demonstrate how to carefully retract, or pull in, the tape measures. Establish and enforce the two-inch "no zap" rule: *Do not push the button to "zap" the tape measure if more than two inches show.* Yardsticks are not to be used as toys or weapons.

inch marks. If so, briefly explain that 12 inches make a foot.) Review how to mark off and count each foot when using a 12-inch ruler.

Working with a partner, have children use various tools to measure objects in the room to the nearest foot. Provide ample time for children to explore the tools and practice measuring. Encourage them to measure curved as well as straight objects. Afterward, discuss which tool is best for a specific job and why.

Place the measuring tools in the Math Center and encourage children to use them often. They should draw and record the length of an item and the tool they used to measure it on page 6 of their math books. Children learn measuring best by practicing.

▶ **Playing** *Domino Concentration* (Revisit Activity 3•5, p. 148)

In the Math Center, put out sets of dominoes and matching number cards for *Domino Concentration.* Increase difficulty by using double-9 dominoes and 0–18 number cards, or by including multiple dominoes that show different combinations to get the same number. (Color-code the sets so they don't get mixed up.)

B | **Teaching Options**

EXTRA PRACTICE

▶ **Measuring Long Chains** (*Center Activity Cards,* 24)

Children can make a long line of connecting cubes, links, or blocks; measure its length using rulers, a tape measure, or a yardstick; and then record the measurement on the writing and drawing pages in their math books.

LITERACY CONNECTION

▶ **Reading** *Building a House*

Read *Building a House* by Byron Barton (HarperTrophy, 1990). Discuss the different kinds of measurements and measurement tools used to build a house.

Measuring with Standard Measuring Tools

Use a standard measuring tool to measure an object.

Draw the object you measured.

Record your measurement. _____

Draw the measuring tool you used.

Answers vary.

6   Use with Activity 5•12.

My First Math Book, p. 6

Links to the Future

This and other measuring activities using standard units are meant to be exploratory and to provide preliminary experiences with measurement. Learning to measure with standard linear measuring tools is a Grade 1 Goal and a Grade 2 Goal.

Pet Bar Graph

◎ **Objective** To help children make and interpret a graph about pets.

CCSS Mathematical Practices
SMP2, SMP3, SMP4, **SMP6, SMP7**
Content Standards
K.MD.3, K.CC.5

☑ Whole Group ☐ Partners
☐ Small Group ☐ Center

Key Concepts and Skills

• Construct a bar graph. [Data and Chance Goal 1]

• Draw conclusions and answer questions based on a graph. [Data and Chance Goal 2]

Terms to Use bar, total, some, none, all, more, fewer, bar graph

Materials *My First Math Book*, p. 7; posterboard; index cards or paper (pre-cut to fit the graph); drawing materials; tape or glue; book about pets (optional)

Planning Tip *Pet Show!* by Ezra Jack Keats (Puffin, 2001) is a great story to introduce the graphing activity.

A Core Activities

▶ Graphing Pets *(My First Math Book, p. 7)*

If possible, read and discuss a book about pets to begin the activity. Talk about the different types of pets people have, as well as the fact that many people do not own pets for various reasons. Next, give each child a piece of paper or index card on which to draw a picture of their own pet. Children who do not own a pet can mark their paper with an X, 0, or other No Pet symbol. Children with more than one *type* of pet should draw each type of pet on a separate paper or card.

Have children place their papers in piles according to type of animal (for example, all dog papers in one pile; all fish papers in another). Also make a pile with the "no pet" papers. With children, use this information to figure out how many columns you need on your graph (one column for each type of pet, and one No Pet column). Model how to draw and label the columns. Next, invite children to attach their pictures in the appropriate column. Talk with children about how to label the sides of the graph.

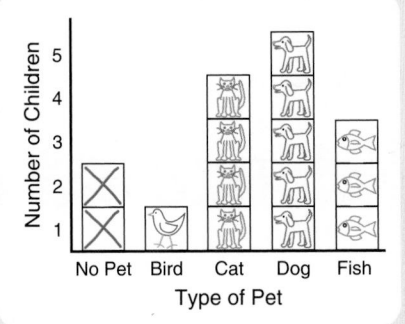

NOTE A similar activity can be done with stuffed animals to make a real-object graph titled "Our Stuffed Animals." Ask children in advance to each bring one small stuffed animal from home. Mark columns on the floor with masking tape, and have children place their stuffed animals in the appropriate columns based on the type of animals they are.

A good title is also important. Children can propose titles and vote on them. (Tally marks are a good way to record votes.)

When the graph is finished, ask: *What do you notice? What information does the graph tell us?* If discussion lags, prompt with more specific questions, such as:

- How many children have dogs? Cats? Which pet is the most common in our class?

- Do some of the children in our class have pets? Do all children have pets?

- Which bar (category) has 2 pets? Which bars are equal?

- Are there more children with fish than children with birds? How many more?

After the discussion, children should use the graph to record information on page 7 of their math books. Save this graph to use again in Activity 6-6.

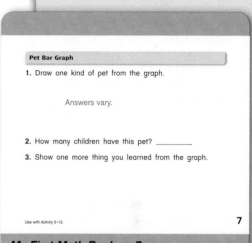

Pet Bar Graph

1. Draw one kind of pet from the graph.

Answers vary.

2. How many children have this pet? _____

3. Show one more thing you learned from the graph.

Use with Activity 5•13.   7

My First Math Book, p. 7

▶ Following Craft-Stick Patterns

(Revisit Activities 4•5 and 5•2, pp. 196 and 238)

Place craft sticks in the Math Center (perhaps with other small manipulatives, such as counters). Have children use the materials to begin a pattern, then change places with a partner to extend and describe their partner's pattern.

 B Teaching Options

MATHEMATICS IN THE WRITING CENTER

▶ Writing Pet Stories

With the class, develop a shared writing piece about the information gathered from the graph. Some children may be inspired to draw or write stories about their pets.

SCIENCE CONNECTION

▶ Researching Pets

Children may be interested in learning and sharing interesting facts about their pets.

Ongoing Assessment:
Recognizing Student Achievement

Use **Graphing Pets** to assess children's ability to answer questions based on a bar graph. Children are making adequate progress if they can tell how many children have each type of pet and if they can compare categories by seeing which bars are longer and which are shorter. Some children may be able to figure out how many more or how many fewer items are in each category when comparing bars.

[Data and Chance Goal 2]

Attribute Spinner Game

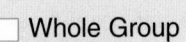

CCSS Mathematical Practices
SMP2, **SMP4, SMP6,** SMP8
Content Standards
K.MD.1

Objective To introduce a game to help children focus on multiple attributes of attribute blocks.

☐ Whole Group
☑ Small Group
☑ Partners
☑ Center

Key Concepts and Skills
• Choose blocks based on multiple attributes. [Patterns, Functions, and Algebra Goal 1]

Terms to Use words describing size, color, and shape; thick, thin, attributes

Materials Game Masters (*Math Masters,* pp. 118 and 119); set of attribute blocks; cardstock; glue; paper clips; sharp pencils

Planning Tip Prepare four attribute spinners by attaching the circles on *Math Masters,* pages 118 and 119, to cardstock. (See Activity 2-4, page 94 for information about making and using paper clip spinners.) Shade each section of the color spinner with the appropriate color.

A Core Activities

▶ Playing the *Attribute Spinner Game* (*Math Masters,* pp. 118 and 119)

Remind children how to use paper clip spinners and demonstrate how to play the game. Begin with three attribute spinners: shape, color, and size. On their turn, children spin the spinners and choose the block that reflects the attributes shown on all three spinners (the large, blue triangle, for example).

Children take turns spinning and collecting blocks until all the blocks are gone. Encourage children to decide as a group what to do if the designated block has already been taken (skip a turn, spin one spinner again, spin all three spinners again, and so on). Leave the spinners and attribute blocks in the Math Center and encourage children to play with a partner or in small groups. Add the thickness spinner when children are ready for more complexity.

Adjusting the Activity

Remove one spinner for children who need a simpler game.

AUDITORY ◆ KINESTHETIC ◆ TACTILE ◆ VISUAL

Ongoing Assessment:

Informing Instruction

Watch for children who are not able to work with multiple attributes simultaneously. Children who are having difficulty should start playing with two spinners and add a third when they are comfortable doing so. Before they play, these children should also practice describing attribute blocks using multiple attributes.

▶ Tallying Class Data (Revisit Activity 5•9, p. 252; *Math Masters*, p. 43)

Show children the blank Cookie Survey Tally Chart (*Math Masters*, page 43). You might want to enlarge it or draw it on the board or on chart paper. Call on each child to name his or her favorite cookie on the chart. Use tally marks to record and total their responses. Then count the tallies together and compare the totals.

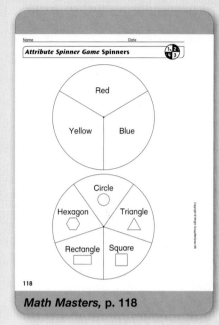

Math Masters, p. 118

B **Teaching Options**

READINESS

▶ Describing Blocks and Other Objects with Multiple Attributes

Have children choose attribute blocks and describe each block's color, size, shape, and thickness. Use simple pictures or the spinners to remind children of attributes to include in their descriptions. Also invite children to describe multiple attributes (length, weight, shape, and color) of other objects, such as unit blocks, books, and items from nature. Help children use tools to measure the items in various ways.

ENRICHMENT

▶ Making Attribute Trains (*Center Activity Cards*, 25)

Children can create a train of attribute blocks in which each part of the train differs from its neighbor by only one attribute. For example, a blue, small, thin triangle can be placed beside a red, small, thin triangle.

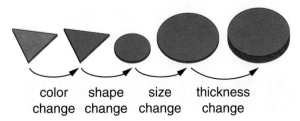

color   shape   size   thickness
change   change   change   change

Introduction to the Number Grid

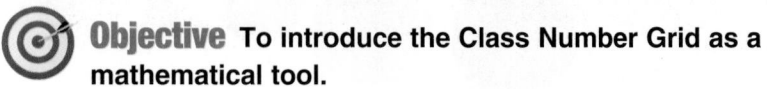

Objective To introduce the Class Number Grid as a mathematical tool.

CCSS Mathematical Practices
SMP1, SMP2, **SMP3, SMP4**, SMP5, SMP6, SMP7, SMP8
Content Standards
K.OA.1, K.OA.2

☑ Whole Group
☑ Small Group
☐ Partners
☐ Center

Key Concepts and Skills
• Identify and locate numbers on the Class Number Grid. [Number and Numeration Goal 3]
• Order numbers on the Class Number Grid. [Number and Numeration Goal 6]
• Discover number patterns on the Class Number Grid. [Patterns, Functions, and Algebra Goal 1]

Terms to Use number grid, row, column

Materials Class Number Grid; wipe-off marker; stick-on notes

Planning Tip Laminate your Class Number Grid so you can use it with wipe-off markers. If you cannot laminate your grid, modify the first part of the Core Activity by having children point to the indicated numbers.

A Core Activities

▶ **Getting to Know the Class Number Grid**

Present the Class Number Grid and discuss what children notice about it. Invite children to look for patterns on the grid and share their observations. Keep the discussion casual and open-ended.

Familiarize children with the grid by having them use a wipe-off marker to mark numbers on the grid according to cues such as:

● Draw a line through the numbers from 1 to 10, 11 to 20, and so on.

● Circle the numbers we say when we count by 5s (or 10s), starting at 0.

● Circle the number 10. Underline the number that comes before it. Put an X on the number that comes after it.

Ongoing Assessment: Informing Instruction

Watch for children who have difficulty locating numbers on the number grid. Make sure children understand the arrangement of numbers on the grid (left to right and top to bottom, like words in a book). It may help to have children track the numbers on the grid with their fingers as they (and you) count aloud by 1s.

- Circle all the numbers that start with 3 (or 5, 7, and so on).

- Draw a line through all the numbers that end with 2 (or 4, 7, and so on).

Next, cover a number with a stick-on note and have children identify the hidden number and explain how they figured it out. Repeat for several numbers.

Post the Class Number Grid in a prominent place in the classroom where children can see it and reach it. Encourage children to use the grid as a reference for *Minute Math* problems and other problem-solving situations. Invite them to share discoveries they make about the Class Number Grid as they gain experience with it.

▶ Writing Number Models for Number Stories

(Revisit Activity 4◆15, p. 218)

Tell a few "joining" and "removing" number stories for children to solve. Also have children categorize the stories as addition or subtraction stories and try to write a number model for each story on slates or on the writing and drawing pages in their math books. Share and discuss their responses.

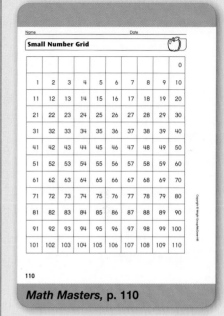

Math Masters, p. 110

B Teaching Options

EXTRA PRACTICE

▶ Using Write On/Wipe Off Number Grids (*Math Masters*, p. 110)

Make and laminate several copies of the small number grid for the Math Center. Pairs of children can give clues for finding and marking numbers on the grids with wipe-off markers.

LITERACY CONNECTION

▶ Reading *How the Stars Fell into the Sky*

Read the Navajo myth, *How the Stars Fell into the Sky* as told by Jerrie Oughton (Houghton Mifflin, 1996). Encourage children to compare the "order in the stars" with the order on the Class Number Grid.

Number-Grid Search Game

Objective To develop understanding of number sequence and patterns on the Class Number Grid using a game.

Mathematical Practices
SMP3, **SMP6, SMP7,** SMP8

☑ Whole Group
☑ Small Group
☑ Partners
☑ Center

Key Concepts and Skills
• Locate and identify numbers on the number grid. [Number and Numeration Goal 3]
• Explore number patterns. [Patterns, Functions, and Algebra Goal 1]

Terms to Use number grid, row, column, right, left

Materials Class Number Grid; stick-on notes; blindfold (optional)

A Core Activities

▶ Playing *Number-Grid Search*

To warm up for the game, quickly point to a number on the number grid and have children say the number. Call on someone to describe where the number is on the grid (*near the top, in the middle, on the right side,* and so on). Invite other children to add more details, as needed (*top row, second column* or *second number,* for example).

Call on two children to help you demonstrate the game. One will be a Searcher; the other will be a Guide. Call out a number between 0 and 100. With eyes covered or closed, the Searcher tries to place a stick-on note on that number on the Class Number Grid. The Guide gives direction clues (*higher, lower, the other way, up, near the top, to the right side,* and so on) to help the Searcher. (You may need to prompt the Guide until children become familiar with the game.) Decide with the class how many direction clues (perhaps 3) should be given before the Searcher places the stick-on note on the grid and checks to see how close he or she came to the selected number. (The game

Links to the Future

When playing the game, children will begin to assimilate the pattern of numbers on the chart. For example, they will discover that smaller numbers are near the top; numbers with 2 in the ones place are toward the left, and so on. Number grids are used throughout the primary grades to help children understand number patterns, basic operations, and place value, which are Kindergarten, Grade 1, and Grade 2 Goals.

should move quickly so children don't get restless waiting for a turn!) Explain that the object is to come close to the number and that it is unlikely that someone will be able to place a note precisely in the correct location. (You might compare the game to Pin the Tail on the Donkey.)

Play this game throughout the year to help children solidify number recognition skills and gain experience navigating the Class Number Grid.

▶ Playing the *Matching Coin Game* (Revisit Activity 2◆8, p. 104)

Set out money cubes, money trays, and a collection of coins in the Math Center for children to play the *Matching Coin Game*. This informal game will help prepare children for the more formal introduction of pennies, nickels, and dimes in the next section.

Also remember to use *Minute Math* during spare moments in the day.

B Teaching Options

ENRICHMENT

▶ Playing the *Number-Grid Game* (Math Masters, pp. 110 and 129)

Children can use a small number grid (*Math Masters,* page 110) and the instructions and table on *Math Masters,* page 129, to play an operations game on the number grid. You may wish to enlarge the number grid to make it easier for children to move their markers, or use only part of the grid to make the game less challenging.

EXTRA PRACTICE

▶ Playing a Mini *Number-Grid Search* Game (Math Masters, p. 110)

Children can use counters and a small number grid (*Math Masters,* page 110) to play *Number-Grid Search* in the Math Center.

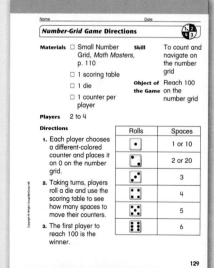

Math Masters, p. 129

The 100th Day of School

PROJECT 5

CCSS Mathematical Practices
SMP1, SMP2, SMP4,
SMP5, SMP6
Content Standards
K.MD.1, K.MD.2

◎ **Objective** To deepen children's understanding of 100 through a variety of activities that celebrate the 100th day of school and apply children's growing mathematical knowledge and skills.

Terms to Use one hundred, groups of ten, collection

Materials

Collections of 100: 100th Day Museum
- ☐ children's 100 Collections
- ☐ index cards
- ☐ pan balance and other measuring tools

Number Hunt and 100 Chart
- ☐ small 0–100 number cards made from cardstock, index cards, or small stick-on notes
- ☐ posterboard
- ☐ tape or glue stick

Food and Other Fun
- ☐ materials vary according to teacher choices

NOTE See Looking Ahead to the 100th Day in Activity 5-2, page 239 and Home Link 5-2 (*Math Masters*, page 37) for more information about children's "100 Collections."

Introduction

There is probably no other occasion in Kindergarten that generates as much mathematical activity as preparing for and celebrating the 100th day of school. It's a party! It honors math. And it summons up all the children's energy and enthusiasm (as well as yours)!

Before the big day, you'll need to talk with children about what type of object each of them would like to collect for their "100 Collection." Discuss how to deal with problems that may come up. This is a good opportunity for group problem solving and collaboration to address issues and questions such as:

▷ "We don't have 100 things in our house."
▷ "How can I carry 100 things to school?"
▷ "How can I count out 100 things? Can I get my grandma to help me?"
▷ "If I share my collection with the class, how many will each person get?"

A collection of 100 stickers

Consider doing your own 100 Collection to share with the group. Some teachers prepare the materials (100 cards and a sheet of posterboard) for the Number Hunt and 100 Chart activity, which is described on page 270, as their 100 Collection.

Some 100th Day activities can extend beyond the 100th day of school. The suggestions are far from exhaustive. Allow your class to lead you in new mathematical directions.

Activity Options

▶ Collections of 100: A 100th Day Museum

☑ **Whole Group**

In a central area, set up a table or large desk to serve as a museum display area for children's 100 Collections. On the 100th day, consider using children's collections as the basis for some of the following activities:

▷ Have children tell how they decided what to collect, how they counted or grouped their items, any challenges they encountered, and anything else they'd like to share about the experience. You might write on index cards what children say about their collections and display the cards with the collections in the Museum.

▷ Invite guests (children or teachers from other classrooms, parents, or school staff) to tour the museum.

▷ Weigh and measure the collections. Encourage children to predict which collection is heaviest, lightest, tallest, shortest, and so on. Then have them test their predictions. Children can create index cards to display with their collections that include length, height, weight, and other attributes of their items. If the collection as a whole is too difficult to measure, have children choose one item from their collections and describe its measurable attributes. Deciding how to measure the collections is a good collaborative problem-solving activity!

▷ Play 20 Questions. Children ask questions to try to figure out which collection you are thinking of.

▷ If children want to share their collections, help them figure out how many of the items each child in the class will get.

Keep the Museum open for a period of time after the 100th day.

► Number Hunt and 100 Chart

✔ **Whole Group**

In advance, draw lines to divide a posterboard into 110 equal spaces (11 rows × 10 columns). Make 101 small cards (about 2 in. × 2 in.) out of cardstock or index cards, and label each card with a number between 0 and 100. (Alternately, you can write the numbers on small stick-on notes.) While children are out of the classroom or before they arrive at school, hide the number cards around the room. (Don't hide them so well that children won't find them quickly!)

When children come into the classroom, have them search the room to find the number cards. (To be fair, you might set a limit on how many cards each child can find before they stop and wait for others to finish. You can collect any remaining cards yourself.)

After all the cards have been found, have children work together to assemble a 100 Chart on the posterboard grid. Begin by attaching 0 to the upper right space on the grid. (The rest of the spaces on the top row will remain empty.) Then ask who has the next number. Attach each number card in order to the grid. Encourage children to think ahead so they will know when the number they are holding will come up. Keep the pace brisk and energetic during the assembly process so children will remain interested and focused throughout. (You might have another adult or an older child help attach the numbers to move the process along quickly.)

After the chart is assembled, children can use it as a reference tool or for games, just as they use the Class Number Grid.

Math Masters, p. 110

Children assemble a 100 Chart that resembles the number grid pictured above.

▶ Food and Other Fun

☑ **Whole Group** ☑ **Small Group** ☑ **Center**

These activities are fun and appropriate for the 100th day of school:

▷ Make necklaces out of 100 beads, tube-shaped pasta, or cereal with holes. You might dye the pasta or use colorful cereal and encourage children to make patterns.

▷ Use a pan balance to find out which weighs more, 100 kernels of popped popcorn or 100 kernels of unpopped popcorn. Be sure to have children make predictions first! Help them figure out how to share the popped popcorn equally.

▷ Compare 100 pretzels to 100 raisins. Ask: *Which takes up more room? What size container do we need for each?*

▷ Mix 100 pieces of popcorn, 100 pretzels, 100 raisins, and 100 chocolate chips together to make a yummy trail-mix snack.

▷ Have children help you decorate a cake with 100 candles, raisins, nuts, colored candies, or other items. Eat the cake!

▷ Lead the class in 100 physical exercises (10 jumping jacks, 10 toe touches, 10 sit ups, 10 squats, and so on).

⬤ **Literature Link** There are many books about the number 100 and about the 100th day of school. Here are a few that you might want to read on and before the big day:

Centipede's 100 Shoes by Tony Ross (Henry Holt and Co., 2003);
Counting Our Way to the 100th Day! by Betsy Franco (Margaret K. McElderry, 2004);
Emily's First 100 Days of School by Rosemary Wells (Hyperion, 2000);
Fluffy's 100th Day of School by Kate McMullen (Cartwheel, 2000);
From One to One Hundred by Teri Sloat (Puffin Books, 1995);
Miss Bindergarten Celebrates the 100th Day of Kindergarten by Joseph Slate (Dutton Children's Books, 1998);
The 100th Day of School by Brenda Haugen (Picture Window Books, 2003);
100th Day Worries by Margery Cuyler (Simon & Schuster, 2000);
100 Days of School by Trudy Harris (Millbrook, 2000);
One Hundred Hungry Ants by Elinor J. Pinczes (Houghton Mifflin, 1993).

A necklace with 100 pieces of cereal

Section 6

Overview

Section 6 has several main areas of focus:

◆ To introduce pennies, nickels, dimes, and coin exchanges,

◆ To introduce 3-dimensional shapes and review 2-dimensional shapes and symmetry,

◆ To explore various ways to measure and compare time,

◆ To extend graphing skills to include making individual survey graphs,

◆ To extend patterning skills to include representing patterns with symbols,

◆ To introduce skip counting by 2s and to continue other counting, estimation, and numeration activities,

◆ To introduce the concept of half,

◆ To develop strategies for solving simple addition and subtraction problems, including joining, take-away, and comparison situations, and

◆ To continue measurement activities using standard and nonstandard tools and units.

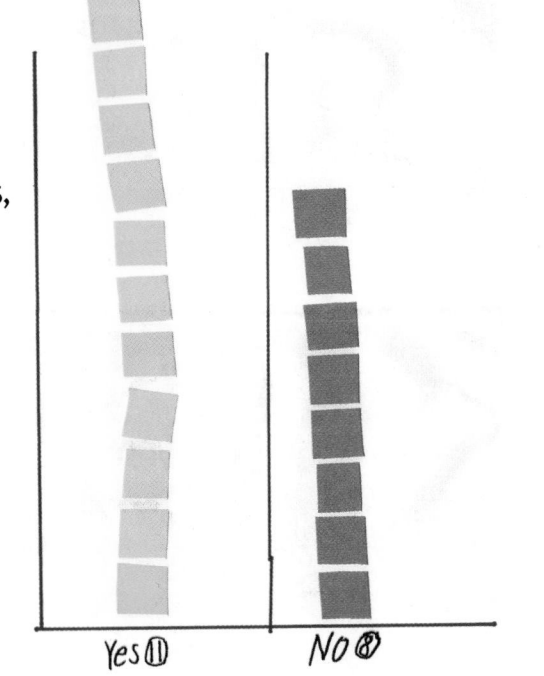

Maintaining Ongoing Daily Routines

Doing the Routines

In addition to Section 6 activities, continue to do the following Ongoing Daily Routines:

- Number of the Day
- Attendance
- Job Chart
- Monthly Calendar
- Daily Schedule
- Weather Observation
- Recording Daily Temperature
- Survey

Adjusting the Routines

Each Ongoing Daily Routine can be adjusted periodically according to children's progress and interests. Ongoing Daily Routines are powerful tools for practicing and reinforcing the skills that are introduced in the activities. If you haven't already done so, use the following routines to introduce new ideas and ask different questions during and after Section 6:

- **Attendance** Consider changing your attendance recording system to one that is more challenging. See page 12 for suggestions.
- **Number of the Day** Because coins will be formally introduced during this section, consider substituting pennies for craft sticks or straws for your Concrete Number Count or adding a penny-exchange component to the routine. After ten days, children can trade ten pennies for a dime and move it to the "10s" container. Ten dimes can be traded for a dollar.

Using Routines for Ongoing Assessment

All of the Ongoing Daily Routines offer opportunities for ongoing assessment of a variety of skills and concepts. You might want to use the following routines for ongoing assessment during Section 6:

- **Temperature** Do children use appropriate vocabulary (hot, warm, cool, cold, and so on) to describe the temperature? Are they able to use the color zones to read the thermometer? Do they correctly use probability language as they predict and describe temperature trends?
- **Number of the Day** Do children know when to bundle straws or sticks during the Concrete Number Count? Do they understand why these exchanges can be made?

Learning in Perspective

Core Activities

Activity	Objective	Revisit Activity	Page
6·1	**Introduction of the Penny** To introduce the penny.	**Counting Steps on a Number Line** (Activity 4-1, p. 188)	282
6·2	**Introduction of the Nickel** To introduce the nickel. 👟 **Links to the Future** Children will continue to work with money values throughout Kindergarten and in Grades 1 and 2.	**Playing the *Growing and Disappearing Train Game*** (Activities 3-13 and 4-15, Extra Practice, pp. 166 and 219) 👟 **Links to the Past** Children played the *Growing and Disappearing Train Games* with green and red dice in earlier sections. By now they should be using dice with + and − signs.	284
6·3	**Solid Shape Museum** To introduce 3-dimensional shapes and review 2-dimensional shapes.	**Making Symmetrical Hearts and Other Designs** (Activity 2-15, p. 120)	286
6·4	**Counts to Measure Time** To introduce counting as a way to measure and compare time. 👟 **Links to the Future** Children will begin to learn about hours, minutes, and analog and digital clocks in Section 8. Telling time is a focus in Grades 1 and 2.	**Playing *The Raft Game*** (Activity 5-10, p. 254)	290
6·5	**Surveys and Graphs** To develop children's ability to conduct surveys and graph their results.	**Counting to the Number of the Day** (Activities 3-15, and 5-8, pp. 170 and 250)	292
6·6	***I Spy* with Shapes** To review characteristics of 2-dimensional and 3-dimensional shapes.	**Making a "Number of Pets" Graph** (Activity 5-13, p. 260)	294
6·7	**Introduction of the Dime** To introduce the dime.	**Playing the *Attribute Spinner Game*** (Activity 5-14, p. 262)	296
6·8	**Coin Exchanges** To provide practice with exchanging pennies, nickels, and dimes.	**Playing *Guess My Number* and Counting Backward** (Activity 5-4, p. 242)	298

Core Activities, *continued*

Activity	Objective	Revisit Activity	Page
6·9	**Comparison Number Stories** To introduce comparison number stories. 👟 **Links to the Future** Children will represent comparison number stories with number models in Grade 1.	**Measuring in Different Ways** (Activity 5-12, p. 258; *My First Math Book*, p. 10) 👟 **Links to the Past** Children explored both standard and nonstandard measurement tools and units in Activity 3-7 and in Section 5.	300
6·10	**Count by 2s** To introduce skip counting by 2s. 👟 **Links to the Future** Children will explore number patterns and sequences in later grades.	**Estimating Nickels or Dimes** (Activities 2-13 and 3-2, pp. 114 and 140; *My First Math Book*, p. 11)	302
6·11	**Divide Groups in Half** To introduce the concept of half. 👟 **Links to the Future** Children touch upon odd and even numbers in this activity, but will explore them more fully in Grade 1.	**Playing *Teen Frame* and *Top-It*** (Activities 3-16, 4-2, and 4-7, pp. 172, 190, and 202; *Math Masters*, pp. 137 and 108)	304
6·12	***Read My Mind* Game** To reinforce the use of attribute clues and rules through a group game.	**Playing *Monster Squeeze*** (Activity 3-6, p. 150)	306
6·13	**Tools for Measuring Time** To introduce tools for measuring short periods of time.	**Playing *Number-Grid Search*** (Activity 5-16, p. 266)	308
6·14	**Skip Count with Calculators** To demonstrate how to skip count on a calculator.	**Making Coin Patterns** (Activity 5-2, p. 238) 👟 **Links to the Past** Children learned to skip count by 10s, 5s, and 2s in earlier activities.	310
6·15	**Symbolic Representations of Patterns** To deepen children's understanding of patterns by introducing a way to represent patterns with symbols. 👟 **Links to the Future** Children will work extensively with numeric patterns in later grades.	**Flipping a Coin** (Activity 3-11, p. 162; *My First Math Book*, p. 14) 👟 **Links to the Past** Children have explored probability and ways to describe it in earlier activities.	312
6·16	**Division of Whole Objects into Halves** To expand children's understanding of the concept of *half*.	**Writing Number Models for Number Stories** (Activity 4-15, p. 218)	314

Section Opener

Ongoing Learning and Practice

Practice through Games

Games are an essential component of practice in the *Everyday Mathematics* program. Games offer skills practice and promote strategic thinking. These games are introduced in this section:

Activity	Game	Skill Practiced
6◆2	*Penny-Nickel Exchange*	Counting coins and making exchanges [MRF Goal 2]
6◆3	*Stand Up If . . .*	Identifying 3-dimensional shapes [G Goal 1]
6◆7	*Penny-Dime Exchange*	Counting coins and making coin exchanges [MRF Goal 2]
6◆11	*Cover Half*	Counting objects by ones and recognizing half of a region or collection [NN Goals 2 and 4]
6◆12	*Read My Mind*	Using multiple attributes to describe and select objects [PFA Goal 1]

Home-School Connection

Home Links provide homework and home communication. The following activities contain Home Links: 6-3, 6-8, 6-12, 6-14, 6-16.

Home Connection Handbook provides more ideas to communicate effectively with parents. ▶

◀ *Mathematics at Home Books 1–4* provide additional ideas for enjoyable mathematics activities that families can do together, as well as lists of children's books related to topics in each strand area. Families can do activities from *Mathematics at Home* **Book 3** during Section 6.

Balanced Assessment

Use the **Assessment Management Spreadsheets** to collect, review, and share information about children's progress.

Ongoing Assessment

⭐ Recognizing Student Achievement

Opportunities to assess children's progress toward Kindergarten Goals:

Activity	Content Assessed
6◆7	Count by 10s. [Number and Numeration Goal 1]
6◆8	Identify pennies, nickels, and dimes. [Measurement and Reference Frames Goal 2]
6◆9	Use nonstandard measuring tools and units to measure length. [Measurement and Reference Frames Goal 1]
6◆12	Use attribute rules to find an object. [Patterns, Functions, and Algebra Goal 1]
6◆15	Use basic probability terms. [Data and Chance Goal 3]

⭐ Informing Instruction

To anticipate common trouble spots and highlight problem-solving strategies:

Activity 6◆6
Identify and name 2- and 3-dimensional shapes

Activity 6◆16
Understand the meaning of half

Portfolio Opportunities

- ◆ Survey lists and graphs, **Activity 6-5**
- ◆ Attribute collages, **Activity 6-12** Teaching Option

Assessment Handbook

- ◆ Kindergarten Goals, pp. 27–33
- ◆ Section 6 Assessment Overview, pp. 60–61
- ◆ Assessment Overviews by Strand, pp. 66–75
- ◆ Individual Profile of Progress and Class Checklist (Sections 5–6), pp. 81–82
- ◆ Cumulative Individual Profile of Progress (Sections 5–8), pp. 99–102

Periodic Assessment

Mid-Year assessment tasks were completed in Sections 4 and 5. End-of-Year assessment tasks will be completed in Section 8.

Differentiated Instruction

Teaching Options

Use optional Part B activities as time permits to meet individual and class needs and to integrate mathematics throughout the Kindergarten classroom and schedule.

ELL SUPPORT

6•6	Going on a shape scavenger hunt
6•9	Acting out comparison stories
6•11	Sharing cookies equally

READINESS

6•5	Making concrete graphs
6•8	Playing exchange games and making an exchange chart

CONNECTIONS

Literacy

6•1	Reading about pennies
6•3	Reading a 3-dimensional adventure
6•4	Discussing "The Tortoise and the Hare"
6•5	Reading about surveys
6•6	Making a solid shapes book
6•10	Reading and counting by 2s
6•16	Reading about dividing things

Science

6•13	Exploring tools for timing

Art

6•1	Making penny rubbings
6•2	Making nickel rubbings
6•7	Making dime rubbings
6•12	Making attribute collages

Music

6•15	Playing instrument patterns

Movement

6•13	Timing minutes and half minutes

ENRICHMENT

6•8	Making and recording coin exchanges
6•14	Solving problems using skip counting

EXTRA PRACTICE

6•1	Buying penny snacks
6•2	Playing *Penny-Nickel Exchange*
6•3	Playing *Stand Up If ...*
6•4	Timing other activities
6•6	Feeling for shapes
6•7	Playing *Penny-Dime Exchange*
6•7	Comparing coins by feel
6•9	Solving comparison pocket problems
6•10	Marking "2s" on write on/wipe off number grids
6•11	Playing *Cover Half*
6•12	Playing *Guess Who?*
6•15	Making a pattern book

CENTERS

Block Center

6•3	Describing block shapes and sizes

Dramatic Play Center

6•2	Playing store
6•16	Making half-and-half pizzas

TECHNOLOGY

6•3	Exploring shapes with technology
6•14	Skip counting by other numbers

Language Support

Everyday Mathematics provides activity-specific suggestions to help *all* young children develop the language necessary to acquire, process, and express mathematical ideas. Activities that provide additional support for non-native English speakers are marked by **ELL SUPPORT** and **ELL**.

Connecting Math and Literacy

Activity 6◆1   *Benny's Pennies* by Pat Brisson (Dragonfly Books, 1995)

Activity 6◆3   *Captain Invincible and the Space Shapes* by Stuart J. Murphy (HarperCollins, 2001)

Activity 6◆4   a version of Aesop's fable "The Tortoise and the Hare"

Activity 6◆10   *How Many Feet in the Bed?* by Diane Johnston Hamm (Aladdin, 1994)

Activity 6◆11   *The Doorbell Rang* by Pat Hutchins (Mulberry Books, 1989)

Activity 6◆16   *Give Me Half!* by Stuart J. Murphy (HarperTrophy, 1996)

See pages 293, 303, 311, and 315 for more literature suggestions.

Using the Projects

Use Maps and Mapping (Project 6, page 316) during or after Section 6 to reinforce skills and concepts related to measurement, distances, and spatial relationships.

Adjusting the Activity

AUDITORY   ◆   **KINESTHETIC**   ◆   **TACTILE**   ◆   **VISUAL**

Activity 6◆16   Dividing Objects in Half

Language & Vocabulary

Use these terms informally with children.

2-dimensional	odd
3-dimensional	one half
attributes	pair
cent	part
cents	pattern
circle	penny
coin	plus
comparison number story	rectangle
	repeat
cone	represent
count by 2s	seconds
cube	skip count
cylinder	sphere
data	square
difference	steady pace
dime	survey
divide	symbol
equal/equals	trade
even	triangle
exchange	uneven
graph	value
half	whole
halves	worth
nickel	

Planning Tips

Pacing
Pacing depends on a number of factors, such as children's individual needs and how long your school has been using *Everyday Mathematics*. Use the optional Part B activities throughout Section 6 if you have extended mathematics instructional time. See page 278 for a list of these activities.

	←——— MOST CLASSROOMS ———→	
FEBRUARY	MARCH	APRIL

Teaching Resources

Resources for the Kindergarten Classroom provides additional teaching ideas, including suggestions for bringing mathematics into thematic instruction as well as using games, literature, technology, and rhymes to support mathematics learning. ▶

Minute Math provides brief activities for transition times and for spare moments throughout the day. During Section 6, use the activities in Part 2, pages 67–196.

NCTM Standards

Content Standards: 1 Number and Operations, **2** Algebra, **3** Geometry, **4** Measurement, **5** Data Analysis and Probability
Process Standards: 6 Problem Solving, **7** Reasoning and Proof, **8** Communication, **9** Connection, **10** Representation

Section 6 Activities	6·1	6·2	6·3	6·4	6·5	6·6	6·7	6·8	6·9	6·10	6·11	6·12	6·13	6·14	6·15	6·16
NCTM Standards	1, 4, 9	1, 4, 9	3, 8, 9	1, 4, 8	5, 10	3	1, 4, 9	1, 4, 9	1, 6, 8, 10	1, 10	1, 8, 9	1, 6	1, 4, 9	1	1, 10	1, 8, 9

Professional Development

Teacher's Reference Manual Links

Activity	Topic	Section	Activity	Topic	Section
6·1	Money Facts	12.9.1	**6·7**	Money Facts	12.9.1
6·2	Money Facts	12.9.1	**6·9**	Addition and Subtraction Use Classes	9.3.1
6·3	Space and 3-D Figures	11.5	**6·11**	Odd and Even Number Patterns	15.1.2

Materials

Activity	Masters	Materials	
6·1	*My First Math Book,* p. 8	• pennies • small plastic bags	• magnifying lenses • paper or slates*
6·2		• nickels and pennies	• magnifying lenses
6·3	Home Link Master, p. 44	• items that represent common 3-dimensional shapes (balls,	ice cream cones, party hats, cans, boxes, paper towel rolls, and so on)
6·4	*My First Math Book,* p. 9	• drum or metronome	
6·5		• large sheets of construction paper • colored paper (cut into small squares)	• class lists • clipboard (optional)
6·6		• 2-dimensional and 3-dimensional items in the classroom	
6·7		• dimes and pennies	• magnifying lenses
6·8	Home Link Master, p. 45	• large collection of pennies, nickels, and dimes	• slips of paper and pencils
6·9		• slates* or sheets of paper	• counters

Activity	Masters	Materials	
6·10		• Growing Number Line	• Class Number Grid (optional)
6·11	*My First Math Book,* p. 12	• counters or pennies	
6·12	Home Link Master, p. 46	• attribute blocks*	
6·13		• an assortment of timers (stopwatch, clock or watch with second hand, kitchen timer*)	
6·14	Home Link Master, p. 47	• calculators	• large signs or transparencies displaying [ON/C] or [AC], [+], and [=]
6·15	*My First Math Book,* p. 13	• chalkboard and chalk	
6·16	Home Link Master, p. 49	• graham crackers	• chalkboard and chalk

Technology
Assessment Management Spreadsheets, Section 6: See the *iTGA.*

* Indicates items in the Kindergarten manipulative kit.

 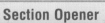

ACTIVITY 6·1

Introduction of the Penny

(◎) **Objective** To introduce the penny.

☑ Whole Group
☐ Small Group
☑ Partners
☑ Center

Key Concepts and Skills
- Count pennies and record the total using the cents symbol. [Number and Numeration Goal 2]
- Explore the characteristics of the penny. [Measurement and Reference Frames Goal 2]
- Learn about the value of the penny. [Measurement and Reference Frames Goal 2]

Terms to Use penny, coin, cent, worth, value, symbol

Materials *My First Math Book,* p. 8; pennies; small plastic bags; magnifying lenses; paper or slates

---

Planning Tip Make sure you have enough coins to conduct this activity and later coin activities in this section. Prior to doing the activity, you might want to prepare bags with a handful of pennies for each child or pair of children. You can use these penny bags again for Activity 6-11.

A Core Activities

▶ **Exploring the Penny** (*My First Math Book,* p. 8)

Invite children to share what they know about money. You might ask them what money is used for or why there are different kinds of money.

Give each child a penny. Have them share the magnifying lenses to look closely at their penny. Discuss the size, shape, color, and markings children notice. Ask if anyone knows the coin's name. Explain that it has two names; it can be called *1 cent* or *1 penny. A penny is worth 1 cent.* To support English language learners, discuss the meaning of the words *worth* and *value.* Ask whether 1 cent buys a lot or a little. Make a pile of everyone's pennies and count the total together. Discuss what could be purchased with the total amount.

Write the cent symbol (¢) and explain that this symbol means "cents"; for example, *22¢ means 22 cents.* Demonstrate how to use the symbol by writing the class total

NOTE You might mention that sometimes money amounts are written with a $ sign, but use the ¢ sign for the Kindergarten coin activities so you will not need to write with decimal notations.

of cents on the board. Children can practice writing the ¢ sign in the air or on slates.

Give each child (or pair of children) a handful of pennies and a small plastic bag. Have children count their pennies and write the total on a sheet of paper or slate using the ¢ sign. Then have each child (or pair of children) trade bags with another child (or pair) to double-check the penny counts. Children should record the number of pennies in their bags on page 8 of their math books. Place the bags of pennies in the Math Center for counting and writing totals.

▶ **Counting Steps on a Number Line** (Revisit Activity 4•1, p. 188)

Pose several problems for children to act out and solve on a walk-on number line. Also model the problems with finger hops on a wall number line.

My First Math Book, p. 8

B **Teaching Options**

EXTRA PRACTICE
▶ **Buying Penny Snacks**

Set out an assortment of food items, such as raisins or jelly beans, that children can buy for one cent each. Give children an equal number of pennies to purchase the snacks.

LITERACY CONNECTION
▶ **Reading about Pennies**

Read and discuss *Benny's Pennies* by Pat Brisson (Dragonfly Books, 1995).

ART CONNECTION
▶ **Making Penny Rubbings** (*Center Activity Cards*, 26)

Children can make rubbings of both sides of a penny using the side of a crayon and a piece of paper or the writing and drawing pages in their math books.

NOTE See Chapter 12 of the *Teacher's Reference Manual* for information about Abraham Lincoln and the penny that you might share with children as a Social Studies connection.

Introduction of the Nickel

CCSS

Mathematical Practices
SMP1, SMP2, SMP3, SMP4, SMP6

Content Standards
K.OA.1, K.OA.4

ACTIVITY 6·2

◎ **Objective** To introduce the nickel.

- ✔ Whole Group
- ☐ Small Group
- ✔ Partners
- ✔ Center

Key Concepts and Skills
- Skip count by 5s. [Number and Numeration Goal 1]
- Make exchanges with pennies and nickels. [Measurement and Reference Frames Goal 2]
- Explore the characteristics of the nickel. [Measurement and Reference Frames Goal 2]
- Learn about the value of the nickel. [Measurement and Reference Frames Goal 2]

Terms to Use nickel, coin, cent, worth, penny, exchange, value

Materials nickels and pennies; magnifying lenses

Planning Tip Make sure you have enough pennies and nickels so that partners will have a handful of each to practice trading. (You'll need more pennies than nickels.) Include some of the new nickel designs that the U.S. Mint introduced in 2004 and 2005.

A Core Activities

▶ Exploring the Nickel

Give a nickel to each child. Have children share magnifying lenses to look closely at the nickel. Discuss the size, shape, color, and any markings children notice. Ask if anyone knows the name of this coin. Explain that it has two names; it can be called *a nickel* or *5 cents. A nickel is worth 5 cents.* Invite children to estimate how much money they will have if they put all of their nickels together. Make a pile of everyone's nickels and count by 5s to get the total with the class. Use the cents sign to write the total for children to see. Discuss what might be purchased with the total.

Ask: *How many pennies will I get if I trade, or exchange, my nickel for pennies?* Demonstrate by trading 1 nickel for 5 pennies. Count the pennies out loud (*1 cent, 2 cents, 3 cents,* and so on) to draw attention to the equivalent value.

NOTE Depending on the number of children in your class, counting by 5s may take you well over $1.00. You and a few children may be the only ones counting toward the end, but it helps all children to hear the 5s-count pattern.

Have children work with partners, one acting as a banker and one acting as a trader. Give the traders a handful of pennies and the bankers a handful of nickels. Traders group their pennies into stacks of 5 and trade them with the bankers for nickels. (They may have some pennies left over.) Then have partners switch roles. Place nickels in the Math Center (along with the pennies) for continued exploration.

▶ Playing the *Growing and Disappearing Train Game*

(Revisit Activities 3◆13 and 4◆15, Mathematics Extension, pp. 166 and 219)

Have children use + and − dice to play the *Growing and Disappearing Train Game*.

B Teaching Options

EXTRA PRACTICE

▶ Playing *Penny-Nickel Exchange*

Children can roll a die and collect that number of pennies. When they get 5 pennies, they trade them for a nickel. The game ends when someone collects 5 nickels.

MATHEMATICS IN THE DRAMATIC PLAY CENTER

▶ Playing Store

Set up a play store. Mark items to sell—stuffed animals, school supplies, empty food containers—with a price tag. (Begin with prices less than 20 cents; you can add higher-priced items later.) Supply a cash register and coins. Children can take turns being clerks and shoppers. A parent or older child might help with this activity.

ART CONNECTION

▶ Making Nickel Rubbings

Children can make rubbings of both sides of a nickel using the side of a crayon and a piece of paper or the writing and drawing pages in their math books.

Links to the Future

Children will do preliminary work with coin and paper money values and exchanges and with counting mixed collections of coins in *Kindergarten Everyday Mathematics*. However, mastering these skills takes more practice and experience. Children will continue to work with money in Grade 1 and Grade 2.

NOTE See Chapter 12 of the *Teacher's Reference Manual* for information about Thomas Jefferson and the nickel that you might share with children as a Social Studies Connection.

Solid Shape Museum

Objective To introduce 3-dimensional shapes and review 2-dimensional shapes.

CCSS
Mathematical Practices
SMP1, SMP4, **SMP6**, SMP7
Content Standards
K.MD.1, K.G.1, K.G.2, K.G.3, K.G.4, K.G.5

☑ Whole Group
☑ Small Group
☐ Partners
☑ Center

Key Concepts and Skills
- Explore and describe geometric properties of common objects. [Geometry Goal 1]
- Identify, compare, and analyze 2-dimensional and 3-dimensional shapes. [Geometry Goal 1]
- Model and create 2-dimensional and 3-dimensional shapes with everyday materials. [Geometry Goal 1]
- Measure and describe objects according to various size attributes.
  [Measurement and Reference Frames Goal 1]

Terms to Use 2-dimensional, square, circle, triangle, rectangle, 3-dimensional, cube, sphere, cylinder, cone

Materials Home Link Master (*Math Masters,* p. 44); items that represent common 3-dimensional geometric shapes (balls, ice cream cones, party hats, cans, boxes, paper towel rolls, and so on)

Planning Tip Collect a few objects of different geometric shapes for initial exploration and to start the classroom Shape Museum. Allow children to add to the museum over the course of several days or weeks. Plan to discuss new items periodically.

NOTE See Chapter 11 of the *Teacher's Reference Manual* for definitions and explanations of solid geometric shapes.

A Core Activities

▶ Making a Shape Museum

Pass around your object collection for children to explore and handle. Promote observation, thought, and discussion with questions such as: *What do you notice about the shapes of these items? Do any of them look the same? How are they alike? What are some differences?* Discuss children's observations about various shapes. (Each face of the cube is a square; two ends of the cylinder are circles; and so on.) Informally use proper shape names throughout the discussion.

Hold up a spherical object and draw a circle on the board. Ask: *Are these 2 shapes the same? How are they different?* Repeat the exercise, this time comparing a square and a cube. In the course of discussion, introduce the terms **2-dimensional** (to describe the flat circle and square) and **3-dimensional** (to describe the sphere and cube), and gather children's ideas about the differences between the two. (For example, children may share that the 2-dimensional shapes are flat and the 3-dimensional shapes are not; or that you can put your hands around the sphere and the cube but not the circle and square.)

Set up a Shape Museum to display the objects you collected, as well as the objects children collect from home. Encourage children to create additional objects from clay, straws, toothpicks, paper, and other materials. Talk about the properties and shapes of new objects as they are added to the classroom museum. You might have children sort and organize similar shapes together and then compare all the spheres, all the cubes, and so on. In addition to helping children describe the geometric properties of the objects (the shapes of the faces, the number of edges, and so on), ask them to describe the sizes of the objects (height, weight, and so forth). Encourage children to use tools, such as rulers and a scale or pan balance, to measure the objects in various ways.

Links to the Future

Do not get bogged down with technical definitions; rather, use children's words and ideas to promote understanding of the concepts. Children's experiences with 3-dimensional shapes in Kindergarten are mostly exploratory. Identifying spheres and cubes is a Kindergarten Goal. Learning the names and properties of other 3-dimensional shapes are Grade 1, 2, and 3 Goals.

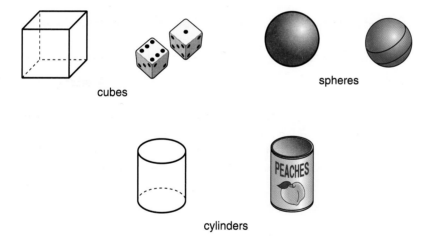

cubes

spheres

cylinders

cones

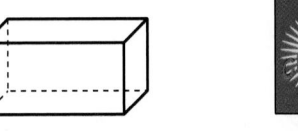

rectangular prisms

 **Home Link 6·3** (*Math Masters*, p. 44)

Children bring items from home to add to the Shape Museum.

▶ Making Symmetrical Hearts and Other Designs

(Revisit Activity 2◆15, p. 120)

Show children how to make hearts by folding a sheet of paper and cutting half of a heart outline along the fold. You might do this in conjunction with a Valentine's Day project. Encourage children to cut other symmetrical shapes and designs, too. Try to locate some small mirrors and have children use them to check whether their shapes and designs are the same on either side of the fold. If they are the same, the complete shape will show in the mirror when it is placed along a line of symmetry (in this case, the fold). Children will enjoy experimenting with the mirrors.

Also remember to use *Minute Math* during spare moments in the day.

Name   Date

6·3 **Solid Shape Museum**

Family Note Manipulating, exploring, and discussing 3-dimensional objects helps children learn the names of these objects and build spatial sense. Many familiar objects are common 3-dimensional geometric shapes: balls are spheres and dice are cubes, for example. Children have been learning about 2-dimensional and 3-dimensional shapes and noticing shapes all around them. At home, encourage your child to think about 2- and 3-dimensional shapes as he or she looks for objects to place in our classroom Shape Museum.

Look around your home for objects that have 3-dimensional geometric shapes.

See if you can find examples like these:

Sphere: ball, globe
Cube: dice, square box
Cylinder: can of food
Cone: ice cream cone, party hat
Rectangular prism: cereal box, book

Bring in a few objects to add to our classroom Shape Museum.

sphere   rectangular prism   cylinder

44

Math Masters, p. 44

B Teaching Options

EXTRA PRACTICE

▶ Playing *Stand Up If ...*

Give each child a 3-dimensional shape. Say: *Stand up if you have a sphere (cube, cylinder ...)*. Hold up an example of each solid shape as you name it. Have children say the name of the object and the shape when they stand up (*ball and sphere*, for example).

MATHEMATICS IN THE BLOCK CENTER

▶ Describing Block Shapes and Sizes

Children can identify and compare the shapes and sizes of blocks. Spark their thinking and observations with questions such as: *Which blocks have square faces? Rectangular? Which blocks have the same shape, but different sizes? How could you measure these blocks? How would you sort them?*

LITERACY CONNECTION

▶ Reading a 3-Dimensional Adventure

Read *Captain Invincible and the Space Shapes* by Stuart J. Murphy (HarperCollins, 2001). Encourage children to find shapes in the Shape Museum that correspond to the shapes in the story.

TECHNOLOGY

▶ Exploring Shapes with Technology

Children can explore 2- and 3-dimensional shapes on the computer using games and activities such as those on *Mighty Math: Carnival Countdown* and *Mighty Math: Zoo Zillions*. See *Resources for the Kindergarten Classroom* for other software suggestions.

CCSS
Mathematical Practices
SMP2, SMP3, SMP5, SMP6, **SMP7, SMP8**

ACTIVITY 6·4

Counts to Measure Time

🎯 **Objective** To introduce counting as a way to measure and compare time.

☑ Whole Group
☑ Small Group
☑ Partners
☐ Center

Key Concepts and Skills
• Use counting to measure time. [Number and Numeration Goal 1]
• Compare time required for various tasks. [Measurement and Reference Frames Goal 4]

Terms to Use steady pace

Materials *My First Math Book,* p. 9; drum or metronome

A Core Activities

▶ Beating Out Time (*My First Math Book,* p. 9)

Ask: *Will it take longer to walk or to tiptoe across the room?* Invite children to give reasons for their predictions and to share ideas about how to test their responses *without* using a watch, clock, or timer. If no one mentions it, explain that counting can be used to measure and compare time. Use something to mark a steady beat, such as a drum, metronome, or hand claps, and have children count the beats out loud. Call on one child to walk across the room while the class counts out loud at the steady pace you mark. Record the final number and write "counts" as the unit (for example, "9 counts"). Repeat, this time have the same child tiptoe across the room. Try to mark the same steady counting pace as you did for walking. Compare and discuss the results for walking versus tiptoeing.

Help children consider the rate of counting. You might say: *It took ___ counts for Serena to walk across the room. What number do you think we will get if we count faster while*

NOTE Always label your results with a unit. If you recount using a different tempo, change your label to reflect the tempo, such as *slow counts* or *fast counts*.

she walks? After getting responses, have the same child walk across the room while you mark a faster pace for children to count. Record the number of counts and compare it with the results you got previously. Discuss the reasons for the difference. Prompt with questions such as: *Why did we get different numbers each time? What would happen if we mixed slow and fast counting? Do you think counting is the best way to measure time? Why or why not?*

Have children work with a partner to complete page 9 in their math books. One child walks and tiptoes across the room while his or her partner counts at a steady beat. Then they switch roles. Children record the counts for their own movements in their math books. Children then choose a new way to move across the room, time each other, and record the counts.

▶ **Playing *The Raft Game*** (Revisit Activity 5•10, p. 254)

Encourage children to play *The Raft Game* and practice counting beans by 5s in the Math Center.

B Teaching Options

(EXTRA PRACTICE)

▶ **Timing Other Activities**

Children can count and compare how long it takes to do other things, such as sing a song, get in line, or clean up the classroom. They can record the results on the writing and drawing pages in their math books.

(LITERACY CONNECTION)

▶ **Discussing "The Tortoise and the Hare"**

Read or retell a version of Aesop's fable "The Tortoise and the Hare." Discuss why the tortoise won the race.

Using Counting as a Measure of Time

1. How many counts did it take you to cross the room? Write the number below.

    walking _____ counts

    tiptoeing _____ counts   Answers vary.

2. Choose a new way to cross the room. _____

3. Write the number of counts it took. _____ counts

4. Which way took the longest time? _____

5. Which way took the shortest time? _____

Use with Activity 6•4.   **9**

***My First Math Book*, p. 9**

ACTIVITY 6·5

Surveys and Graphs

Objective To develop children's ability to conduct surveys and graph their results.

CCSS Mathematical Practices
SMP2, **SMP4,** SMP6, **SMP7,** SMP8
Content Standards
K.CC.1, **K.MD.3**

☐ Whole Group
☑ Small Group
☐ Partners
☑ Center

Key Concepts and Skills
- Make graphs using survey information. [Data and Chance Goal 1]
- Answer questions based on graphs. [Data and Chance Goal 2]

Terms to Use survey, graph, data

Materials large sheets of construction paper; colored paper (cut into small squares); class lists; clipboard (optional)

Planning Tip Spread this activity over several days by having just a few children do a survey and a graph each day. Some children may require extra assistance, especially with creating the graph.

A Core Activities

▶ Graphing Survey Data

Have each child think of a survey question such as: *"Do you have a pet?"* Children who are not yet comfortable with conducting and graphing surveys should stick to questions with a *yes* or *no* answer. Children with more experience can ask questions with a wider range of possible responses. Help children write their questions at the top (or on the back) of a class list of names and use the list to record responses.

After their surveys are complete, children should make a graph for their survey data on a large sheet of construction paper. Provide assistance as needed, but encourage children to do the bulk of the work themselves. The following procedure works well for many children:

1. Count how many different answers they got, and draw vertical lines to create that number of columns on their papers. (For *yes* or *no* questions, only two columns are needed.) Many children will need help with this step.

NOTE This activity builds upon the Survey Routine (page 32) as each child conducts his or her own survey and then graphs the results. If the children in your class are already independently conducting surveys, use this activity to help them think about how to display their survey results on a graph. Encourage children to continue graphing their survey results as the year progresses.

2. Write each answer ("yes" and "no," for example) at the bottom of a column.

3. Glue the correct number of precut paper squares in each column to represent the number of people who gave each answer.

4. Add a title to the graph. (The survey question can be the title, if desired.)

Allow each child to share his or her graph and pose questions for other children to answer based on the graph. Display children's survey response sheets (the class list) and their survey graphs together, or compile them into a class book.

▶ Counting to the Number of the Day

(Revisit Activities 3•15 and 5•8, pp. 170 and 250)

Choral count by 1s, 5s, and then 10s to the number on your Growing Number Line.

B Teaching Options

READINESS

▶ Making Concrete Graphs

Children can use connecting cubes to create graphs. They make stacks of cubes (one color per stack) to represent the correct number of each response. For example, for results of 14 *yes* and 6 *no* responses, a child could stack 14 red cubes to represent the *yes* responses and 6 yellow cubes to represent the *no* responses. Some children may benefit from making a concrete graph before making a graph on paper.

LITERACY CONNECTION

▶ Reading about Surveys

Read *The Best Vacation Ever* by Stuart J. Murphy (HarperTrophy, 1997). Discuss how the family uses surveys and graphs to decide where to take a family vacation.

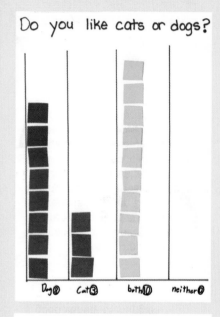

Do you like cats or dogs?

Dog⑧   Cat③   both①   neither⓪

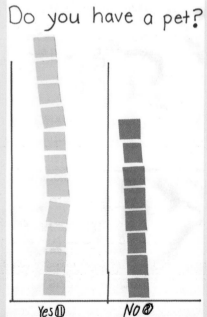

Do you have a pet?

Yes⑪   NO⑨

I Spy with Shapes

ACTIVITY 6·6

🎯 **Objective** To review characteristics of 2-dimensional and 3-dimensional shapes.

CCSS

Mathematical Practices
SMP1, SMP2, SMP4, SMP6, SMP7, **SMP8**

Content Standards
K.CC.5, K.CC.6, K.MD.3, **K.G.1, K.G.2, K.G.3, K.G.4**

☑ Whole Group
☑ Small Group
☐ Partners
☐ Center

Key Concepts and Skills
- Identify 2-dimensional and 3-dimensional shapes. [Geometry Goal 1]
- Describe 2-dimensional and 3-dimensional shapes. [Geometry Goal 1]

Terms to Use 2-dimensional shape names; 3-dimensional shape names

Materials 2-dimensional and 3-dimensional representations or items in the classroom

Planning Tip Prepare for the game by finding examples of shapes that may not otherwise be obvious in your classroom: spheres, cylinders, cubes, and a good variety of triangles.

A Core Activities

▶ Playing *I Spy* with Shapes

Play *I Spy* using clues for 2-dimensional shapes. For example, say: *I spy a square on the bulletin board.* Call on children to guess what you are thinking of. (To support English language learners, explain the meaning of "I spy.") Include different properties in your clues. *For example:*

- I spy a shape on the door that has 3 corners (or angles).
- I spy a shape near the windows with 4 sides that are the same size.

Next, tell children that you will include 3-dimensional shapes.

- I spy an object on my desk that has a square on all sides, including the top and bottom. (dice/cube)
- I spy an object on the shelf that is the same shape as a ball. (globe/sphere)
- I spy something to write with that is a cylinder. (marker)

NOTE Before incorporating 3-dimensional shapes, elicit children's thoughts about the differences between 2- and 3-dimensional shapes. Reinforce that 2-dimensional shapes are flat, like rectangles, circles, and triangles, and that 3-dimensional shapes are solid objects that they can hold, like cubes, spheres, and cones.

Allow children to take turns choosing objects and giving clues. You can expand the game to include other attribute clues, such as color and size.

▶ Making a "Number of Pets" Graph (Revisit Activity 5·13, p. 260)

With the class, create a bar graph that shows how many children have 0 pets, 1 pet, 2 pets, and so on. When the graph is complete, have the class count and compare the number of children in each category. *(Do more children have 0 pets or 3 pets? How many more? How did you figure it out?)* Have children order the results from least to most common response. Put the graph next to the "types of pets" graph from Activity 5-13. Prompt children to explain the information each graph shows and what they find interesting about each graph. Have children discuss whether each graph's title is accurate and pose questions for each other about the graphs.

B Teaching Options

EXTRA PRACTICE

▶ Feeling for Shapes *(Center Activity Cards, 27)*

Children can reach in a Feely Box or Bag and find a 3-dimensional object you describe by its attributes or its shape name.

ELL SUPPORT

▶ Going on a Shape Scavenger Hunt

Give each pair or small group of children a list (or drawing) of 3-dimensional shapes. Children work together to find objects that match the shapes and then record their discoveries (with pictures and/or words) on their lists.

LITERACY CONNECTION

▶ Making a Solid Shapes Book

Take photographs of 3-dimensional objects, label them, and compile them into a class book.

Ongoing Assessment:
Informing Instruction

Watch for children who are having difficulty using clues to identify 2-dimensional and 3-dimensional shapes. At this point, most children should be able to identify and name circles, squares, rectangles, and triangles. Many will also be able to identify and name cubes and spheres. Provide opportunities for children to explore the objects in the Shape Museum.

ACTIVITY 6·7

Introduction of the Dime

◎ **Objective** To introduce the dime.

CCSS Mathematical Practices
SMP1, SMP2, SMP4,
SMP6, **SMP7, SMP8**
Content Standards
K.CC.1, K.MD.1

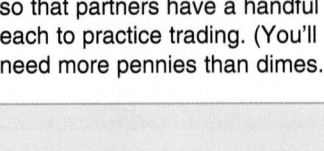

☑ Whole Group
☐ Small Group
☑ Partners
☑ Center

Key Concepts and Skills
- Skip count by 10s. [Number and Numeration Goal 1]
- Make exchanges with pennies, nickels, and dimes. [Measurement and Reference Frames Goal 2]
- Explore the characteristics of the dime. [Measurement and Reference Frames Goal 2]
- Learn about the value of the dime. [Measurement and Reference Frames Goal 2]

Terms to Use dime, nickel, penny, exchange, value, coin, cents

Materials dimes and pennies; magnifying lenses

Planning Tip Make sure you have enough pennies and dimes so that partners have a handful of each to practice trading. (You'll need more pennies than dimes.)

A Core Activities

▶ Exploring the Dime

Give a dime to each child. Have children share magnifying lenses to look closely at the dime. Discuss size, shape, color, and any markings children see. Ask if anyone knows the name of this coin. Explain that it has two different names; it can be called *a dime* or *10 cents. A dime is worth 10 cents*. Invite children to estimate how much money they will have if they put all of their dimes together. Make a pile of everyone's dimes and count by 10s with the class to get the total number of cents. Use the cent sign to write the total for children to see. Discuss what might be purchased with the total.

Ask: *How many pennies will I get if I trade, or exchange, my dime for pennies?* Count the pennies out loud (*1 cent, 2 cents, 3 cents,* and so on) to draw attention to their equivalent value.

NOTE It may be confusing for many children that the dime is worth more than the penny and the nickel, even though it is smaller in size. You might suggest a trick for remembering—"tiny" and "ten cents" both start with the same sound.

Have children work in pairs, one acting as a banker and one acting as a trader. Give the traders a handful of pennies and the bankers a handful of dimes. The traders group their pennies into piles of 10 and trade them with the bankers for dimes. (They may have some pennies left over.) Then, partners should switch roles.

Add dimes to the Math Center for continued exploration.

▶ Playing the *Attribute Spinner Game* (Revisit Activity 5•14, p. 262)

Encourage children to play the *Attribute Spinner Game* in the Math Center.

B Teaching Options

EXTRA PRACTICE

▶ Playing *Penny-Dime Exchange*

Children roll a die and collect that number of pennies. When they get 10 pennies, they trade them for a dime. The game ends when someone collects 4 dimes.

EXTRA PRACTICE

▶ Comparing Coins by Feel

Children compare a penny and a dime, visually and by touch. Put a coin in a Feely Box or Bag and have children guess, by touch only, which coin it is. Then, put one or more of each type of coin in the Feely Box and see if children can identify and pull out the coin you name. When children are ready, add a nickel to the box.

ART CONNECTION

▶ Making Dime Rubbings

Children can make rubbings of both sides of a dime using the side of a crayon and a piece of paper or the writing and drawing pages in their math books.

Ongoing Assessment:
Recognizing Student Achievement

Use **Exploring the Dime** to assess children's ability to count by 10s. Children are making adequate progress if they can count the total number of cents in a handful of coins (dimes or piles of pennies) by 10s.

[Number and Numeration Goal 1]

NOTE See Chapter 12 of the *Teacher's Reference Manual* for information about Franklin Delano Roosevelt and the dime that you might share with children as a Social Studies Connection.

Coin Exchanges

Objective To provide practice with exchanging pennies, nickels, and dimes.

CCSS
Mathematical Practices
SMP1, SMP2, **SMP3,**
SMP4, SMP6
Content Standards
K.OA.5

☐ Whole Group
✔ Small Group
✔ Partners
✔ Center

Key Concepts and Skills
• Count a collection of pennies. [Number and Numeration Goal 2]
• Identify pennies, nickels, and dimes. [Measurement and Reference Frames Goal 2]
• Exchange pennies, nickels, and dimes. [Measurement and Reference Frames Goal 2]

Terms to Use exchange, penny, value, trade, nickel, dime, coin, worth

Materials Home Link Master (*Math Masters,* p. 45); large collection of pennies, nickels, and dimes; slips of paper and pencils

Planning Tip Plan to conduct this activity with small groups of children over the course of several days.

A Core Activities

▶ Making Coin Exchanges

Give each child a handful of pennies (20–25 per child). Children count their pennies and write the value of their collections on slips of paper. Introduce the exchange activity by saying: *You don't want to carry a big pile of pennies to the store. Do you want to trade any of your pennies for these nickels and dimes?*

Children take turns making exchanges. They tell you which exchange they want to make, and you confirm the exchange. For example, a child says: *I want to trade 5 pennies for 1 nickel.* You reply: *I will take your 5 pennies and give you 1 nickel.* Continue around the group for several turns, allowing each child to make one exchange per turn. Make suggestions if children seem stuck on a particular kind of exchange. Children will learn from each other about "fancier" trades, such as 2 nickels or 5 pennies and 1 nickel for 1 dime.

Ongoing Assessment:
Recognizing Student Achievement

Use **Coin Exchanges** to assess whether children are able to identify pennies, nickels, and dimes. Children are making adequate progress if they are able to tell the difference between the coins. Some children may be able to make exchanges independently.

[Measurement and Reference Frames Goal 2]

At the end of the activity, help children count the value of their coins and compare their ending and beginning values. See if they can explain why the value of each handful remains the same, even though the beginning and ending piles look different. After trading up from pennies, children can trade their nickels and dimes back for pennies.

 Home Link 6·8 (*Math Masters*, p. 45)
Children make coin exchanges with the pennies in their family Penny Jar.

▶ Playing *Guess My Number* and Counting Backward

(Revisit Activity 5◆4, p. 242)

Play several rounds of *Guess My Number*. Use addition and subtraction clues, as well as clues related to place value. (See page 242 for sample clues.) When children guess the number, have the class count backward from the number (go back at least 5 numbers) using the number line or number grid as a reference.

B Teaching Options

READINESS

▶ Playing Exchange Games and Making an Exchange Chart

Children can play *Penny-Nickel Exchange* (Activity 6-2, page 284) and *Penny-Dime Exchange* (Activity 6-7, page 296) to practice making exchanges. You might help children construct a chart for reference that shows exchanges (5 pennies for a nickel; 10 pennies for a dime; and so on). Attach real coins to the chart or use coin stamps or pictures. Keep the chart in the Math Center. Add to it when quarters are introduced.

ENRICHMENT

▶ Making and Recording Coin Exchanges

Place coins, a stamp pad, and coin stamps in the Math Center for making and recording coin exchanges. Children can use the writing and drawing pages in their math books.

Technology
Children can play a version of *Coin Exchanges* on the computer using *EM Online Games.*

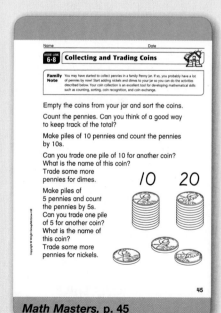

Math Masters, p. 45

Comparison Number Stories

CCSS
Mathematical Practices
SMP1, SMP2, SMP4,
SMP5, SMP6
Content Standards
K.OA.1, K.OA.2

 **Objective** To introduce comparison number stories.

☑ Whole Group ☐ Partners
☑ Small Group ☐ Center

Key Concepts and Skills
• Use manipulatives to represent numbers. [Number and Numeration Goal 3]
• Model and solve comparison number stories with counters. [Operations and Computation Goal 1]

Terms to Use comparison number story, difference

Materials slates or sheets of paper; counters

NOTE Most of the subtraction stories the class has done so far have been take-away situations. Comparison situations (how many more, how many less) are another important use of subtraction.

A Core Activities

▶ Telling Comparison Stories

Give each child a sheet of paper or a slate and 10 counters. Have children count their counters. Tell a comparison number story such as: *Mary has 5 bears and 3 ducks. Does she have more bears or more ducks? How many more?* Ask if anyone can think of a way to use counters to act out the story and figure out the answer. If no one suggests it, show children how to place 5 counters in a row across their papers or slates and line up 3 counters directly below them. Model how to count the unmatched counters to find out how many more. Help children understand they are using one-to-one matching, then counting to determine the difference. You may wish to tell them this is another kind of number story—a comparison story. To support English language learners, discuss and model the meaning of the word *compare* by comparing different piles or rows of objects. Share more comparison stories for children to model using counters. *For example:*

• Brian has 8 toy cars. Leo has 4. How many more cars does Brian have?

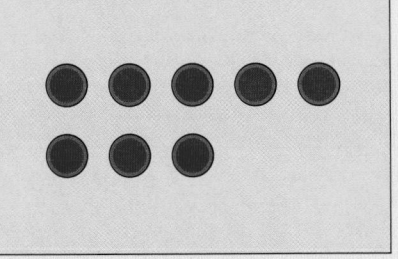

Children use one-to-one matching and count the leftover counters.

 **Links to the Future**

Children will represent comparison stories with number models in Grade 1. In later grades, making change (with money) is an important application of comparison stories.

- Maggie is inviting 6 friends to her birthday party. She made 7 invitations. Did she make too many or not enough? How many extras did she make?

Continue to share and model comparison stories. Occasionally record (or have children record) them with pictures. (There are many comparison stories in the *Minute Math* book.) Do not be concerned with using number sentences at this time.

▶ Measuring in Different Ways (Revisit Activity 5•12, p. 258; *My First Math Book*, p. 10)

Set out a variety of measuring tools that children have used, including rulers, tape measures, foot cutouts (children's and standard), and connecting cubes. Invite children to use the tools to measure items in the classroom and to record their findings with drawings and numbers on page 10 in their math books. (Remind children to include units with their measurements. Provide help as needed.) Prompt children to measure the same item with different tools and discuss why the results are different. Leave the measuring tools in a prominent place for several days or as long as interest continues.

Also remember to use *Minute Math* during spare moments in the day.

B Teaching Options

EXTRA PRACTICE

▶ Solving Comparison Pocket Problems

Use two envelopes as pockets to model comparison stories. (For example, put 6 counters in one envelope, 2 in the other, and ask: *Which pocket has more? How many more?*)

ELL SUPPORT

▶ Acting Out Comparison Stories

Provide materials, such as stuffed animals and snacks, for children to use as they tell and act out number stories. Children love to be included in the stories.

Ongoing Assessment:
Recognizing Student Achievement

Use **Measuring in Different Ways** to assess children's ability to use nonstandard measuring tools for measuring length. Children are making adequate progress if they correctly use connecting cubes, foot cutouts, or other nonstandard tools. Some children may be able to use standard measuring tools and units.

[Measurement and Reference Frames Goal 1]

Measuring with Different Tools

1. Measure an object using different tools. Draw the object you measured.

2. Record measurements for each tool you used. Write the measurement unit, such as cubes or my feet.

_____ _____
units

_____ _____
units

Answers vary.

10   Use with Activity 6•9.

My First Math Book, p. 10

ACTIVITY 6·10

Count by 2s

◎ **Objective** To introduce skip counting by 2s.

Key Concepts and Skills
- Skip count by 2s. [Number and Numeration Goal 1]
- Use objects to represent groups of 2s. [Number and Numeration Goal 3]
- Recognize a growing number pattern on a number line or grid. [Patterns, Functions, and Algebra Goal 1]

Terms to Use count by 2s, pair, skip count

Materials Growing Number Line; Class Number Grid (optional)

CCSS

Mathematical Practices
SMP1, SMP4, **SMP6, SMP7,** SMP8

☑ Whole Group
☐ Small Group
☐ Partners
☐ Center

NOTE Skip counting is a more efficient way to count things. It is also good preparation for recognizing and extending numeric patterns.

A Core Activities

▶ Counting by 2s

Have children stand in a circle. Tell them you want to find out how many feet are in the room. Walk around counting their feet by 1s, creating a rhythmic chant by emphasizing the even numbers. Ask if anyone knows how to count by 2s. Invite children to join in as you repeat the count, this time counting by 2s. Ask children to think of other things that come in 2s (or pairs), such as shoes, socks, ears, hands, and so on. List their ideas and lead another choral count by 2s to count something else on the list. (Later, you might have children create a class display by drawing things that come in pairs, such as boots, mittens, eyes, or hands. Label the growing total with numbers: 2, 4, 6, 8, and so on.)

Involve children in marking the multiples of 2 on your Growing Number Line. Beginning with 0, use your finger to hop 2 spaces, then circle, underline, or highlight the 2. Hop 2 more spaces and mark the 4. Continue through at least 20, saying each

Here are two counting chants:

2, 4, 6, 8
Who do we appreciate?
Kindergartners, Kindergartners, Yeah!

2, 4, 6, 8
Mary's at the garden gate,
Eating cherries off the plate,
2, 4, 6, 8!

number as you mark it. You might repeat the process using a wipe-off marker on your Number Grid. Discuss patterns that children observe.

Explain that today they have been skip counting by 2s. Ask what other types of skip counting they have learned (counting by 5s and 10s). Ask: *Why would we want to skip count? When does it make sense to count by 2s? By 5s? By 10s?* During the discussion, refer back to their ideas of what comes in 2s (and 5s and 10s).

NOTE See Activity 3-2, page 141 for suggestions about collecting and graphing children's estimates.

▶ Estimating Nickels or Dimes

(Revisit Activities 2•13 and 3•2, pp. 114 and 140; *My First Math Book*, p. 11)

Place about 50 nickels (or dimes) in your estimation jar and invite children to make and record estimates. Count the coins and have children compare the total to their estimates. Have children record their estimates, and whether they were "way too high," "way too low," or "pretty close," on page 11 in their math books. Next, count the total value of the coins, counting by 5s (or 10s) to make piles of 100 cents each, and then combine the piles to get the total number of dollars. Discuss what you might buy with the total.

B **Teaching Options**

EXTRA PRACTICE

▶ Marking "2s" on Write On/Wipe Off Number Grids

(*Math Masters*, p. 110; *Center Activity Cards*, 28)

Children count by 2s and color every second number on laminated number grids using wipe-off markers.

LITERACY CONNECTION

▶ Reading and Counting by 2s

Read *How Many Feet in the Bed?* by Diane Johnston Hamm (Aladdin, 1994). Count the feet by 2s as the family gets in and out of bed. *Two Ways to Count to Ten* by Ruby Dee (Henry Holt, 1988) is another great story about counting by 2s.

Recording Estimates

1. Write your estimate.

_____

2. Circle one. My estimate was

　way too high.　　　way too low.　　　pretty close.
　Answers vary.

Use with Activity 6•10.　　　　　　　　　　**11**

My First Math Book, p. 11

NOTE Encourage children to describe number patterns they notice when they count or mark numbers by 2s. For example, they might notice the 2, 4, 6, 8, 0 cycle that repeats in the ones digit.

Divide Groups in Half

CCSS Mathematical Practices
SMP1, **SMP2, SMP4,**
SMP6, SMP7
Content Standards
K.CC.4a, K.CC.4b, K.CC.6,
K.CC.7, K.NBT.1

(◎) **Objective** To introduce the concept of half.

☑ Whole Group ☑ Partners
☐ Small Group ☐ Center

Planning Tip You can use the penny bags from Activity 6-1 as a source of counters for the partner activity. Add or remove pennies so that each bag has an even number.

Key Concepts and Skills
• Count and compare numbers in groups. [Number and Numeration Goal 2]
• Divide a group of objects in half. [Number and Numeration Goal 4]

Terms to Use half, halves, divide, equal, even, odd, uneven, whole, part

Materials *My First Math Book,* p. 12; counters or pennies

NOTE Activity 6-16 focuses on dividing objects, rather than groups, in half. Children's examples will undoubtedly relate to both types of situations, which is fine.

A Core Activities

▶ Dividing a Group into Halves (*My First Math Book,* p. 12)

Elicit children's ideas about *half* by asking them to share ways they have heard the term used. List the examples children share. (Save the list to refer to later in this activity and in Activity 6-16.) Encourage children to explain what they think *half* means in each case. Children may mention half a sandwich or cookie, half a glass of milk, half an hour, 5 and a half years old, and so on.

Call 6 children to the front of the room. Direct this group to divide in **half,** or into 2 equal groups. Children probably won't have trouble doing this using equal sharing; that is, one child joins one group, the next joins the other, and so on. Ask: *Are the groups the same size? How do you know?* Count each group to verify that they are the same, and explain that each group is one-half of the whole group. Write $\frac{1}{2}$ on the board. Have other groups of children repeat the process, including at least one odd-numbered group. As children try to divide the odd-numbered group in half, ask why it doesn't work.

Links to the Future

This activity provides an informal introduction to the idea of odd and even numbers. Understanding odd and even numbers is a Grade 1 Goal.

Be sure children understand that dividing something in half means that both halves must be equal (same size or number). Talk about real-life instances when they need to divide collections into halves (forming teams, dealing cards, and so on). Ask: *Why does it sometimes matter if 2 groups are the same size?*

Distribute an even number of counters to partners and have them divide the counters into 2 equal groups, then count to check that the groups are equal. Children record their results on page 12 in their math books.

▶ Playing *Teen Frame* and *Top-It*

(Revisit Activities 3•16, 4•2, and 4•7, pp. 172, 190, and 202; *Math Masters*, pp. 137 and 108)

Have children play *Teen Frame* in the Math Center and record a "10 + _____" number model to represent their numbers for each round. (See the Revisit activity on page 202.) Children who are proficient with teen numbers can play *Top-It* with numbers greater than 20. Use blank number cards (*Math Masters,* page 108) to create cards with higher numbers.

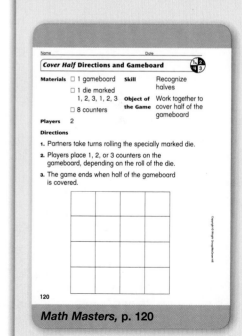

Recording Half Groups

Divide a handful of counters into 2 equal groups. Draw counters in the boxes to show the 2 equal groups.

Sample answer:

12   Use with Activity 6•11.

My First Math Book, p. 12

B Teaching Options

ELL SUPPORT

▶ Sharing Cookies Equally

Read *The Doorbell Rang* by Pat Hutchins (Mulberry Books, 1989) and discuss the way cookies are shared as more and more people arrive at the door. You might want to reenact the story with the class!

EXTRA PRACTICE

▶ Playing *Cover Half* (Math Masters, p. 120)

Children can play a new game called *Cover Half.* Players work together to cover half of the gameboard using a die and counters. See *Math Masters,* page 120, for directions and a gameboard. Players may cover the top, bottom, left, or right side of the board. Or they may cover the squares using a pattern.

Name _____ Date _____

Cover Half Directions and Gameboard

Materials	☐ 1 gameboard	**Skill**	Recognize halves
	☐ 1 die marked 1, 2, 3, 1, 2, 3	**Object of the Game**	Work together to cover half of the gameboard
	☐ 8 counters		

Players 2

Directions

1. Partners take turns rolling the specially marked die.
2. Players place 1, 2, or 3 counters on the gameboard, depending on the roll of the die.
3. The game ends when half of the gameboard is covered.

120

Math Masters, p. 120

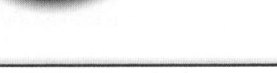

Read My Mind Game

CCSS Mathematical Practices
SMP1, SMP3, SMP6, SMP8
Content Standards
K.CC.7

Objective To reinforce the use of attribute clues and rules through a group game.

☑ Whole Group
☑ Small Group
☐ Partners
☑ Center

Key Concepts and Skills
• Use multiple attributes to describe objects. [Patterns, Functions, and Algebra Goal 1]
• Use rules based on attributes to select an object from a collection. [Patterns, Functions, and Algebra Goal 1]

Terms to Use attributes

Materials Home Link Master (*Math Masters,* p. 46); attribute blocks

A Core Activities

▶ Playing *Read My Mind*

Place the attribute blocks where children can see them. Tell children that you are going to choose a mystery block, then they will try to "read your mind" and guess the block. For this game children ask *yes* or *no* questions; for example: *Is it red? Is it small? Is it the large, blue triangle?*

After children ask a question, they remove attribute blocks according to the answer they receive. For example, if the answer to *Is it red?* is *yes,* the child who asked the question removes all the blocks except the red blocks. Continue in this manner until only the mystery block remains or until someone guesses the correct block. When children are comfortable with the process, have a child choose the mystery block and respond to the questions. Encourage children to play the game with each other in the Math Center.

NOTE You might use tally marks to keep track of how many guesses it takes to identify the block. Children can add a tally mark after they ask a question, or you might designate someone as the official tally recorder for each game.

▶ Playing *Monster Squeeze* (Revisit Activity 3•6, p. 150)

Play a few rounds of *Monster Squeeze*. Try playing with clues only—no monsters—and choosing higher numbers. Ask children if they notice any similarities between *Monster Squeeze* and *Read My Mind*. (Both use questions and clues to identify an object or number.) You might also try varying *Monster Squeeze* by using only *yes* or *no* questions such as, *Is the mystery number higher than 10? Lower than 15?*

Home Link 6•12 (*Math Masters*, p. 46)

Children practice using a calendar at home.

B Teaching Options

EXTRA PRACTICE

▶ Playing *Guess Who?*

Introduce the commercial game *Guess Who?* In this game, players use the process of elimination by attributes to identify a "mystery person." See the Teaching Options in Activity 4-14, page 217, for a similar game in which children are the subjects.

ART CONNECTION

▶ Making Attribute Collages (*Center Activity Cards*, 29)

Set out a variety of collage materials, including magazines, small objects, and paper of different colors. Children can make a collage using materials that have something in common (for example, things that are red, or soft, or have a picture of an animal on them). Display the collages and invite others to guess the common attribute.

Ongoing Assessment:
Recognizing Student Achievement

Use **Read My Mind** to assess children's ability to use attribute rules to find an object. Children are making adequate progress if they are able to figure out what to eliminate after getting a response. Some children may still have difficulty formulating *yes* or *no* questions that elicit new or relevant information.

[Patterns, Functions, and Algebra Goal 1]

Name _____ Date _____

6·12 Reading the Calendar

Family Note Calendars offer valuable opportunities for children to count and read numbers. Help your child record important family appointments, events, and occasions on a calendar at home.

Look at your calendar to find answers to the following questions:

♦ How many days are in this month?
♦ How many Wednesdays? Fridays? Sundays?
♦ What day of the week is the first? The fifth?
♦ What is today's date?
♦ How many days are left in this month?
♦ Are there any birthdays, holidays, or special days this month? When are they? Circle or mark them on your calendar.

Math Masters, p. 46

Tools for Measuring Time

ACTIVITY 6·13

🎯 **Objective** To introduce tools for measuring short periods of time.

CCSS

Mathematical Practices
SMP3, SMP4, **SMP5,**
SMP6, **SMP7,** SMP8

☑ Whole Group
☑ Small Group
☐ Partners
☐ Center

Key Concepts and Skills
• Compare time measurements. [Number and Numeration Goal 6]
• Use tools to measure and compare time. [Measurement and Reference Frames Goal 4]

Terms to Use seconds

Materials an assortment of timers (stopwatch, clock or watch with second hand, kitchen timer)

A Core Activities

▶ Timing Activities

Remind children about counting beats to compare times. (See Activity 6-4, page 290.) Ask: *Did it matter how fast we counted? Did we get a different number when we counted fast compared to when we counted slowly? Was it tricky to count at a steady beat?* Discuss with children what they might use at home to keep track of short periods of time—a microwave timer, oven timer, clock, watch, kitchen timer, or stopwatch, for example. Explain that these types of timers keep a steady beat, so they are a good, reliable way to measure time. Show children the second hand on a clock and explain that it helps measure time in seconds. To demonstrate how long a second is, use the second hand to count out loud at a 1-per-second rate. Say: *1 second, 2 seconds, 3 seconds . . .* to emphasize that you are counting seconds, not simply oral counting.

Use a clock or a stopwatch to time a few children as they move across the room (one at a time) in a particular way, such as hopping, walking, or skipping. After each turn, record

NOTE As you time children with a clock or stopwatch, call out the time at 5-second intervals.

the action and the time in seconds (for example, hopping: 12 seconds). You may want to invite children to take turns as "timing assistant."

Have children sit in a circle and play Pass the Beanbag. Use a stopwatch or the second hand on a clock to time how long it takes them to pass a beanbag around the circle without dropping it. If the beanbag drops, start the time over again. Keep a record and compare the times. Children enjoy trying to beat their previous times.

▶ **Playing *Number-Grid Search*** (Revisit Activity 5◆16, p. 266)

Play a few rounds of *Number-Grid Search* with the class. You might use a timer to add a time component to the game (60 seconds per turn, for example).

Also remember to use *Minute Math* during spare moments in the day.

B Teaching Options

(MOVEMENT CONNECTION)

▶ **Timing Minutes and Half Minutes**

Have children do the same type of activity (jumping, dancing, clapping) for 30 or 60 seconds. Establish start and stop signals, and keep track of the time using a clock or stopwatch. Invite children to help with the timing and recording. Repeat often to give children a sense of the length of these time intervals.

(SCIENCE CONNECTION)

▶ **Exploring Tools for Timing**

Display an assortment of timers for children to explore and use. Have children talk about when and how the different types of timers are used. For example, ask: *Why are hourglasses used in many games? When are stopwatches used?*

NOTE Use timers to keep track of and regulate time during everyday classroom life. For example, time cleanup over several days and discuss results; use timers to indicate length of turns at the computer or sand table and indicate the amount of time left until music or lunch.

Links to the Future

Children explore the length of an hour and a minute in Activity 8-2 and Activity 8-11. They also begin to learn about estimating time using the hour hand of an analog clock in Section 8.

Skip Count with Calculators

ACTIVITY 6·14

CCSS Mathematical Practices
SMP1, SMP2, SMP3, SMP5, **SMP7, SMP8**
Content Standards
K.CC.1

◎ **Objective** To demonstrate how to skip count on a calculator.

☑ Whole Group
☑ Small Group
☐ Partners
☐ Center

Key Concepts and Skills
• Use calculators to skip count by 2s, 5s, and 10s. [Number and Numeration Goal 1]
• Use the symbols + and −. [Patterns, Functions, and Algebra Goal 2]

Terms to Use skip counting, plus, equals, pattern, repeat

Materials Home Link Master (*Math Masters,* p. 47); calculators; large signs or transparencies displaying [ON/C] or [AC], [+], and [=]

Planning Tip You may want to use the large display signs for the [+], [=], and clear keys that you made for Activities 4-7 and 5-5 to demonstrate the key sequences. Each child or pair of children should have a calculator for this activity, so you may need to conduct it with small groups.

A Core Activities

▶ Skip Counting with Calculators

Remind children that skip counting involves counting by numbers other than 1, such as counting by 2s, 5s, and 10s. Practice some choral skip counting. Then tell children they can use their calculators to skip count. Explain and demonstrate one way (the long way) to count by 2s on their calculators:

1. Press [ON/C] or [AC] to clear the calculator.
2. Press ; ... Continue until you reach 20.

NOTE Have children count aloud each time they skip count on the calculators.

Ask and discuss: *Why do you think this makes the calculator skip count by 2s?* Next, tell children there is a faster way to skip count on a calculator. Explain that most calculators have a key that tells the calculator to repeat a particular step, such as adding 2 (or 5, or 10). Demonstrate as you explain how to set the repeat function to count by 2s:

1. Press [ON/C] or [AC] to clear the calculator.

2. Press [2] [+] [=] (for TI-108 or similar calculator models) or [2] [+] [+] [=] (for Casio SL-450 or similar calculator models).

3. Keep pressing [=] to count to 40 (or higher) by 2s.

Ask for suggestions for counting by 5s on the calculator. When children are ready, have them press the clear key, substitute [5] for [2] in the above sequence, and count to 115 (or higher) by 5s on the calculator and aloud. Next, remind children to clear their calculators, then have them count to 110 (or higher) by 10s.

Home Link 6·14 (*Math Masters*, p. 47)
Children count by 2s, 5s, and 10s at home.

▶ Making Coin Patterns (Revisit Activity 5·2, p. 238)

Use coins to create patterns for children to describe and extend (for example, 2 pennies, 2 nickels; 2 pennies, 2 nickels; ...). You can use the heads and tails sides of the coins to make more subtle patterns (heads, heads, tails; heads, heads, tails; ...).

B Teaching Options

ENRICHMENT

▶ Solving Problems Using Skip Counting

Read *The King's Commissioners* by Aileen Friedman (Scholastic, 1995) and discuss how skip counting is used to solve the king's problem.

TECHNOLOGY

▶ Skip Counting by Other Numbers

Children can figure out how to use a calculator to skip count by other numbers.

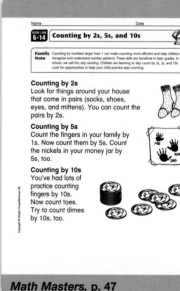

Math Masters, p. 47

Symbolic Representations of Patterns

ACTIVITY 6·15

CCSS

Mathematical Practices
SMP1, **SMP2, SMP4,** SMP6, SMP7, SMP8

Objective To deepen children's understanding of patterns by introducing a way to represent patterns with symbols.

☑ Whole Group
☑ Small Group
☑ Partners
☐ Center

Key Concepts and Skills
• Create and extend patterns. [Patterns, Functions, and Algebra Goal 1]
• Use symbols to represent and follow a pattern. [Patterns, Functions, and Algebra Goal 1]

Terms to Use symbol, represent

Materials *My First Math Book,* p. 13; chalkboard and chalk

Links to the Future

This activity provides exposure to pattern representation. Representing and recording patterns with symbols lays the groundwork for working with numeric patterns in later grades. At this point, children may need assistance to record their patterns, so you might have children do page 13 in their math books with a partner or a small group.

A Core Activities

▶ Representing a Pattern (*My First Math Book,* p. 13)

Demonstrate two movements such as touching your head and clapping one time; then have children copy the movements. Ask the class if they can think of a way for you to tell them which movement to do without using words or actions. Discuss and try their suggestions. If children do not bring it up, ask if you could draw or write something to tell them what to do. Point out that drawing the whole picture could take a lot of time. Ask: *Can we think of something I could draw quickly to represent the movement?* Discuss the meaning of the word *represent.* (You might ask whether anyone has heard of using Xs and Os to mean kisses and hugs when writing a note.) If children need further prompting, draw the symbol ‖ on the board and sketch hands touching a head alongside it. Write "touch head" underneath the symbol. Similarly, indicate that an X will represent a clap. Point to the symbols in a random order and have children perform the actions indicated.

Draw a pattern with the symbols ‖ X ‖ X ‖ X. Have the class do the motions as you point to the symbols. Ask if anyone can make another pattern using the same movements and

NOTE You might use colors, instead of (or in addition to) symbols to indicate each motion. For example, red means "hands on head"; yellow means "clap." Children can represent their patterns with colored counters.

symbols. Follow their suggestions or write a new pattern, such as X X ‖ X X ‖ X X ‖. Again, point and have the class do the movements. Repeat with several patterns. Add new symbols for new motions as needed.

Direct children to create their own movement patterns and draw symbols to represent their patterns on page 13 in their math books. Have each child trade books with another child, explain the symbols, and follow each other's patterns.

▶ Flipping a Coin (Revisit Activity 3•11, p. 162, *My First Math Book*, p. 14)

Ask children why a coin toss is a fair way to decide between two things. Ask: *Is it possible that you will get tails? Are you certain to get heads? Is it impossible to get heads?* Through discussion, elicit that there is an equal chance of getting heads or tails. Children can test this by flipping a coin numerous times and tallying the number of times they get heads and tails on page 14 of their math books. Compile children's results and compare and discuss the total number of heads and tails.

B Teaching Options

EXTRA PRACTICE

▶ Making a Pattern Book (*Math Masters*, p. 48)

Children can draw symbols to represent a pattern on *Math Masters,* page 48. Compile the pages into a book. Periodically choose a page, assign new movements to the symbols, and have children follow the pattern.

MUSIC CONNECTION

▶ Playing Instrument Patterns

Children can represent the sounds of various simple instruments with symbols, and then use the symbols to create patterns (triangle, maraca, bell; triangle, maraca, bell; and so on). Have children follow and play each others' musical patterns.

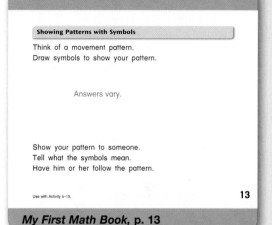

Showing Patterns with Symbols

Think of a movement pattern.
Draw symbols to show your pattern.

Answers vary.

Show your pattern to someone.
Tell what the symbols mean.
Have him or her follow the pattern.

Use with Activity 6•15.

13

My First Math Book, p. 13

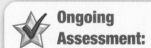 **Ongoing Assessment:**

Recognizing Student Achievement

Use **Flipping a Coin** to assess children's ability to describe events using basic probability terms. Children are making adequate progress if they can use the terms *certain, impossible,* and *possible* (or similar terms) correctly. Many children will be able to use terms such as *more likely, less likely,* and *equally likely* to describe events.

[Data and Chance Goal 3]

Division of Whole Objects into Halves

ACTIVITY 6·16

CCSS Mathematical Practices
SMP1, SMP2, SMP3, SMP4, SMP6, SMP8
Content Standards
K.OA.1, K.OA.2

 **Objective** To expand children's understanding of the concept of *half*.

- [x] Whole Group
- [ ] Small Group
- [ ] Partners
- [ ] Center

Key Concepts and Skills
- Represent half of a whole using concrete objects. [Number and Numeration Goal 4]

Terms to Use whole, part, half, divide, equal, one half

Materials Home Link Master (*Math Masters*, p. 49); graham crackers; chalkboard and chalk

> **Planning Tip** Have half as many crackers as there are children. You might also use other items, such as oranges or cookies.

 **A** **Core Activities**

▶ Dividing a Whole into Halves

Show the class the graham crackers and tell them there are not enough for the whole group. Elicit ideas about how they might share them. When children think of breaking the crackers in half, ask what that means. Draw a cracker on the board and draw a line that divides it unequally. Ask: *Is the cracker divided in half? Why not?* Draw various other lines (horizontal, vertical, diagonal) to divide the cracker into two parts. Use some lines to divide the cracker into two equal parts and other lines to divide the cracker into two unequal parts. Each time, ask and discuss whether the cracker is divided in half. Use this exercise to reiterate that dividing something in half means there must be two equal parts. Show children that one-half is written as $\frac{1}{2}$.

With the class, count the crackers. Draw that number of crackers on the board. Call on children to draw lines to show breaking the crackers into halves. (They can draw any line that divides the cracker into two equal parts.) Point to each half as you count again with the children to confirm that everyone will get a half. Break the crackers in half, some vertically and some horizontally, and distribute them.

 **Adjusting the Activity** **ELL**

To help children visualize and compare equal and unequal divisions, draw 2 identical crackers on the board. Divide one in half with a vertical line. Divide the other into unequal portions with a vertical (or horizontal) line. Talk with children about the difference in the way the crackers are divided: *How are they different? Which one is divided into half? Why?*

AUDITORY ◆ KINESTHETIC ◆ TACTILE ◆ VISUAL

Home Link 6•16 (*Math Masters*, p. 49)

Children divide food items in half to create a half snack.

▶ Writing Number Models for Number Stories (Revisit Activity 4•15, p. 218)

Tell a few "joining" and "removing" number stories for children to solve. Have children categorize the stories as addition or subtraction stories and try to write a number model on their slates or on the writing and drawing pages of their math books for each story.

Also remember to use *Minute Math* during spare moments in the day.

B Teaching Options

MATHEMATICS IN THE DRAMATIC PLAY CENTER

▶ Making Half-and-Half Pizzas (*Center Activity Cards*, 30)

Set out paper plate "pizzas" and a selection of paper pepperoni, mushrooms, and other toppings. Children can order and make pizzas with different toppings on each half. For children who are ready, introduce the term *fraction* and invite them to experiment with other fractional parts of the pretend pizzas, such as fourths and thirds.

LITERACY CONNECTION

▶ Reading about Dividing Things

Read *The Little Mouse, the Red Ripe Strawberry, and the Big Hungry Bear* by Don and Audrey Wood (Child's Play International Ltd., 1993). Talk about how the characters solve a problem by sharing equally. Another good book, *Give Me Half!* by Stuart J. Murphy (HarperTrophy, 1996), tells how a brother and sister share lunch.

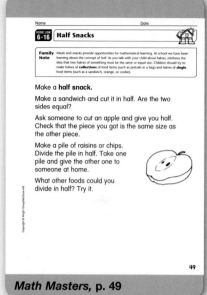

Math Masters, p. 49

⭐ Ongoing Assessment: Informing Instruction

Watch for children who do not realize that when you divide something in half, both sides must be equal. To help them understand that halves of a whole or a collection are equal parts or groups, provide concrete experiences with both whole objects, such as crackers, and collections of objects, such as raisins.

Maps and Mapping

CCSS
Mathematical Practices
SMP1, SMP2, SMP4, SMP6
Content Standards
K.G.1

◎ **Objective** To enrich children's understanding of measurement, distances, and spatial relationships through various mapping activities.

Terms to Use map, orientation, forward, backward, left, right, up, down

Materials

Mapping the Classroom
☐ Home Link Master (*Math Masters,* p. 79) (optional)
☐ large piece of paper
☐ small pieces of paper
☐ fine-tipped black markers
☐ glue sticks

Creating and Following Maps and Mapping the Route to School
☐ paper
☐ pencils
☐ markers or crayons

Making a Treasure Map
☐ book on pirates, such as *Pirates* by Gail Gibbons
☐ paper
☐ pencils
☐ markers or crayons
☐ treat to serve as treasure

Literature Link
Any of the following books would be a good introduction or complement to the mapping activities:

Mapping Penny's World by Loreen Leedy (Henry Holt and Co., 2000); *Me on the Map* by Joan Sweeney (Knopf Books for Young Readers, 1996); *My Map Book* by Sara Fanelli (HarperCollins, 1995); *Where Do I Live?* by Neil Chesanow (Barron's Juveniles, 1995).

Introduction

Mapping is an excellent way to integrate mathematics with literacy and art and to focus on spatial orientation and relationships. Mapping is about more than just getting from one place to another; it involves analyzing the relationships between things and representing those relationships in a diagram.

Begin making maps as a group, then have children make their own maps. At first, children's maps may look similar to one another, but as they become more familiar and adept at creating maps, children's maps will become more individualized.

Before beginning mapping activities, encourage children to discuss what they know about maps, where they have seen maps, and how the maps have been used. Many children may be familiar with road maps or maps of places such as museums or zoos. Invite children to bring in maps to share with the class. Consider reading some of the books listed in the Literature Link on page 316 to introduce the topic and to help children understand maps and their uses.

There are several activities included in the project. While the activities support one another, they may also be done independently. Choose activities that are appropriate for your class.

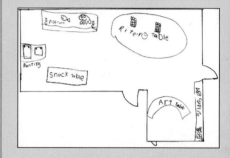

Activity Options

▶ # Mapping the Classroom   ✔ **Whole Group**   ✔ **Small Group**

Post a large piece of paper with the same general proportions as your classroom. Hang it where everyone can see and reach it. Choose one familiar thing in the room as a focal point or point of orientation (for example, a rug, group meeting space, classroom door, large table, or window). Have the class help you figure out where it should be drawn on the paper to begin the classroom map.

Give each child a small sheet of paper. Have the child draw his or her favorite place in the classroom using a black, fine-tipped marker (color can be added later), and then cut around the drawing. Children then add their favorite places to the classroom map, using the focal point to figure out where to place their cutout drawings. Issues of placement, direction, and size can be discussed by the group as pictures are added. If several children chose the same area, discuss how they might put their drawings on the map (stack them, choose one, and so on). If children are concerned about relative sizes, drawings can be resized on a copier. When all drawings have been added, ask the class what things are still missing. Over time, continue to add parts of the room to the map.

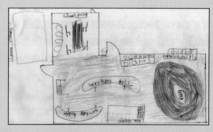

Child-drawn classroom maps

⊙ **Literacy Connection** Children can write or dictate something about their favorite places in the classroom. They might accompany their writing with a drawing. Display the writings around the classroom map or create a class book of everyone's work.

NOTE It is a good idea to copy children's favorite-place drawings, as they may come in handy for additional work.

Home Link Suggestions (*Math Masters,* p. 79)

Children can map a room in their home or another place where they spend time. Send *Math Masters,* page 79, home with a cutout rectangle to represent a bed, a kitchen table, a sofa, or another important object in the room. Tell children to place the rectangle on a piece of paper to serve as a reference point, and then add drawings or cut out pieces of paper to represent other things in the room. Encourage them to begin by looking carefully at where in the room the bed, table, or other object is (for example, near a door or closet) before adding more items. They can label the objects in the room or create a key to accompany their map. Invite children to bring their room maps to school to share with the class.

► Creating and Following Maps   ☑ Whole Group ☑ Small Group

Show your class an assortment of maps, and discuss how maps are used. Individually or as a group, map the path to an often-visited area in the school, such as the playground, library, or main entrance. Before beginning to draw the map, walk the route with the group. Think about relative distances, turns, stairs, or other landmarks they pass along the way. After they finish making the map, have children walk the route as they hold their maps. (Make copies if the class collaborated on a group map.) Allow children to add details they notice as they walk. They might also count the steps between different points and label these distances on the map.

Encourage children to use and make maps often. Simple line maps can be created when children need to deliver something to another classroom or office. Provide materials for children to make their own maps. Create a book of child-made maps to keep in the classroom and use as a reference.

Library

109

108

Room 102   *104*   *106*

103   *105*   *107*

► Mapping the Route to School   ☑ Whole Group ☑ Small Group ☑ Center

After they've had some experience with mapping, invite children to make maps of their routes to school. They might begin by drawing their home as a starting place. Provide a

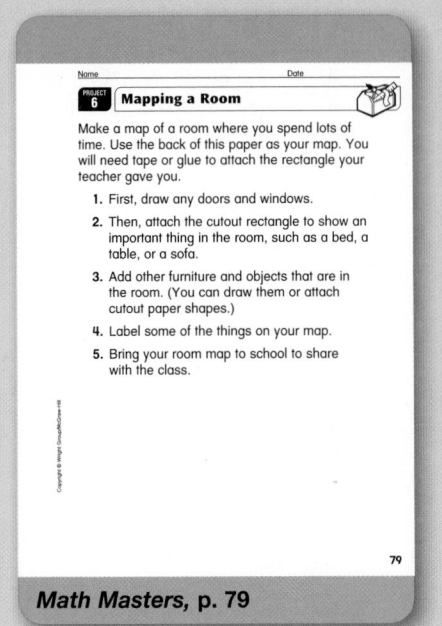

Math Masters, p. 79

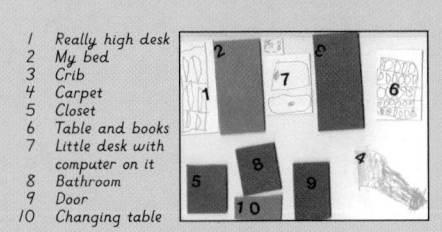

One child's map of a room

picture of the school for children to add to their maps. Prompt children to show on their maps whether they walk, bike, or take a bus or car to school. Have them think about when and where they turn, what they pass, existing traffic signals or stop signs, and whether it takes a long time or a short time to get to school. Have children work on their maps over several days so that they can take note of things they see as they travel to and from school.

You might try some of these related activities:

▷ Add written descriptions to children's maps.
▷ Make a class graph that shows how children come to school (how many children take a car, take a bus, walk, or ride their bike, for example).
▷ Use a simple computer-mapping program to create maps between school and familiar locations.

▶ Making a Treasure Map

✔ Whole Group ✔ Small Group

NOTE As children work with maps, encourage them to use directional words such as *forward, backward, left, right,* and so on.

Talk about treasure maps and how they are used to find hidden treasure. Encourage children to draw treasure maps, perhaps using the playground or classroom as the area where the treasure is hidden.

If you made a map of your classroom, mark the map to show where you have hidden a treasure in the classroom. Allow children to use the map to try to find the treasure. More than one child can act as finder if you direct the children to look for, but not point to or pick up, the treasure. After all the finders have had a chance to locate the treasure, call on someone to identify its location and pick it up.

Encourage children to make their own maps of the classroom or playground to use as treasure maps for others to follow. (You might provide small treats to use as treasures.)

Section 7

Overview

Section 7 has a number of main areas of focus:

◆ To introduce the concept of 10s and 1s and place value using concrete materials,

◆ To introduce name collections through continued exploration of equivalent names for numbers,

◆ To introduce quarters and reinforce the names and values of other coins,

◆ To reinforce addition and subtraction skills and the use of number sentences to model addition and subtraction number stories,

◆ To extend data collection and graphing skills,

◆ To continue activities with 2- and 3-dimensional shapes,

◆ To continue to explore "What's My Rule?" activities with sorting and patterning, and

◆ To reinforce and extend counting, estimation, and other numeration skills.

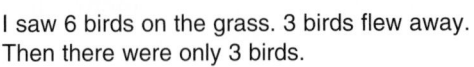

I saw 6 birds on the grass. 3 birds flew away.
Then there were only 3 birds.

Maintaining Ongoing Daily Routines

Doing the Routines

In addition to Section 7 activities, continue to do the following Ongoing Daily Routines:

- ◆ Number of the Day
- ◆ Attendance
- ◆ Job Chart
- ◆ Monthly Calendar
- ◆ Daily Schedule
- ◆ Weather Observation
- ◆ Recording Daily Temperature
- ◆ Survey

Adjusting the Routines

Each Ongoing Daily Routine can be adjusted periodically according to children's progress and interests. The routines are powerful tools for practicing and reinforcing the skills that are introduced in the activities. If you haven't already done so, use the following routines to introduce new ideas and ask different questions during and after Section 7:

- ◆ **Survey** Continue to encourage children to conduct and graph surveys independently, as described in Activity 6-5, page 292.
- ◆ **Weather Observation** Have children compare weather data from different months and look for weather patterns or trends. *Which month had the most snowy days? Which month had more sunny days: September or February? How do our graphs show that the seasons have changed?*

Using Routines for Ongoing Assessment

All of the Ongoing Daily Routines offer opportunities for ongoing assessment of a variety of skills and concepts. You might want to use the following routines for ongoing assessment during Section 7:

- ◆ **Survey** Can children collect, organize, and display survey data? Can they answer questions based on survey data?
- ◆ **Weather Observation** Can children compare weather data from different months? Do they correctly use probability language as they make or check predictions and describe weather patterns or trends?

Learning in Perspective

Core Activities

Activity	Objective	Revisit Activity	Page
7·1	**Money Cube Game** To reinforce the names and values of coins and provide practice with coin exchanges.	**Counting to the Number of the Day** (Activity 6-10, p. 302)	330
7·2	**Class Collections** To reinforce counting and data collection skills through the use of a class collection.	**Writing Number Models for Number Stories** (Activity 4-15, p. 218)	332
7·3	**Class Number Story Book** To deepen children's understanding of mathematical symbols and language through number stories.	**Playing Shape Games** (Activities 6-3 and 6-6, pp. 286 and 294)	336
7·4	**Marshmallow and Toothpick Shapes** To provide experiences with building 2-dimensional and 3-dimensional shapes.	**Dividing Groups in Half** (Activity 6-11, p. 304) **Links to the Past** Children learned about the concept of half in Section 6.	340
7·5	**Introduction of the Quarter** To introduce the quarter. **Links to the Future** In Grade 1, children will make exchanges between pennies, nickels, dimes, quarters, and dollar bills.	**Graphing Sums of Dice Rolls** (Activity 4-8, p. 204; *My First Math Book,* p. 16 or *Math Masters,* p. 34)	342
7·6	**Dice Addition and Subtraction Games** To reinforce addition and subtraction skills and provide practice with addition and subtraction facts within 5.	**Creating Number Stories** (Activity 7-3, p. 336; *My First Math Book*, p. 17)	344
7·7	**Late-in-the-Year Counting** To reinforce and extend children's oral counting skills.	**Counting the Class Collection** (Activity 7-2, p. 332; *My First Math Book,* p. 15)	346
7·8	**10s and 1s with Craft Sticks** To deepen children's understanding of place value by using craft sticks to represent 10s and 1s. **Links to the Future** In Grade 1, children will read, write, and represent numbers up to 1,000.	**Playing *Number-Grid Search*** (Activity 5-16, p. 266)	348

Core Activities, *continued*

Activity	Objective	Revisit Activity	Page
7•9	**Name Collections with Craft Sticks** To provide opportunities to explore equivalent names for numbers. 🔗 **Links to the Past** Children's work with Number Books, dominoes, and *Guess My Number* laid groundwork for understanding equivalent names for numbers.	**Working with Attribute Blocks** (Activity 5-14, p. 262)	350
7•10	**Number Scrolls** To deepen children's understanding of number patterns and place value and to provide number writing practice.	**Estimating Quarters** (Activity 2-13, p. 114; *My First Math Book*, p. 19)	352
7•11	**Decade Count** To develop children's understanding of place value through a counting and recording routine.	**Playing Dice Addition and Subtraction Games** (Activity 7-6, p. 344)	354
7•12	***Plus or Minus Game*** To reinforce the meanings of the + and − symbols and to practice complements of 10 and addition and subtraction facts with small numbers.	**Counting the Class Collection** (Activity 7-2, p. 332; *My First Math Book*, p. 15)	356
7•13	**Double Digits with Dice** To develop children's understanding of place value through building and comparing 2-digit numbers. 🔗 **Links to the Future** Children are introduced to place value in Kindergarten, but work on place value continues through Grade 6.	**Playing *Money Cube*** (Activity 7-1, p. 330) 🔗 **Links to the Past** Children learned to play *Money Cube* in Activity 7-1. Some might be ready to add a quarter to the game.	358
7•14	**Numbers in Sequence** To reinforce the skill of ordering numbers.	**Graphing Lengths of Names and Discussing Probability** (Activities 5-13 and 3-10, pp. 260 and 160)	360
7•15	**"What's My Rule?" with Patterns** To deepen children's understanding of patterns by comparing patterns and identifying patterning rules. 🔗 **Links to the Future** In Activity 8-10, children will play *"What's My Rule?"* with numbers.	**Making Name Collections** (Activities 1-16 and 7-9, pp. 73C and 350)	362
7•16	**Bead String Name Collections** To provide additional experiences with name collections.	**Playing *Monster Squeeze*** (Activity 3-6, p. 150)	364

Section Opener

Ongoing Learning and Practice

Practice through Games

Games are an essential component of practice in the *Everyday Mathematics* program. Games offer skills practice and promote strategic thinking. These games are introduced in this section:

Activity	Game	Skill Practiced
7♦1	Money Cube Money Grid	Identifying coins and their values, and exchanging coins of equal value [MRF Goal 2]
7♦6	Dice Addition and Subtraction Games	Adding and subtracting dice rolls and comparing sums and differences [OC Goal 1]
7♦12	Plus or Minus Game Plus or Minus Steps	Recognizing the + and − symbols, adding and subtracting items, and finding complements of 10 [OC Goals 1 and 2; PFA Goal 2] Recognizing the + and − symbols and moving forward and backward [PFA Goal 2]
	Clear the Board Cover the Board	Adding numbers and subtracting or adding items to a board [OC Goals 1 and 2]
7♦13	Number-Grid Grab	Reading and comparing 2-digit numbers [NN Goal 6]
7♦14	High Low	Comparing numbers 0–30 and thinking about probability [DC Goal 3]

Home-School Connection

Home Links provide homework and home communication. The following activities contain Home Links: 7-2, 7-4, 7-7, 7-9, 7-14.

Home Connection Handbook provides more ideas to communicate effectively with parents. ▶

◀ *Mathematics at Home* Books **1–4** provide additional ideas for enjoyable mathematics activities that families can do together, as well as lists of children's books related to topics in each strand area. Families can do activities from **Book 4** during Section 7.

Balanced Assessment

Use the **Assessment Management Spreadsheets** to collect, review, and share information about children's progress.

Ongoing Assessment

 Recognizing Student Achievement

Opportunities to assess children's progress toward Kindergarten Goals:

Activity	Content Assessed
7♦1	Know the names of coins. [Measurement and Reference Frames Goal 2]
7♦3	Use + , − , and = symbols in a number sentence and distinguish addition and subtraction situations. [Patterns, Functions, and Algebra Goal 2; Operations and Computation Goal 2]
7♦4	Model half of a collection. [Number and Numeration Goal 4]
7♦6	Add and subtract small numbers. [Operations and Computation Goal 1]
7♦8	Use manipulatives to model numbers and make exchanges. [Number and Numeration Goal 3]
7♦11	Add and subtract small numbers. [Operations and Computation Goal 1]
7♦14	Compare and order numbers. [Number and Numeration Goal 6]

Informing Instruction

To anticipate common trouble spots and highlight problem-solving strategies:

Activity 7♦2
Count objects by 1s and 10s

Activity 7♦7
Count on past 70

Activity 7♦10
Write and sequence 2-digit numbers

Portfolio Opportunities

◆ Number stories, **Activities 7-3 and 7-6**
◆ Marshmallow/toothpick shapes, **Activity 7-4**
◆ Connecting cube representations, **Activity 7-9**
◆ Number scrolls, **Activity 7-10**

Assessment Handbook

◆ Kindergarten Goals, pp. 27–33
◆ Section 7 Assessment Overview, pp. 62–63
◆ Assessment Overviews by Strand, pp. 66–75
◆ Individual Profile of Progress and Class Checklist (Sections 7–8), pp. 83–84
◆ Cumulative Individual Profile of Progress (Sections 5–8), pp. 99–102

Periodic Assessment

Mid-Year assessment tasks were completed in Sections 4 and 5. End-of-Year assessment tasks will be completed in Section 8.

Differentiated Instruction

Teaching Options

Use optional Part B activities as time permits to meet individual and class needs and to integrate mathematics throughout the Kindergarten classroom and schedule.

ELL SUPPORT

7◆3	Reading a book of number stories
7◆12	Playing *Plus and Minus Steps*
7◆15	Making movement patterns in a song

READINESS

7◆1	Reviewing coin exchanges
7◆2	Counting objects in scattered configurations
7◆9	Playing *Guess My Number*
7◆10	Playing games on the number grid
7◆11	Representing decade counts with sticks
7◆13	Building Numbers as 10s and 1s

CONNECTIONS

Literacy

7◆6	Reading a + story
7◆15	Identifying patterns in stories and songs
7◆16	Reading about name collections

Science

7◆2	Collecting recyclables

Art

7◆2	Making an art project
7◆4	Drawing with shapes
7◆5	Making quarter rubbings

ENRICHMENT

7◆1	Playing *Money Grid*
7◆5	Playing *Money Cube* with quarters
7◆6	Playing Dice Game variations
7◆7	Skip counting

ENRICHMENT Continued

7◆8	Using coins to represent 10s and 1s	7◆10	Number scrolling
		7◆14	Playing *High Low*

EXTRA PRACTICE

7◆1	Using coins in games	7◆8	Generating and representing numbers
7◆3	Writing number models for pocket problems and train games	7◆9	Representing numbers with connecting cubes
7◆4	Making shapes with straws	7◆12	Playing *Clear the Board* and *Cover the Board*
7◆5	Comparing coins by feel	7◆13	Playing *Number-Grid Grab*
7◆7	Playing counting games		

CENTERS

Block Center

7◆16	Making different buildings with the same number of blocks

Dramatic Play Center

7◆14	Making a grocery list

Writing Center

7◆3	Making individual number story books

TECHNOLOGY

7◆10	"Counting On" using calculators
7◆11	Using a computer game to explore place value
7◆13	Entering and comparing numbers on the calculator

HALF-DAY AND FULL-DAY PROGRAMS ◆ CROSS-CURRICULAR INTEGRATION ◆ CENTERS-BASED LEARNING

Language Support

Everyday Mathematics provides activity-specific suggestions to help *all* young children develop the language necessary to acquire, process, and express mathematical ideas. Activities that provide additional support for non-native English speakers are marked by **ELL SUPPORT** and **ELL**.

Connecting Math and Literacy

Activity 7♦3 *12 Ways to Get to 11* by Eve Merriam (Simon & Schuster, 1993)

Activity 7♦15 *I Went Walking* by Sue Williams (Voyager Books, 1992)

Activity 7♦16 *Math Fables* by Greg Tang (Scholastic Press, 2004)

See pages 341 and 345 for more literature suggestions.

Using the Projects

Use Weaving (Project 7, page 366) during or after Section 7 to reinforce skills and concepts related to patterning, hand-eye coordination, and directionality.

Adjusting the Activity

AUDITORY   ♦   **KINESTHETIC**   ♦   **TACTILE**   ♦   **VISUAL**

Activity 7♦1   Counting and totaling a collection of coins

Activity 7♦8   Making bundles with more than 100 sticks

Activity 7♦10   Adapting number grids for scrolling

Activity 7♦11   Using place-value boxes for recording numbers

Planning Tips

Pacing Pacing depends on a number of factors, such as children's individual needs and how long your school has been using *Everyday Mathematics*. Use the optional Part B activities throughout Section 7 if you have extended mathematics instructional time. See page 326 for a list of these activities.

		MOST CLASSROOMS		
MARCH		APRIL		MAY

Teaching Resources

Resources for the Kindergarten Classroom provides additional teaching ideas, including suggestions for bringing mathematics into thematic instruction as well as using games, literature, technology, and rhymes to support mathematics learning.

Minute Math provides brief activities for transition times and for spare moments throughout the day. During Section 7, use the activities in Part 3, pages 197–258.

NCTM Standards

Content Standards: 1 Number and Operations, **2** Algebra, **3** Geometry, **4** Measurement, **5** Data Analysis and Probability
Process Standards: 6 Problem Solving, **7** Reasoning and Proof, **8** Communication, **9** Connection, **10** Representation

Section 7 Activities	7•1	7•2	7•3	7•4	7•5	7•6	7•7	7•8	7•9	7•10	7•11	7•12	7•13	7•14	7•15	7•16
NCTM Standards	4	1, 5, 10	1, 2, 6, 8, 10	3, 8	4, 8, 9	1	1	1, 10	1, 2, 10	1, 2	1, 4, 9	1, 2, 10	1, 10	1	2, 10	1, 10

Professional Development

Teacher's Reference Manual Links

Activity	Topic	Section	Activity	Topic	Section
7•2	Data Collection, Organization, and Analysis	10.2	**7•5**	Money Facts	12.9.1
			7•13	Numeration and Place Value	8.2.1

Materials

Activity	Masters	Materials	
7·1		• die* marked 1¢, 5¢, 10¢ (each value on two sides)	• bank of pennies, nickels, and dimes • calculators (optional)
7·2	My First Math Book, p. 15 Home Link Master, p. 50	• large storage container • small plastic bags	• items for a class collection
7·3		• chart paper or chalkboard • paper	• writing and drawing materials
7·4	Home Link Master, p. 51	• miniature marshmallows	• round toothpicks • cardstock
7·5		• quarters, pennies, nickels, and dimes	• magnifying lenses
7·6		• customized dice	• counters*
7·7	Home Link Master, p. 52		
7·8	My First Math Book, p. 18	• craft sticks* • small rubber bands*	• cups or similar containers labeled "10s" and "1s" • small plastic bags
7·9	Home Link Master, p. 53	• craft sticks*	• chart paper (optional)
7·10	Teaching Aid Master, p. 111	• pencils	• Class Number Grid
7·11		• chalkboard, chalk, eraser	

Activity	Masters	Materials	
7·12	Game Master, p. 135	• die* marked +1, +2, +3, −1, −2, 0	• counters*
7·13	My First Math Book, p. 20	• two dice*: one marked 0, 1, 2, 3, 4, 5, the other marked 4, 5, 6, 7, 8, 9 • chalkboard and chalk	• craft sticks* (bundles of 10 and singles) • number line* or Class Number Grid (optional)
7·14	Home Link Master, p. 54 Teaching Masters, pp. 105–108	• number line* and/or Class Number Grid	• index cards to create additional number cards (optional)
7·15		• coins* • craft sticks*	• connecting cubes* of different colors
7·16	My First Math Book, p. 21	• string or pipe cleaners • beads	• shoes, blocks, or other objects

Technology

Assessment Management Spreadsheets,
Section 7: See the *iTGA.*

* Indicates items in the Kindergarten manipulative kit.

 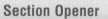

ACTIVITY 7·1

Money Cube Game

(⊙) **Objective** To reinforce the names and values of coins and provide practice with coin exchanges.

CCSS

Mathematical Practices
SMP1, SMP4, SMP6, **SMP7**

☐ Whole Group
☑ Small Group
☑ Partners
☑ Center

Key Concepts and Skills
• Identify names and values of coins. [Measurement and Reference Frames Goal 2]
• Make exchanges with coins. [Measurement and Reference Frames Goal 2]

Terms to Use dime, penny, nickel, cents, exchange

Materials cube marked 1¢, 5¢, 10¢ (each value on two sides); bank of pennies, nickels, and dimes; calculators (optional)

Planning Tip Each group of players will need one money cube and about 20 pennies, 10 nickels, and 10 dimes for their bank.

A **Core Activities**

▶ Playing *Money Cube*

Demonstrate the game and then put it in the Math Center for small groups (2 to 5 children) to play on their own. Players take turns rolling the money cube and selecting a coin (or coins) from the bank that matches the value rolled. Children should say the name of each coin they select. As players accumulate coins, they can make exchanges (5 pennies for 1 nickel; 2 nickels for 1 dime; 1 nickel and 5 pennies for 1 dime; or 10 pennies for 1 dime). (To support English language learners, discuss and model the meaning of *exchange*.) To encourage exchanges, set an exchange period after every round. Play ends when there are no dimes left in the bank.

After you introduce the quarter (Activity 7-5), you can modify the game by replacing one of the 1¢ sides on the money cube with 25¢ and adding about 8 quarters to the bank. Play ends when there are no quarters left in the bank.

Adjusting the Activity

Players can count their coins and determine their totals at the end of the game. They may need help counting a mixed collection of coins. Some children may recognize this as a good time to use calculators.

AUDITORY ◆ KINESTHETIC ◆ TACTILE ◆ VISUAL

► Counting to the Number of the Day (Revisit Activity 6•10, p. 302)

Choral count by 1s, then 2s, to the last number on your Growing Number Line. Incorporate a rhythm or pattern to maintain interest.

B Teaching Options

READINESS

► Reviewing Coin Exchanges

Revisit Coin Exchanges (Activity 6-8, page 298) with children who are not yet ready to play the *Money Cube* game independently.

ENRICHMENT

► Playing *Money Grid* (Math Masters, p. 125)

Players take turns rolling a money cube (labeled 10¢, 5¢, 5¢, 1¢, 1¢, 1¢) and taking a corresponding coin (or coins) to add to their Money Grid (*Math Masters,* page 125). Players can take coins off their grid to exchange for other coins of equivalent value. They can save coins on the side of their grids until they collect enough to trade for a coin to place on the grid. The game ends when one child's grid is filled.

EXTRA PRACTICE

► Using Coins in Games

Children can use coins instead of dice or spinners to generate numbers for familiar games such as *Spin a Number* (Activity 2-4) or *Go Forward, Back Up* (Activity 4-1). Players close their eyes and pick a penny, a nickel, or a dime from a tray. Or they roll a cube labeled with coin pictures (1 dime, 2 nickels, 3 pennies) and move the number of spaces that match the value (in cents) of the coins (5 spaces for a nickel, for example).

Ongoing Assessment:
Recognizing Student Achievement

Use **Money Cube** to assess whether children know the names of the coins. Children are making adequate progress if they can correctly identify each coin. Some children may be able to identify values and make exchanges with coins.

[Measurement and Reference Frames Goal 2]

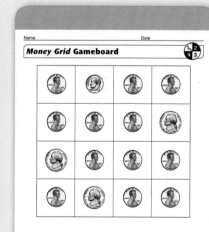

Math Masters, p. 125

ACTIVITY 7·2

Class Collections

🎯 **Objective** To reinforce counting and data collection skills through the use of a class collection.

CCSS Mathematical Practices
SMP1, SMP2, SMP4, SMP6
Content Standards
**K.CC.1, K.CC.4a, K.CC.4b,
K.CC.5,** K.OA.1, K.OA.2

☑ Whole Group
☐ Small Group
☐ Partners
☐ Center

Planning Tip With the class, choose a type of item to collect. Then build and track the collection over a period of 1 to 2 weeks or longer. When interest in the initial collection wanes, you can repeat these activities with different types of collections.

Key Concepts and Skills

• Practice counting by groups (skip counting). [Number and Numeration Goal 1]

• Count objects in a collection. [Number and Numeration Goal 2]

• Read and write 2- and 3-digit numbers. [Number and Numeration Goal 3]

• Record and display data. [Data and Chance Goal 1]

Materials *My First Math Book,* p. 15; Home Link Master (*Math Masters,* p. 50); large storage container; small plastic bags; items for a class collection

A Core Activities

▶ Collecting Objects (*My First Math Book,* p. 15)

Ask for children's ideas about what they would like to collect as a class. Encourage them to consider items that are easily accessible so they can accumulate a large collection in a relatively short period of time. (Some suggestions are bottle caps, yogurt lids, frozen juice tops, or loose buttons.) Children can vote to decide which item to collect. Use tally marks to record and total the votes. Once children have decided what to collect, provide a large container for the collection and invite children to bring examples of the chosen item to class.

Class Collection

1. Our class is collecting Answers vary.

2. Record how the class collection is growing.
   Answers vary.

Date	How many **new** items did we add?	How many items do we have **all together**?

Use with Activity 7·2.   **15**

My First Math Book, p. 15

As the collection accumulates, periodically ask some children to count (or have the group count) how many items are in the collection. Each time the collection is counted, help children record the date, the number of *new* items, and the *total* number of items on a class chart and on the chart on page 15 in their math books. If desired, the class can also create a different type of display to track the growing total (such as the thermometer-style graph pictured in the margin). Children can use different colors each time they update the display.

Class Collection Recording Chart

Date	How many **new** items did we add?	How many items do we have all together?
February 15	38	38
February 17	17	55
February 23	13	68
February 26	7	75

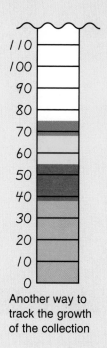

Another way to track the growth of the collection

NOTE Tables are one of the most basic formats for displaying data. Using a variety of data displays encourages children to "see" the data in different ways and helps them to better understand the data. See "Data and Chance," *Teacher's Reference Manual,* Chapter 10.

When the total number of items gets large enough, suggest that children group the items by 10s. (They can put each group of 10 in a small plastic bag.) Model different ways to count the collection, including counting by 10s and "counting on" (starting with an already-known quantity rather than always starting at 1). Children may have other ideas for ways to count the collection, which they should try out and discuss. If the collection goes beyond 100 items, you might group 100 items together for ease in counting. (Children can count on from 100.)

The class might participate in some of the following additional activities:

▷ Periodically weigh the collection on a bathroom scale.

▷ Sort the objects in the collection by attribute (depending on the type of object).

▷ Use collection data to generate number stories. For example, say: *We had 25 objects yesterday, and today we added 6 more. How many do we have now? Or Juana brought 2 objects today, Yasmin brought 3, and Patrick brought 5. How many objects are we adding to the collection today?*

Home Link 7·2 (*Math Masters*, p. 50)

Children bring in items from home to add to the class collection.

▶ Writing Number Models for Number Stories (Revisit Activity 4·15, p. 218)

Tell a few "joining" and "removing" number stories for children to solve. Have children categorize the stories as addition or subtraction stories and try to write a number model for each story on slates or on the writing and drawing pages in their math books. Children will create their own number stories and represent them with drawings and number models in Activity 7-3.

Also remember to use *Minute Math* during spare moments in the day.

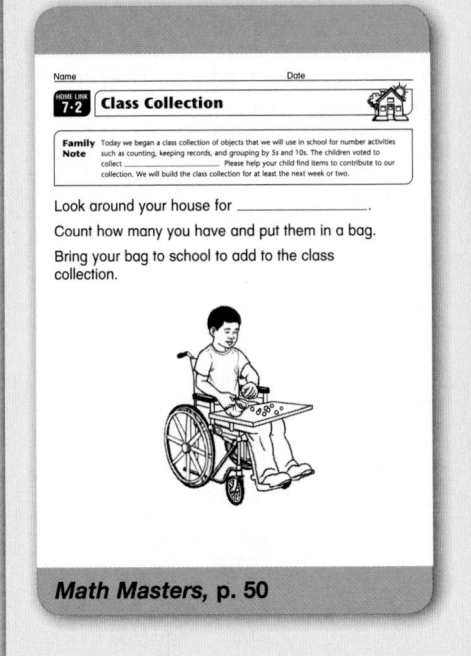

Math Masters, p. 50

B Teaching Options

READINESS

▶ Counting Objects in Scattered Configurations

Some children may have difficulty counting objects that are in scattered configurations. To address this, present children with a small pile of objects and elicit their strategies for counting the objects. Model the following strategies if no one suggests them:

▷ Line up the objects before or while counting.

▷ Move the objects to the side as they are counted.

Give children an opportunity to practice by having them grab handfuls of objects and then count the collections using one of the modeled strategies. You might also have children estimate how many objects they grabbed before counting.

ART CONNECTION

▶ Making an Art Project

When the class decides the collection is complete, the materials from the collection might be used along with glue or other materials to create an art project.

SCIENCE CONNECTION

▶ Collecting Recyclables

The class can collect recyclable materials and track the growth of their collection. Discuss the importance of recycling. Children may want to learn more about the process of recycling, the uses of recycled materials, or other related topics.

ACTIVITY 7·3

Class Number Story Book

◎ **Objective** To deepen children's understanding of mathematical symbols and language through number stories.

CCSS **Mathematical Practices**
SMP1, SMP2, **SMP3,**
SMP4, SMP5, SMP6,
SMP7, **SMP8**
Content Standards
K.OA.1, K.OA.2, K.OA.3, K.MD.1,
K.G.1, K.G.2, K.G.3, K.G.4, K.G.5

✔ Whole Group
✔ Small Group
☐ Partners
☐ Center

Key Concepts and Skills

• Use pictures to represent and solve addition and subtraction stories. [Operations and Computation Goal 1]

• Identify addition and subtraction number stories. [Operations and Computation Goal 2]

• Use the +, −, and = symbols to write number models for number stories.
[Patterns, Functions, and Algebra Goal 2]

Terms to Use number story, addition, subtraction, add, subtract, plus, minus, equal, symbol, number sentence

Materials chart paper or chalkboard; paper; writing and drawing materials

NOTE See Activity 2-14, page 116 and Activity 4-15, page 218 to review number story development and for a complete list and description of the stages of number story development.

A Core Activities

▶ Creating Number Stories

Review the idea that number stories can be told with pictures, words, or numbers. Tell and write a story, such as: *There were 4 squirrels on the ground. 1 squirrel ran up a tree. 3 squirrels were still on the ground.* Draw pictures to depict the story and cross out the squirrel that left. Invite the class to help you write a number sentence to model the story ($4 - 1 = 3$). If children seem stuck, begin by prompting them to think about whether the story is an addition or a subtraction story. Repeat the procedure with a few more stories.

NOTE To support English language learners, ask questions to connect the sequence of events with mathematical terms. For example: *What happened first? How many squirrels were on the ground? What happened next? How many squirrels ran up the tree?*

Give each child a piece of paper and tell children they will each create a number story to include in a class book. Assist children as they think of number stories, draw pictures to illustrate their stories, and write corresponding number sentences. Provide counters (or small pictures of objects, animals, or other number story subjects) for children who may need to model their stories before drawing them. Bind the completed pages into a book and place it in your classroom library or Math Center. Make a copy of each child's page for portfolio assessment if you use portfolios. Allow children to share their stories with the class during a read-aloud time. You might also allow children to borrow the Class Number Story Book (or a copy of it) to share with their families. Provide frequent opportunities for children to create and share number stories during the remainder of the year.

I saw 6 birds on the grass. 3 birds flew away. Then there were only 3 birds.

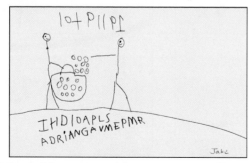

I had 10 apples. Adrian gave me 9 more.

NOTE Make connections across number stories by discussing similarities and differences. Ask children to identify words or contexts that indicate addition or subtraction. For example, "flying away" or "eating something" may indicate subtraction.

Ongoing Assessment:
Recognizing Student Achievement

Use **Creating Number Stories** to assess children's ability to identify addition and subtraction situations and to use the $+$, $-$, and $=$ symbols to represent number stories with number sentences. Children are making adequate progress with distinguishing addition and subtraction if they correctly identify their story as an addition or subtraction story.

[Operations and Computation Goal 2]

Children are making adequate progress with using mathematical symbols if they write a number sentence that corresponds to their number story.

[Patterns, Functions, and Algebra Goal 2]

Sometimes children use arrows to show addition or subtraction.

This child organized her drawing to show groups of objects being added.

▶ Playing Shape Games (Revisit Activities 6◆3 and 6◆6, pp. 286 and 294)

Play several rounds of *I Spy* using clues related to 2- and 3-dimensional shapes. Use clues that help children think about the differences between 2- and 3-dimesional shapes. For example: *I spy a 2-dimensional (flat) shape with no corners,* or *I spy a solid, 3-dimensional shape with 6 flat square faces.* You might also play *Stand Up If …,* as suggested in the Teaching Options for Activity 6-3.

B **Teaching Options**

EXTRA PRACTICE

▶ Writing Number Models for Pocket Problems and Train Games

Children can record number models that correspond to pocket problems that you pose for them or they pose for each other. (See Activity 3-8, page 156.) They might also record number models for each of their moves as they play any of the train games from Activity 3-13, page 166. Children can record number models on the writing and drawing pages in their math books.

ELL SUPPORT

▶ Reading a Book of Number Stories

To give children some ideas and examples of number stories, read *12 Ways to Get to 11* by Eve Merriam (Simon & Schuster, 1993). Talk to children about how each page in the book depicts a number story with pictures and words. (You might also want to have children model some of the stories with objects.) Enlist children's help in writing a number sentence that corresponds to the number story on each page. Discuss the language in the story that corresponds with the number sentence.

MATHEMATICS IN THE WRITING CENTER

▶ Making Individual Number Story Books

Portfolio Ideas

Place materials and counters in the Writing Center so children can make their own number story books. You might assign children a particular number and ask them to write a variety of stories whose answers are that number. Have children begin by exploring different ways to decompose the target number, then use each decomposition as the basis for a number story. Some children may enjoy making thematic number story books in which all the number stories relate to a favorite topic, such as sports or the circus. Have children write number models for each of their stories.

Marshmallow and Toothpick Shapes

CCSS Mathematical Practices
SMP1, SMP2, **SMP3**, **SMP6**, SMP7, SMP8
Content Standards
K.G.2, K.G.3, K.G.4, K.G.5, K.G.6

Objective To provide experiences with building 2-dimensional and 3-dimensional shapes.

☐ Whole Group
☑ Small Group
☐ Partners
☑ Center

Key Concepts and Skills

- Construct 2- and 3-dimensional shapes and explore their properties. [Geometry Goal 1]
- Identify names of 2- and 3-dimensional shapes. [Geometry Goal 1]

Terms to Use dimension, 2-dimensional and 3-dimensional shape names

Materials Home Link Master (*Math Masters*, p. 51); miniature marshmallows; round toothpicks; cardstock

Planning Tip Slightly stale marshmallows work best for this activity.

A Core Activities

▶ Making Geometric Shapes

Portfolio Ideas

Place marshmallows and toothpicks in the Math or Art Center. Demonstrate how to connect the toothpicks and marshmallows to make 2- and 3-dimensional shapes and structures, then encourage children to see what they can make with the materials. Children might make flat creations, or they might build upward or outward. They may make designs, discrete shapes (triangles, cubes, and so on), or representational models, such as houses or rocket ships. In each case, talk with children about the shapes you notice in their constructions (for example, a triangular roof on a 2-dimensional house or a cube as the base of a 3-dimensional house). Promote exploration and discovery with questions about children's work, such as: *How did you make that window? What shapes did you use? Have you figured out how to make a cube? How many marshmallows and toothpicks do you need? Can you think of a way to attach those triangles to each other?* Place children's shape creations on pieces of cardboard or cardstock and display them around the room. If you use portfolios, take photographs of children's creations to place in their portfolios.

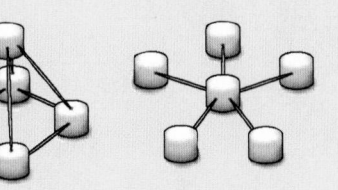

Home Link 7·4 (*Math Masters*, p. 51)

Children use toothpicks and marshmallows to make shapes at home.

▶ Dividing Groups in Half (Revisit Activity 6·11, p. 304)

Show children different numbers of marshmallows (some odd, some even). Have children work together to divide the collections in half. Discuss and try out children's ideas for dividing the odd-numbered collections equally.

B Teaching Options

EXTRA PRACTICE

▶ Making Shapes with Straws (*Center Activity Cards*, 31)

Children who enjoy working with marshmallows and toothpicks might also enjoy the challenge of building shapes and structures with straws. Demonstrate how to connect straws by bending a twist tie or pipe cleaner in half and inserting half in the opening of one straw and half in the opening of another straw. (A small diameter straw works best.) Place the materials in a center and invite children to continue their shape explorations. Talk with children about the shapes they make.

ART CONNECTION

▶ Drawing with Shapes

Read *Picture Pie* or *Picture Pie 2* by Ed Emberley (Little Brown, 1984 and 1996) and show children how the author makes pictures using various shapes. Encourage interested children to experiment with these techniques on the writing and drawing pages in their math books.

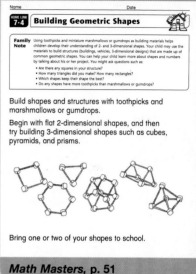

Name _____ Date _____

HOME LINK
7·4 **Building Geometric Shapes**

Family Note Using toothpicks and miniature marshmallows or gumdrops as building materials helps children develop their understanding of 2- and 3-dimensional shapes. Your child may use the materials to build structures (buildings, vehicles, 3-dimensional designs) that are made up of common geometric shapes. You can help your child learn more about shapes and numbers by talking about his or her project. You might ask questions such as:

• Are there any squares in your structure?
• How many triangles did you make? How many rectangles?
• Which shapes keep their shape the best?
• Do any shapes have more toothpicks than marshmallows or gumdrops?

Build shapes and structures with toothpicks and marshmallows or gumdrops.

Begin with flat 2-dimensional shapes, and then try building 3-dimensional shapes such as cubes, pyramids, and prisms.

Bring one or two of your shapes to school.

Math Masters, p. 51

⭐ Ongoing Assessment:

Recognizing Student Achievement

Use **Dividing Groups in Half** to assess children's ability to model half of a collection. Children are making adequate progress if they understand that both halves must be equal.

[Number and Numeration Goal 4]

ACTIVITY 7·5

Introduction of the Quarter

◎ **Objective** To introduce the quarter.

CCSS **Mathematical Practices**
SMP1, SMP2, SMP4, SMP6, SMP7, **SMP8**
Content Standards
K.CC.4a, K.CC.4b, K.OA.1, K.OA.2, K.OA.3, K.OA.5

☑ Whole Group
☐ Small Group
☐ Partners
☑ Center

Key Concepts and Skills
- Make exchanges with pennies, nickels, dimes, and quarters. [Measurement and Reference Frames Goal 2]
- Explore the characteristics of the quarter. [Measurement and Reference Frames Goal 2]
- Learn about the value of the quarter. [Measurement and Reference Frames Goal 2]

Terms to Use quarter, cent, exchange, value, penny, nickel, dime, dollar

Materials quarters, pennies, nickels, and dimes; magnifying lenses

Planning Tip Try to include a variety of state quarter designs in your collection of quarters.

A Core Activities

▶ Exploring the Quarter

Give each child a quarter. Have children use the magnifying lenses to look closely at the quarter. Discuss the size, shape, color, and any markings children notice. Ask if anyone knows the name of this coin. Explain that it can be called by different names: a quarter or 25 cents. Ask children to name some things that they use quarters for. You might tell the children that quarters are the coins used most often for parking meters.

Briefly discuss the meaning of the word **quarter** ($\frac{1}{4}$ of a whole) and explain that 4 quarters make 1 dollar. Ask children to estimate how much money they will have if they put their quarters together. Collect the quarters and put them in stacks of four. Count the stacks (and single quarters) with the class to get the total. Write the total amount on the board. Discuss what could be purchased with the total.

Ask how many pennies you should get if you trade, or exchange, your quarter for pennies. Demonstrate by trading 1 quarter for 25 pennies. Count the pennies out loud (*one cent, two cents,* and so on) to draw attention to their equivalent value. Ask if anyone can think of any other coins they might exchange for a quarter. Put out a collection of mixed coins and invite children to try to make some exchanges. Add quarters to the Math Center for continued exploration.

▶ Graphing Sums of Dice Rolls

(Revisit Activity 4◆8, p. 204; *My First Math Book*, p. 16 or *Math Masters*, p. 34)

Have children work on Dice-Throw Grids using 2 dice in the Math Center. To develop fluency with simple addition facts, encourage children to recall sums for as many combinations as they can.

B   Teaching Options

ENRICHMENT

▶ Playing *Money Cube* with Quarters

Add quarters to the *Money Cube* game for children who are ready. (See Activity 7-1.)

EXTRA PRACTICE

▶ Comparing Coins by Feel

Children can compare a penny, nickel, dime, and quarter, visually and by touch. Put a coin in a Feely Box and have a child guess, by touch only, which coin it is. Then, put one or more of each type of coin in the Feely Box and see if children can pull out the coin you name. Have children say the names and values of the coins.

ART CONNECTION

▶ Making Quarter Rubbings

Children can make rubbings of both sides of a quarter using the side of a crayon and a sheet of paper or the writing and drawing pages in their math books.

Links to the Future

Do not expect that all children will be ready to make exchanges with quarters. See the Enrichment suggestion in the Teaching Options for children who are ready to do so. Making exchanges between pennies, nickels, dimes, and quarters is a Grade 1 Goal.

Technology

Children can play a version of *Money Cube* with quarters on the computer using *Everyday Mathematics EM Games*. The computer version is called *Coin Exchange*.

NOTE See Chapter 12 of the *Teacher's Reference Manual* for information about George Washington and the quarter that you might share with children as a Social Studies Connection. You might also share information about the various state quarter designs.

Dice Addition and Subtraction Games

CCSS Mathematical Practices
SMP2, **SMP3**, SMP4, SMP5, **SMP6**
Content Standards
K.OA.1, K.OA.2, K.OA.3, **K.OA.5**

 **Objective** To reinforce addition and subtraction skills and provide practice with addition and subtraction facts within 5.

☐ Whole Group
✔ Small Group
✔ Partners
✔ Center

Key Concepts and Skills

- Compare sums and differences of dice throws. [Number and Numeration Goal 6]
- Add and subtract numbers from dice throws using various strategies. [Operations and Computation Goal 1]
- Practice addition and subtraction facts within 5. [Operations and Computation Goal 1]

Terms to Use sum, difference, add, subtract, strategy

Materials customized dice (see Planning Tip); counters

Planning Tip Prepare the customized dice for each game. You can create the dice by writing on blank dice or on small wooden cubes. For *Dice Addition,* each player will need a pair of dice: one labeled 0, 0, 1, 1, 2, 2 and the other labeled 1, 1, 2, 2, 3, 3. For *Dice Subtraction,* each player will need two dice, each labeled 0, 1, 2, 3, 4, 5.

A Core Activities

▶ Playing Dice Addition and Subtraction Games

Begin by teaching children how to play *Dice Addition.* Players each roll a pair of customized dice (one labeled 0, 0, 1, 1, 2, 2; the other labeled 1, 1, 2, 2, 3, 3) and announce the sum of the two numbers they roll. The player with the highest sum takes a counter. The game ends when one player has 10 counters. (Children may also practice using tallies by tallying their highest sums rather than using counters to keep track.)

Children can use the counters to model the addition problems if needed, but encourage them to try to recall the facts first.

For *Dice Subtraction,* players use pairs of customized dice labeled 0–5. Players roll their own dice, subtract their lower numbers from their higher numbers, and announce the differences. The player with the larger difference takes a counter (or marks a tally).

Play continues until one player has 10 counters or tallies. As with *Dice Addition,*

encourage children to try to recall the facts before using the counters to find the difference.

Place the customized dice for both games in the Math Center for continued play. You may also create game bags so children can play at home.

▶ **Creating Number Stories** (Revisit Activity 7•3, p. 336; *My First Math Book*, p. 17)

Have children think of original number stories and record them with pictures and number models on page 17 in their math books. You might tell children to leave the answers for their number sentences blank so they can trade books with their partners and solve each others' number stories.

B **Teaching Options**

ENRICHMENT

▶ **Dice Game Variations**

Introduce the following Dice Game variations. Customize the dice to match children's differing skills and needs:

▷ *Counting-On Dice Addition:* Use a numeral die and a standard dot die. Players roll the numeral die and say the numbers that they rolled. Then they roll the dot die and "count on" from the first number to reach the sum.

▷ *Dice Addition with 3 Dice:* Roll and add the dots on 3 dice.

▷ *Dice Addition and Subtraction with Polyhedral Dice:* Play the games using polyhedral dice with more than 6 faces.

LITERACY CONNECTION

▶ **Reading an Addition Story**

Read *Animals on Board* by Stuart J. Murphy (HarperTrophy, 1998). Discuss the number sentences that model the situations in the book.

My First Math Book sidebar

Number Story
Think of a number story.
Show your story with pictures and a number sentence.

Use with Activity 7•6.   **17**

My First Math Book, p. 17

Ongoing Assessment sidebar

Ongoing Assessment:
Recognizing Student Achievement

Use **Dice Addition and Subtraction Games** to assess children's ability to fluently add and subtract small numbers. Children are making adequate progress if they can quickly solve or recall the sums and differences.

[Operations and Computation Goal 1]

Late-in-the-Year Counting

🎯 **Objective** To reinforce and extend children's oral counting skills.

CCSS Mathematical Practices
SMP1, SMP2, SMP4, SMP5, **SMP6,** SMP7
Content Standards
K.CC.1, K.CC.2, K.CC.4a, K.CC.4b, K.CC.5

☑ Whole Group
☑ Small Group
☐ Partners
☐ Center

Key Concepts and Skills
- Count on from various numbers. [Number and Numeration Goal 1]
- Count backward from various numbers. [Number and Numeration Goal 1]
- Count beyond 100. [Number and Numeration Goal 1]
- Read numbers. [Number and Numeration Goal 3]

Materials Home Link Master (*Math Masters*, p. 52)

NOTE Also remember to regularly practice skip counting by 2s, 5s, and 10s with children. Take the counts beyond 100 so that children learn how the pattern continues with higher numbers.

A Core Activities

▶ Counting Forward and Backward from Higher Numbers

Remind children that counting does not always begin with 1 and that they can count forward or backward. Using your signs or signals to start and stop counting, have children choral count forward or backward from various numbers, such as:

▷ the number of children in class

▷ the date on the calendar

▷ randomly-selected numbers on the number line or number grid

▷ the temperature

▷ 2-digit numbers generated by rolling two dice (or flipping two 0–9 number cards) to serve as the digits

Use several starting and stopping numbers (using both forward and backward prompts). To keep the activity interesting, incorporate movement, rhythm, a familiar tune, or a loud/soft pattern as children count. Encourage children to use the number line or number grid as a reference, as needed.

Continue to engage the class in frequent oral counting practice as the year progresses, using the above suggestions as starting points for interrupted counts. Remember to keep the counts brief and playful. At least once a week, the class can choral count up to the number of the day on the Growing Number Line.

 Home Link 7·7 (*Math Masters*, p. 52)
Children practice counting skills at home.

▶ Counting the Class Collection (Revisit Activity 7·2, p. 332; *My First Math Book*, p. 15)

If they haven't done so recently, have the class count the items in the Class Collection that you began in Activity 7-2. Children should record the number of items that have been added since your last count and the total number of items in the collection on page 15 of their math books, as well as on your class chart. If you are keeping a class display of the growing total, update that too.

 B **Teaching Options**

ENRICHMENT

▶ Skip Counting from Different Numbers

Some children might enjoy using a number grid or number line to figure out how to skip count by 2s, 5s, and 10s from various numbers. Children can also use the "repeat" sequence on their calculators to skip count from different numbers.

EXTRA PRACTICE

▶ Playing Counting Games

Children can play *Give the Next Number* (Activity 1-12, page 68), *Count and Sit, Follow the Leader* (Activity 2-6, page 98), and any other counting games you may have introduced using higher numbers and/or backward counting. Use written numerals as starting points to provide practice with reading higher numbers.

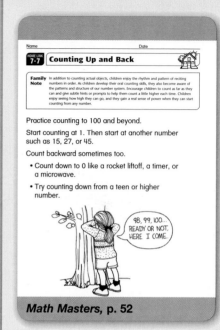

Math Masters, p. 52

 Ongoing Assessment:
Informing Instruction

Watch for children who cannot count higher than 70 or who can only count from 0. Provide extra opportunities for these children to practice their counting skills in small groups so you can determine where they are having difficulty and provide targeted support. Additional experiences with the numeration patterns on the number line or number grid might also be beneficial.

10s and 1s with Craft Sticks

 **Objective** To deepen children's understanding of place value by using craft sticks to represent 10s and 1s.

CCSS Mathematical Practices
SMP1, SMP3, SMP6, **SMP7, SMP8**
Content Standards
K.CC.1, K.NBT.1

☐ Whole Group
☑ Small Group
☐ Partners
☐ Center

Key Concepts and Skills
- Count by 10s and 1s. [Number and Numeration Goal 1]
- Estimate the number of items in a collection. [Number and Numeration Goal 2]
- Represent numbers with manipulatives as 10s and 1s. [Number and Numeration Goal 3]

Terms to Use exchange, bundle, tens, ones

Materials *My First Math Book*, p. 18; craft sticks; small rubber bands; cups or similar containers labeled "10s" and "1s"; small plastic bags

Planning Tip Fill several small plastic bags with a large number of craft sticks (20 to 70 or so; more for some children). You will need one bag of sticks for each child in the small group.

A Core Activities

▶ Bundling Sticks (*My First Math Book*, p. 18)

Set out 40 to 50 craft sticks in the middle of a small group of children. Have the group count the sticks by 1s. Then have them work together to bundle the sticks into groups of 10, leaving the leftover sticks unbundled. Children should put the bundles together in a cup or container labeled "10s" and the single craft sticks together in a cup or container labeled "1s." Ask: *Do we have the same number of sticks as we had before? Why is it easier to have them in bundles of 10s?* (Point out that this is similar to what they do with the items in the Concrete Number Count collection for the Number of the Day Routine.) Count the craft sticks again, this time by 10s (the bundles) and 1s (the unbundled sticks). Write the number. Point out that the number of bundles matches the number on the left, and the number of single sticks matches the number on the right. Say: *Another way to say the number is ____ tens and ____ ones.*

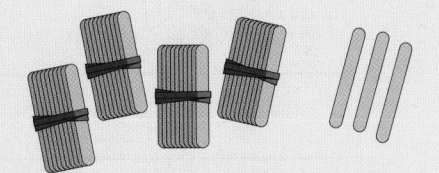

NOTE Help children keep their bundles and sticks separate by providing cups, containers, or different-colored sheets of paper.

Give each child a small plastic bag with at least 20 craft sticks (most children will be ready for more than 20 sticks). Ask children to estimate the number of craft sticks in their bags. Then have them bundle, count, and record the number in the top section of page 18 in their math books. Have them undo their bundles of sticks and trade bags with another child to do the bottom section of their math book page.

Adjusting the Activity

Some children may be ready to use more than 100 sticks. After talking with them about how many bundles of 10 are in 100, help children make a "big bundle" of 100 by putting 10 of the bundles of 10 together.

AUDITORY ◆ KINESTHETIC ◆ TACTILE ◆ VISUAL

▶ **Playing *Number-Grid Search*** (Revisit Activity 5•16, p. 266)

Play a few rounds of *Number-Grid Search* with the class.

B | Teaching Options

ENRICHMENT

▶ Using Dimes and Pennies to Represent 10s and 1s

Children can use dimes and pennies to represent a given number of cents as 10s and 1s. For example, they can show 42 cents as 4 dimes and 2 pennies.

EXTRA PRACTICE

▶ Generating and Representing Numbers (*Center Activity Cards*, 32)

One child can flip over two number cards (0–9) to represent the digits in a number, lay the cards side by side, and read the resulting number. Then a partner represents the number with bundles of 10 and single sticks. Partners can work with numbers in the 100s by flipping three cards and using "big bundles" of 100 sticks.

10s and 1s with Craft Sticks

Bag 1
1. How many bundles of 10 do you have? <u>Answers vary.</u>
2. How many unbundled sticks do you have? <u>Answers vary.</u>
3. How many sticks do you have all together? <u>Answers vary.</u>

Bag 2
1. How many bundles of 10 do you have? <u>Answers vary.</u>
2. How many unbundled sticks do you have? <u>Answers vary.</u>
3. How many sticks do you have all together? <u>Answers vary.</u>

18   Use with Activity 7•8.

My First Math Book, p. 18

 Ongoing Assessment:
Recognizing Student Achievement

Use **Bundling Sticks** to assess children's ability to use manipulatives to model numbers and make exchanges. Children are making adequate progress if they can represent numbers through at least 20 with bundles of 10 craft sticks and single sticks.

[Number and Numeration Goal 3]

Name Collections with Craft Sticks

ACTIVITY
7·9

CCSS Mathematical Practices
SMP1, **SMP2**, SMP3, **SMP8**
Content Standards
K.OA.3, K.MD.1

◎ **Objective** To provide opportunities to explore equivalent names for numbers.

☑ Whole Group
☑ Small Group
☐ Partners
☐ Center

Key Concepts and Skills
• Use craft sticks to find and represent equivalent names for numbers. [Number and Numeration Goal 5]
• Use the + sign to represent equivalent names for numbers. [Patterns, Functions, and Algebra Goal 2]

Terms to Use combinations, name collection, equivalent names

Materials Home Link Master (*Math Masters*, p. 53); craft sticks; chart paper (optional)

A Core Activities

▶ Exploring Equivalent Names for Numbers

Tell children to show 5 fingers on one hand. Then ask them to show 5 fingers using both hands. Point out the combinations they are using—3 fingers on one hand and 2 on the other; 4 fingers and 1 finger; 5 fingers and 0 fingers. Explain that these are different ways to show the number 5.

Give each child 6 craft sticks and count them to confirm the total. Tell children to hold some of the sticks in their right hands and the rest in their left. As children hold up their sticks, list on the chalkboard or chart paper all of the different combinations that children use to make 6 (4 + 2, 5 + 1, and so on). You might want to draw the sticks alongside the number models. Be sure children understand why you include the + symbol as you write the combination. After you make the list, ask children if they can think of any other combinations. Explain that the list is called a *name collection* for the number 6. Invite children to add other ways to show 6, such as 6 tally marks, a sketch

NOTE Children's earlier work with Number Stations (Activity 1-5), dominoes (Activity 3-5), *Guess My Number* (Activity 5-4), and other activities laid the groundwork for recognizing that there are different ways to represent numbers.

of 5 fingers and 1 finger, and so on. Repeat the activity using different numbers of sticks. Invite children to add to the lists as they think of other ways to show each number.

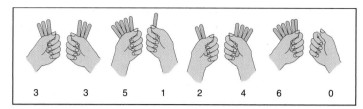

3	3	5	1	2	4	6	0

Name collection for the number 6

Home Link 7·9 *(Math Masters, p. 53)*
Children find different ways of grouping the members of their families.

▶ Working with Attribute Blocks *(Revisit Activity 5·14, p. 262)*

Place attribute blocks in the Math Center and encourage children to play the *Attribute Spinner Game* and/or make "attribute trains." (See Activity 5-14, page 262.)

B Teaching Options

READINESS

▶ Playing *Guess My Number*

Children think of equivalent names for numbers as they give clues (orally, in writing, or using manipulatives) for *Guess My Number*. (See Activity 5-4, page 242.)

EXTRA PRACTICE

▶ Representing Numbers with Connecting Cubes *(Center Activity Cards, 33)*

Children can use connecting cubes of different colors to find ways to represent a given total. For example, they can make a stack of 8 cubes with 5 red and 3 yellow; 4 blue and 4 red; or 5 red, 2 yellow, and 1 blue. Have children record their combinations with pictures and number sentences or equations ($8 = 4 + 4$, for example) on the writing and drawing pages in their math books.

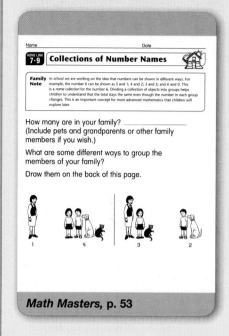

Math Masters, p. 53

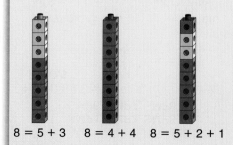

$$8 = 5 + 3 \qquad 8 = 4 + 4 \qquad 8 = 5 + 2 + 1$$

Number Scrolls

ACTIVITY
7·10

◎ **Objective** To deepen children's understanding of number patterns and place value and to provide number writing practice.

☑ Whole Group   ☐ Partners
☑ Small Group   ☑ Center

Key Concepts and Skills

• Write 1-, 2-, and 3-digit numbers. [Number and Numeration Goal 3]
• Notice number patterns. [Patterns, Functions, and Algebra Goal 1]

Terms to Use number grid, scroll

Materials Teaching Aid Master (*Math Masters,* p. 111); pencils; Class Number Grid

Planning Tip You might use an overhead or enlarged copy of the Number Scroll Teaching Aid Master to model number scrolling. Once introduced, keep number scrolls available as an open-ended activity for the rest of the year.

A Core Activities

▶ Making Number Scrolls (*Math Masters,* p. 111)

Portfolio
Ideas

Review the Class Number Grid with children. Have them identify and share number patterns they see on the grid. For example, all numbers in a column end with the same number. Then demonstrate how to begin a number scroll by completing the top two or three rows of a blank number scroll (*Math Masters,* page 111). Distribute blank number scrolls to the children and assist them as they begin to write numbers. Provide ample time for children to get a good start on their scrolls, then tell them that they can continue to add to the scrolls over the next several days, weeks, or longer. You may want to designate a space in the Math Center to save "in-progress" scrolls so children can work on them during free time during the day. Some children may want to tape together additional sheets so they can continue past 100. (See the Enrichment Teaching Option below for suggestions to help children as they write numbers past 100.) As their number scrolls get longer, children can roll them and secure them with rubber bands.

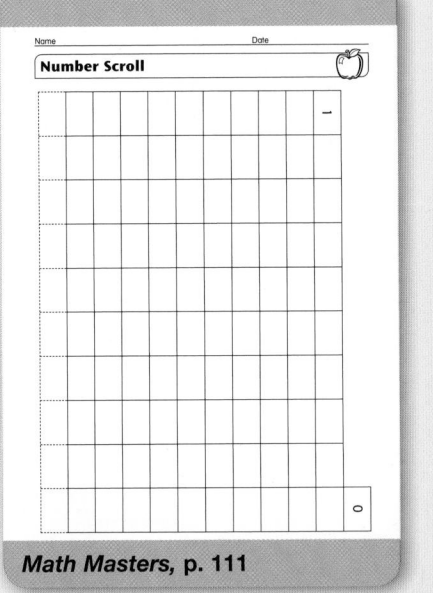

Math Masters, p. 111

▶ Estimating Quarters (Revisit Activity 2•13, p. 114; *My First Math Book*, p. 19)

Place a large number of quarters in your estimation jar. Have children use page 19 of their math books to record their estimates of how many quarters are in the jar. After you count the number of quarters together, have children circle whether their estimates were "way too high," "way too low," or "pretty close." Then stack the quarters in piles of 4 and count the total number of dollars. Discuss what you might buy with the total.

 **Teaching Options**

READINESS

▶ Playing Games on the Number Grid

To increase familiarity with the Class Number Grid, children can play *Number-Grid Search* or mini *Number-Grid Search* in the Math Center. See Activity 5-16, page 266, for directions.

ENRICHMENT

▶ Number Scrolling beyond 100

Children can add sheets to continue scrolling past 100. Remind them that hundreds numbers are always written with 3 digits. You might give children opportunities to practice writing 3-digit numbers on 3 blank horizontal lines.

TECHNOLOGY

▶ "Counting On" Using Calculators

Children can use a calculator to "count on" while making their number scrolls. Some children may find this helpful as they write large numbers. Refer to Activity 5-5, page 244 for more information.

 Adjusting the Activity

Coloring or shading alternate rows on the grid may be useful for children who need help keeping track of their place as they write on their scrolls. You might also provide copies of a small number grid (*Math Masters,* page 110) for children to use as a reference, if needed.

AUDITORY ◆ KINESTHETIC ◆ TACTILE ◆ VISUAL

 Ongoing Assessment:

Informing Instruction

Watch for children who write 2-digit numbers incorrectly or in the incorrect sequence on the number grid. Assist them as they work and encourage them to use the Class Number Grid as a model.

ACTIVITY 7·11

Decade Count

Objective To develop children's understanding of place value through a counting and recording routine.

CCSS Mathematical Practices
SMP2, SMP3, SMP5, SMP7, SMP8
Content Standards
K.OA.1, K.OA.3, K.OA.5

- ☑ Whole Group
- ☐ Small Group
- ☐ Partners
- ☐ Center

Key Concepts and Skills

- Count forward. [Number and Numeration Goal 1]
- Write numbers as 10s and 1s. [Number and Numeration Goal 3]
- Use counting to time an event. [Measurement and Reference Frames Goal 4]

Terms to Use tens, ones

Materials chalkboard, chalk, eraser

A Core Activities

▶ Recording Decades While Counting

Tell the class that you want to show them a different way to keep track of a count. Give a signal to begin counting by 1s. When the count reaches 10, write just the digit 1 as the children continue the count. When the count reaches 20, erase the 1 and write 2 while the children continue counting. As each new decade (count of 10) is reached, erase the previous number and write the next. Stop the count when it has reached a high enough number for the children to recognize the system you are using to track and record the count. Ask for children's ideas about how to complete the number. For example, if the decade is at 8 and you stop the count at 83, write 3 in the appropriate place (the ones place). For counts that go past 99, erase the 9 and write 10 (for a count that ends at 103, write 3 in the ones place).

Use this activity as an enjoyable way to time a classroom cleanup or other transition. It serves not only to focus attention on the patterns in the counting system, but also

Adjusting the Activity

You might use a visual aid to help children understand place value. Create three place-value boxes into which children record the numbers.

AUDITORY ◆ KINESTHETIC ◆ TACTILE ◆ VISUAL

brings the group together as they join in the count. Once children are familiar with recording decades during a count, invite them to be the recorders. You may wish to add a Recorder job to the class job chart. If you do, make sure children know they can ask for all the help they wish with this job. Remind the class that the best way to give help is with a hint, not the answer.

▶ Playing Dice Addition and Subtraction Games

(Revisit Activity 7•6, p. 344)

Have children play Dice Addition and Subtraction Games in the Math Center. You might have children record number sentences for each turn. Consider using some of the variations suggested in the Teaching Options on page 345 for children who are ready.

Also remember to use *Minute Math* during spare moments in the day.

B Teaching Options

READINESS

▶ Representing Decade Counts with Sticks

Make the decade counts more concrete by taking a bundle of 10 sticks each time the count reaches a new decade, then adding the appropriate number of single sticks at the end of the count. Count the sticks by 10s and 1s with the class to confirm that the number of sticks matches the count.

TECHNOLOGY

▶ Using a Computer Game to Explore Place Value

Children can play "Bee's Toy Store Game" on *Piggy in Numberland* (Learning in Motion, 1998) to further explore place value in 2-digit numbers. See *Resources for the Kindergarten Classroom* for other software suggestions.

Ongoing Assessment:

Recognizing Student Achievement

Use **Dice Addition and Subtraction Games** to assess children's ability to fluently add and subtract small numbers. Children are making adequate progress if they can quickly solve or recall the sums and differences.

[Operations and Computation Goal 1]

Links to the Future

Do not expect all children to fully understand this method for recording counts. This activity is an early exposure to place-value concepts. Identifying the places in numbers and the values of the digits in those places is a Grades 1–6 Goal.

ACTIVITY
7·12

Plus or Minus Game

◎ **Objective** To reinforce the meanings of the + and − symbols and to practice complements of 10 and addition and subtraction facts with small numbers.

CCSS **Mathematical Practices**
SMP1, SMP2, SMP6, SMP7, SMP8
Content Standards
K.CC.4a, K.CC.4b, K.CC.5, **K.OA.1, K.OA.4, K.OA.5**

☐ Whole Group
☑ Small Group
☑ Partners
☑ Center

Planning Tip Before you introduce the activity, prepare the die and cut the masters in half to make individual gameboards (one gameboard per player and one die per group of players).

Key Concepts and Skills

- Add and subtract numbers within 10. [Operations and Computation Goal 1]
- Identify pairs of numbers with sums to 10. [Operations and Computation Goal 1]
- Explore the differences between addition and subtraction. [Operations and Computation Goal 2]
- Recognize and use the + and − symbols. [Patterns, Functions, and Algebra Goal 2]

Materials Game Master (*Math Masters*, p. 135); die marked +1, +2, +3, −1, −2, 0; counters

A Core Activities

▶ Playing the *Plus or Minus Game* (*Math Masters*, p. 135)

Demonstrate how to play the game. Children take turns rolling the die. When players roll a + number, they add that number of counters to the board. When players roll a − number, they remove that number of counters from the board unless there are no counters on the board. If a 0 is rolled, there is no move. At the end of each player's turn, that player announces how many counters are on his/her board and how many more counters are needed to get to 10. The game ends when a player's board is covered with an exact roll. Leave the game in the Math Center for children to play with partners or small groups.

You may vary the game to practice and record addition and subtraction facts by having children say and write the number sentence for each turn ($0 + 2 = 2$ for an initial roll of +2, for example).

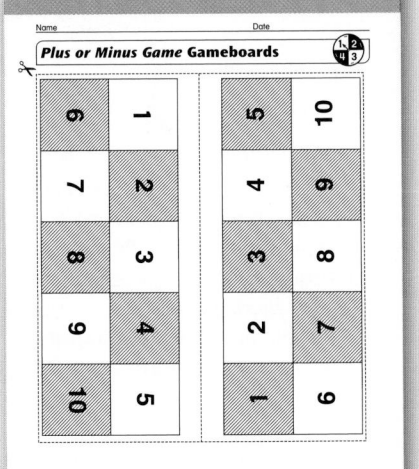

Math Masters, p. 135

▶ Counting the Class Collection

(Revisit Activity 7♦2, p. 332; *My First Math Book*, p. 15)

If they haven't done so recently, have the class count the items in the Class Collection that you began in Activity 7-2, page 332. (You might track the count using the "decade count" system from Activity 7-11, page 354.) Children should record the number of items that have been added since your last count and the total number of items in the collection on page 15 of their math books, as well as on your class chart. If you are keeping a class display of the growing total, update that as well.

B Teaching Options

EXTRA PRACTICE

▶ Playing *Clear the Board* and *Cover the Board* (Center Activity Cards, 34)

Children can play *Clear the Board* by working together to uncover a checkerboard that is covered with checkers or other counters (one counter per square). Players take turns rolling a pair of dice, finding the total, and removing that number of counters from the board until the board is empty. Children also can play *Cover the Board* by rolling dice and adding counters to fill a board that starts off empty.

ELL SUPPORT

▶ Playing *Plus or Minus Steps*

Mark starting and ending lines on opposite sides of an outdoor area, hallway, or large classroom rug. Children take turns rolling a cube (large if possible) marked $+1$, $+2$, $+3$, -1, -2, 0 and taking the correct number of steps forward $(+)$ or backward $(-)$ until someone reaches the ending line. Remind children to take regular walking steps; or, you can vary the steps for each round (hops or baby steps, for example). You can also use a large walk-on number line.

Class Collection

1. Our class is collecting ___Answers vary.___ .

2. Record how the class collection is growing.
   Answers vary.

Date	How many **new** items did we add?	How many items do we have **all together**?

Use with Activity 7-2.   15

My First Math Book, p. 15

Technology

Children can play a version of the *Plus or Minus Game* on the computer using *Everyday Mathematics EM Games*.

Double Digits with Dice

Objective To develop children's understanding of place value through building and comparing 2-digit numbers.

CCSS Mathematical Practices
SMP1, **SMP2,** SMP3,
SMP4, SMP5, SMP6,
SMP7, SMP8
Content Standards
K.CC.6, K.CC.7

☑ Whole Group
☑ Small Group
☑ Partners
☑ Center

Key Concepts and Skills

- Read 2-digit numbers and represent them with manipulatives. [Number and Numeration Goal 3]
- Recognize 2-digit numbers as combinations of 10s and 1s. [Number and Numeration Goal 5]
- Compare numbers. [Number and Numeration Goal 6]

Materials *My First Math Book,* p. 20; two cubes: one marked 0, 1, 2, 3, 4, 5, the other marked 4, 5, 6, 7, 8, 9; chalkboard and chalk; craft sticks (bundles of 10 and singles); number line or number grid (optional)

A Core Activities

▶ Comparing 2-Digit Numbers (*My First Math Book,* p. 20)

Write a pair of numbers on the board, such as 22 and 14. Call on children to read each number and then represent it with bundles of 10 and single sticks. Review and discuss what each representation means (22 is the same as two 10s and two 1s; 14 is the same as one 10 and four 1s). Then have the class compare the two quantities and decide which is larger. Repeat for several pairs of numbers. Choose pairs that highlight place value concepts such as 23 and 43, 32 and 34, and 34 and 43.

Show children the number cubes you made and introduce the activity. With a partner or in a small group, children take turns rolling both number cubes and arranging them to make the larger number. For example, 2 and 5 should be arranged as 52, rather than 25. Encourage children to represent both possible numbers with craft sticks (bundles of 10 and single sticks) to get experience seeing numbers as combinations of 10s and 1s and to help them compare the numbers. A number line or number grid is also a good

NOTE Some children may ask what a number with 0 in the ones place means (for example, 60 compared to 06). You might use the craft sticks to show that 60 means six 10s and zero 1s, and that 06 means zero 10s and six 1s, which is the same as 6. Most children may be confused by this, but it gives them something to think about!

tool for comparing numbers. Have children record information from one of their turns on page 20 in their math books.

Place the number cubes and craft sticks in the Math Center for continued use.

▶ **Playing *Money Cube*** (Revisit Activity 7♦1, p. 330)

Put out materials in the Math Center to play *Money Cube* (with or without quarters).

Teaching Options

(READINESS)

▶ **Building Numbers as 10s and 1s**

Revisit Activity 7-8 (10s and 1s with Craft Sticks) with children who need additional help understanding how numbers can be grouped into 10s and 1s.

(EXTRA PRACTICE)

▶ **Playing *Number-Grid Grab***

Children take turns rolling both number cubes from the main activity and placing a counter on the number grid that matches the larger possible 2-digit number. (For example, if a 2 and 7 are rolled, a counter is placed on 72.) When all players have had a turn, the child with the highest number for the round takes all the counters.

(TECHNOLOGY)

▶ **Entering and Comparing Numbers on the Calculator**

Partners can take turns entering a 2- or 3-digit number on a calculator, and then compare the numbers to determine which is larger. Explain that they must enter numbers they can read.

Double-Digits with Dice
1. Write the two digits you rolled.
_____ and _____
2. Write both 2-digit numbers you can make with those digits.
_____ and _____
3. Circle the larger number.

20   Use with Activity 7♦13.

My First Math Book, p. 20

Links to the Future

Even though Kindergarten children are introduced to place value, they are not expected to understand it fully. For many children, combining digits to form numbers will be more like spelling words than writing numbers. Identifying place value in numbers up to 1,000 is a Grade 1 Goal; work on place value continues through Grade 6. See "Number and Counting," Chapter 8 in the *Teacher's Reference Manual*.

Numbers in Sequence

Objective To reinforce the skill of ordering numbers.

CCSS

Mathematical Practices
SMP1, SMP2, SMP3, **SMP4,** SMP5, SMP6, SMP7, SMP8
Content Standards
K.CC.7, K.MD.3

☑ Whole Group
☑ Small Group
☑ Partners
☐ Center

Key Concepts and Skills

• Read numbers. [Number and Numeration Goal 3]

• Put nonconsecutive numbers in ascending or descending order. [Number and Numeration Goal 6]

Terms to Use smallest, largest, smaller, larger, order

Materials Home Link Master (*Math Masters,* p. 54); Small Number Cards (*Math Masters,* pp. 105–108); number line and/or Class Number Grid; index cards to create additional number cards (optional)

Planning Tip Each pair of children will need 4 number cards. Tailor the numbers on the cards to children's skill levels. You can write higher numbers on the blank cards on the master or on index cards.

A Core Activities

▶ Ordering Numbers

Display a group of nonconsecutive number cards in a row in random order, such as 6, 4, 8, and 2. Have children read each number, then ask them to help you put them in order from smallest to largest. You might prompt by asking: *Which number is the smallest? Which comes next? Next? Which is the largest?* Move the cards into order as they are mentioned. Have children read the numbers from smallest to largest. Repeat with other sets of numbers, gradually using larger numbers. Sometimes direct children to order the numbers from largest to smallest instead of smallest to largest. Encourage children to use the number line or number grid as a reference.

Give partners a set of four cards and have them order them according to your directions (smallest to largest or largest to smallest). Then have them trade cards with another pair of children. Repeat as often as time and interest permit.

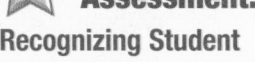

Ongoing Assessment: Recognizing Student Achievement

Use **Ordering Numbers** to assess children's ability to compare and order numbers. Children are making adequate progress if they are able to order numbers through at least 20. Many children will be able to order much higher numbers.

[Number and Numeration Goal 6]

Home Link 7·14 (*Math Masters,* p. 54)

Children order prices from a grocery sales flyer.

► Graphing Lengths of Names and Discussing Probability

(Revisit Activities 3·10 and 5·13, pp. 160 and 260)

Write children's first names on index cards and have them count the number of letters. Make a class bar graph that shows how many letters children have in their names. Put the name cards facedown on a tray and use the graph to discuss probability by asking questions such as: *Am I more likely to pick a name with 3 letters or one with 5 letters? Is it* certain, likely, unlikely, *or* impossible *that I will pick a name with 1 letter? With 8 letters?* To support English language learners, review and discuss the meanings of *certain, likely, unlikely,* and *impossible.*

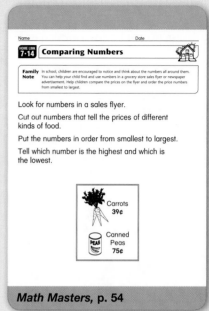

Math Masters, p. 54

B **Teaching Options**

ENRICHMENT

► Playing *High Low*

Shuffle a deck of 0 to 30 number cards and place the deck facedown on the table or desk. Players take turns turning over and reading the top card and guessing whether the next card will be a larger or smaller number. After flipping the next card, the player keeps both cards if the guess was correct. If the guess was incorrect, the player returns both cards to the bottom of the pile. Play continues until the pile is used up.

MATHEMATICS IN THE DRAMATIC PLAY CENTER

► Making a Grocery List

Cut out food pictures and prices from grocery store fliers or newspaper ads. Children can order the items from least to most expensive and tape them on a piece of paper in order. Display the lists in the Dramatic Play Center to use for pretend shopping.

NOTE Look for flyers that do not use decimal points and that have prices in the number range children are comfortable with (probably less than a dollar for most children).

"What's My Rule?" with Patterns

ACTIVITY 7·15

CCSS Mathematical Practices
SMP1, **SMP2**, SMP3, SMP7, **SMP8**
Content Standards
K.OA.3, K.OA.4

Objective To deepen children's understanding of patterns by comparing patterns and identifying patterning rules.

☑ Whole Group
☑ Small Group
☑ Partners
☐ Center

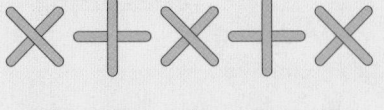

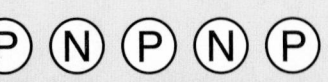

What's My Patterning Rule?

Key Concepts and Skills
- Compare patterns and identify patterning rules. [Patterns, Functions, and Algebra Goal 1]
- Apply patterning rules to create and extend patterns. [Pattern, Functions, and Algebra Goal 1]

Terms to Use pattern, rule, repeat

Materials coins; craft sticks; connecting cubes of different colors

A Core Activities

▶ Comparing Patterns

Show children several patterns made from different materials that follow the same patterning rule. For example, show an alternating pattern with craft sticks and coins, and have children make a sit/stand/sit/stand pattern with their bodies. Say: *These patterns have something in common.* Give a handful of interconnecting cubes to each child and ask this question: *Can you use your cubes to make a similar pattern with colors—a pattern that follows the same rule?* (Children can trade cubes to get the colors they need.) After children make their patterns, ask: *How did you figure out what to do?* Encourage children to use their own words to describe the pattern, for example: "one thing, another thing; one thing, another thing" or "two things taking turns." Discuss their ideas and congratulate them on figuring out your patterning rule.

Repeat with a set of patterns that follows a more complex patterning rule (such as +××+××... or +×−+×−...). Have children figure out the pattern rule and use it to

NOTE Point out that many children used different colors to follow the same pattern rule. Remember that children can identify, describe, and follow pattern rules without necessarily labeling them as ABAB or ABCABC, although you can introduce this type of labeling if you believe it will be helpful to your students at this point.

create a pattern with cubes. Repeat several times showing one or more pattern examples, and invite children to follow the same rules to create their own patterns.

When children seem ready, have them work with a partner. One child creates a pattern with cubes, and the other child follows the same rule to create a pattern using body movements. Then partners reverse roles. (If children are not yet ready to do this independently, continue with the whole class or a small group.)

▶ Making Name Collections (Revisit Activities 1◆16 and 7◆9, pp. 73C and 350)

Give children a collection of 10 craft sticks or other counters. Ask them to split the objects into groups in different ways (7 and 3 or 4 and 6, for example). Record their combinations with pictures and number sentences. Help children connect this activity to earlier "complements of 10" work they have done with ten frames. Repeat for other numbers as time permits.

B Teaching Options

ELL SUPPORT

▶ Making Movement Patterns in a Song

Children can experience different patterns that follow the same patterning rule as they act out and sing "Did You Ever See a Laddie (Lassie)?" (See *Resources for the Kindergarten Classroom* for words.) On "this way and that way," the child in the middle of the circle (the "laddie" or "lassie") moves one way for "this" and a different way for "that." Children take turns being the leader and choosing different movements.

LITERACY CONNECTION

▶ Identifying Patterns in Stories and Songs

See if children can find and describe patterns in repeating stories like *I Went Walking* by Sue Williams (Voyager Books, 1992) and songs like "I Know an Old Lady."

NOTE Children can also apply their patterning rules to create number patterns, such as 1, 2, 2, 1, 2, 2 … or 1, 2, 3, 1, 2, 3….

NOTE Explain that "lad" or "laddie" means *boy* and "lass" or "lassie" means *girl.*

Bead String Name Collections

ACTIVITY 7·16

◎ **Objective** To provide additional experiences with name collections.

☑ Whole Group
☑ Small Group
☐ Partners
☐ Center

Key Concepts and Skills
• Use objects and drawings to represent equivalent names for numbers. [Number and Numeration Goal 5]
• Solve number sentences to find equivalent names. [Operations and Computation Goal 1]
• Record equivalent names with number models. [Patterns, Functions, and Algebra Goal 2]

Terms to Use equivalent names, name collections, number sentences, combinations

Materials *My First Math Book,* p. 21; string or pipe cleaners; beads; shoes, blocks, or other objects

A Core Activities

▶ Making Name Collections (*My First Math Book,* p. 21)

Place 7 objects, such as 7 shoes or 7 blocks, where everyone can see and count them. Ask a volunteer to separate the pile of objects into 2 piles and to count how many are in each pile (4 and 3, for example). Ask another child to separate the pile in a different way (5 and 2, for example). Keep separating the pile in different ways until all possibilities have been tried. Don't forget that one pile can have 0 objects.

Have each child make a counting loop of 8 to 10 beads on a string or pipe cleaner. Be sure the loop is securely fastened. Demonstrate how to move the beads around the loop and group them to show different combinations. For example, on a 10 bead loop, children can move 8 to one side and 2 to the other, or have groups of 5 and 5, or groups of 6 and 2 and 2. Children should record the total number of beads on their loops on page 21 in their math books. Then they should draw at least 3 different ways they grouped the beads on the loops. You may also wish to have children record each of their groupings with a number

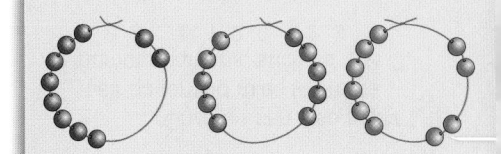

model underneath each loop. Children can add more combinations by drawing more loops and beads on the writing and drawing pages in their math books.

Have children take their bead loops home to show their families how to make different combinations. Also invite children to make some extra loops with different numbers of beads to keep in the Math Center for continued exploration. Be sure to include loops with higher numbers of beads.

▶ Playing *Monster Squeeze* (Revisit Activity 3•6, p. 150)

Play a few rounds of *Monster Squeeze*. You might have children use bundles of 10 and single craft sticks to represent the mystery number after it is guessed.

Also remember to use *Minute Math* during spare moments in the day.

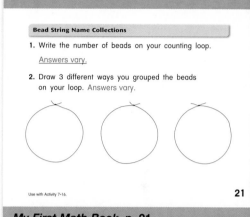

Bead String Name Collections

1. Write the number of beads on your counting loop.
   Answers vary.

2. Draw 3 different ways you grouped the beads on your loop. Answers vary.

Use with Activity 7•16.   21

My First Math Book, p. 21

B Teaching Options

MATHEMATICS IN THE BLOCK CENTER

▶ Making Different Buildings with the Same Number of Blocks

Children can use the same number of blocks to make different structures. For example, have children create a building with 17 blocks, then have them compare their structures with their classmates' 17-block structures. You might create cards that show (with numbers and sketches) the number and type of blocks that can be used (3 cylinders and 6 medium rectangular prisms, for example). After children build using these specifications, photograph their structures to display with the cards.

LITERACY CONNECTION

▶ Reading About Name Collections

Read *Math Fables* by Greg Tang (Scholastic Press, 2004), and discuss how the examples in the book represent name collections for different numbers.

PROJECT 7

Weaving

CCSS Mathematical Practices
SMP7
Content Standards
K.G.1

⊙ **Objective** To provide tactile and visual experiences that promote patterning, hand-eye coordination, and directionality.

○ **Literature Link**
Consider reading and discussing the following books about weaving with your class:

The Goat in the Rug by Charles L. Blood and Martin Link (Aladdin, 1990); *The Chief's Blanket* by Michael Chanin (H. J. Kramer, 1998).

Terms to Use weaving, warp, woof, over, under, back, forth, left, right

Materials

Paper Weaving
- □ construction paper (large sheets and $1\frac{1}{2}$ in.-wide strips the same length as the width of the large sheets)
- □ ruler
- □ pencil
- □ scissors
- □ glue or tape

Weaving on Plastic Baskets
- □ plastic berry baskets and/or large plastic laundry basket
- □ yarn, ribbon, or other similar material for weaving

Weaving on Cardboard Looms
- □ stiff cardboard (about 6 in. x 9 in. per piece)
- □ ruler
- □ scissors
- □ strong string; yarn

Weaving on Straws
- □ straws, yarn, tape

Introduction

The experience of weaving over and under gives children a physical sense of the orderliness of patterning. Teachers have found that weaving fosters a calming and soothing atmosphere in the classroom as children become absorbed in this activity. Weaving provides an opportunity for mastery of a new skill and offers the satisfaction of creating a personal product. A classroom of weavers is a peaceful place!

You may wish to start the weaving project with a few children at a time. Children can work on their looms in the Math Center or Art Center and during free time or finish-up times when various tasks are completed.

▶ Paper Weaving

☑ Small Group ☑ Center

This type of weaving produces a lovely placemat, especially if laminated when complete. In advance, prepare materials for paper weaving using the following steps:

1. Fold a large sheet of construction paper in half so the short sides line up.
2. Use a ruler and pencil to draw lines perpendicular to the fold of the large sheet of paper. Draw the lines $1\frac{1}{2}$ inches apart, stopping $1\frac{1}{2}$ inches from the outside edges of the paper. Cut along the lines to make slits through which to weave. Then unfold the paper. This will provide the **warp** upon which to weave the paper strips.
3. Cut strips of colored construction paper that are $1\frac{1}{2}$ inches wide and the same length as the width of the large sheet of paper. These strips are the **woof** for the weaving.

Show children how to weave the cut strips (the woof) over and under the slits in the construction paper (the warp). If children start weaving their first strip of paper **over** the slit on the edge of the warp, they should start weaving their second strip of paper **under** the slit on the edge of the warp. (See diagram.) Children continue this over/under pattern until the warp is filled. Have them try to keep the strips close together to create a firm weave. When the warp is filled, glue or tape the ends of the strips to the large sheet of construction paper. Laminate the woven mat or cover it with clear contact paper.

▶ Weaving on Plastic Baskets

☑ Small Group ☑ Center

This weaving activity can be done individually, using small berry baskets, or as a group, weaving on a large plastic laundry basket. The baskets provide the warp for the weaving, the ribbon, yarn, or other similar materials provide the woof.

Show children how to insert the yarn or ribbon in the bottom row of the basket and weave around all sides for the first row. (If the yarn or ribbon slips as they weave, help children tie or tape one end to the basket before weaving with the rest of it.) They should continue with the second row (using the rest of the same yarn or ribbon or starting with a new piece), so that the weaving alternates with the in/out pattern of the first row. Children continue alternating rows until the frame of the basket (warp) is filled, then tuck in loose ends of the yarn or ribbon (the woof).

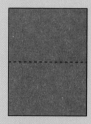

Fold the paper in half.

Cut along the lines to make slits.

Use paper strips as the **woof** for weaving.

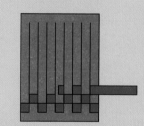

▶ Weaving on Cardboard Looms

✔ **Small Group** ✔ **Center**

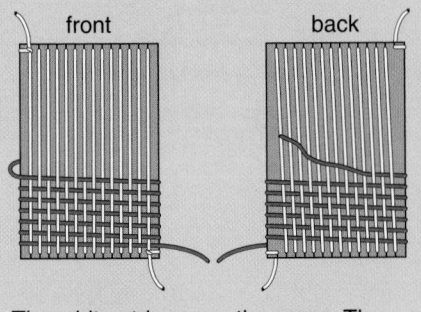

The white strings are the **warp.** The red yarn is the **woof.**

Cardboard looms can be woven on both sides to create a pocket, purse, or a small pillowcase. Alternately, these looms can be woven on one side to create a small rug or blanket.

Follow these steps to prepare the loom:

1. Cut pieces of cardboard, about 6 in. × 9 in.
2. Mark lines that are about $\frac{1}{2}$ inch apart on the narrow ends of each cardboard loom. Cut a small slit (about $\frac{1}{4}$ inch long) at each mark.
3. Tie strong string to one of the corner slits, and then wrap it around the loom, slipping it firmly into the slits. Tie the string ends securely. (These strings are the warp; the weaving yarn that interlaces them is the woof.)
4. Make sure the loom is strung with an odd number of warp strings on one side and an even number on the other, so that the woven rows will alternate as children weave around both sides of their looms.

Teach children to weave on the cardboard looms according to these steps:

1. Choose a color of yarn and cut a length to begin weaving. (The span of a child's outstretched arms is about the right length.)
2. Tie one end of the yarn onto the warp string at a corner of the loom card.
3. Begin weaving over, under; over, under; and so on. (If children are weaving on both sides of the loom, they should continue the same over/under pattern when they turn the loom over to weave on the other side. (If children are weaving on only one side of the loom, they do not need to turn it over.)
4. Children can change colors each time they tie on a new length of yarn. Some children enjoy creating color patterns, such as red, yellow, blue; red, yellow, blue.

When completed, take the weaving off the loom:

▷ For a two-sided loom, push the weaving firmly to the bottom of the loom, then carefully cut the strings at the top, two at a time, and tie them off using square knots. Slide the weaving off the cardboard loom to make a little pocket or purse. If you want to make a little pillow, stuff it at the opening and sew it together.
▷ For a one-sided loom, cut the strings at the top and tie square knots at both ends to make a small rug or blanket. Trim the extra warp strings.

▶ Weaving on Straws

☑ **Small Group** ☑ **Center**

Children can use this type of weaving to make belts or headbands.

Prepare the materials according to the following steps. (Some children will be able to do much of this themselves with demonstration and assistance.)

1. Measure a length of yarn twice around the child's waist or head (either for a belt or a headband). Cut this length and use it to measure and cut 3 additional lengths of yarn.
2. Take 4 straws and thread 1 strand of yarn through each straw. (One easy method is to start the yarn in a straw, and then carefully suck it up the straw.)
3. Tape one end of the yarn to the end of each straw so the yarn is held securely.
4. Tie the other ends of the 4 yarn tails together. This is the loom.

Teach children to weave on their straw looms according to these steps:

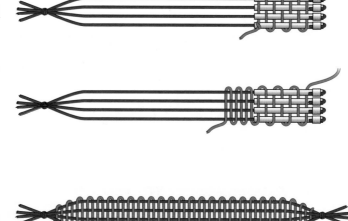

1. Measure and cut a length of yarn equal to the child's arm span (length between outspread arms) and tie the yarn to the top of one of the straws.
2. Hold all the straws in a flat row in one hand. Weave over and under, back and forth across all 4 straws. As the straws fill, push the woven yarn down the warp strings toward the end of the loom.
3. When the loom is full, carefully pull the straws out of the woven yarn so that the finished weaving moves down onto the yarn strands. When the belt or headband is the desired length, remove the straws and tie the ends.

Section 8

Overview

Section 8 has a number of main areas of focus:

- ◆ To introduce the use of the hour hand to estimate time on an analog clock,

- ◆ To introduce the concept of hours and minutes,

- ◆ To introduce Function Machines and function rules,

- ◆ To continue to explore place-value concepts and equivalent names for numbers,

- ◆ To introduce the $1 and $10 bills and reinforce coin names, values, and exchanges,

- ◆ To introduce "missing number" problems and reinforce the use of number models for addition and subtraction stories and situations,

- ◆ To continue activities with 2- and 3-dimensional shapes,

- ◆ To continue graphing and measurement activities, and

- ◆ To reinforce and extend counting, estimation, and other numeration activities.

Maintaining Ongoing Daily Routines

Doing the Routines

In addition to Section 8 activities, continue to do the following Ongoing Daily Routines:

- ◆ Number of the Day
- ◆ Daily Schedule
- ◆ Attendance
- ◆ Weather Observation
- ◆ Job Chart
- ◆ Recording Daily Temperature
- ◆ Monthly Calendar
- ◆ Survey

Adjusting the Routines

Each Ongoing Daily Routine can be adjusted periodically according to children's progress and interests. If you haven't already done so, use the following routines to introduce new ideas and ask different questions during and after Section 8:

- ◆ **Daily Schedule** Use *Math Masters,* page 112, to make clocks to add to your daily schedule. Show the approximate starting time for each event on the schedule. Decide whether to show the times using only the hour hand or the hour and the minute hands.

- ◆ **Monthly Calendar and Number of the Day** Have children suggest equivalent names for the date on the calendar or the number of the day on the Growing Number Line. Encourage them to include number sentences, tens and ones, tally marks, coin equivalents, and other representations for the number.

Using Routines for Ongoing Assessment

All of the Ongoing Daily Routines offer opportunities for ongoing assessment of a variety of skills and concepts. You might want to use the following routines for ongoing assessment during Section 8:

- ◆ **Monthly Calendar** Can children use place-value clues (all days with 4s in the ones place) and addition and subtraction clues (two days whose sum is 8) to find a given date or dates on the calendar?

- ◆ **Number of the Day** Can children read the numbers on the Growing Number Line and tell you how to write the next number? Can they count to the number of the day (or count the objects in the Concrete Number Counts containers) by 1s, 10s, 5s, or 2s? Can they represent the number of the day with sticks or other manipulatives?

Learning in Perspective

Core Activities

Activity	Objective	Revisit Activity	Page
8·1	**Ones, Tens, Hundreds Game** To deepen children's understanding of place value through an exchange game.	**Counting the Class Collection** (Activity 7-2, p. 332; *My First Math Book,* p. 15)	380
8·2	**How Long Is an Hour?** To develop children's sense of the duration of an hour. ∞ **Links to the Future** In Activity 8-11, children will explore the duration of a minute.	**Graphing Favorite Math Games** (games in multiple activities)	382
8·3	**The Hour-Hand Clock** To introduce the analog clock, focusing on the hour hand. ∞ **Links to the Future** In Grades 1 through 3, children will learn to tell time using the hour and minute hands on an analog clock.	**Making Shapes and Structures** (Activities 1-15 and 7-4, pp. 73A and 340)	384
8·4	**High Roller Game** To develop "counting on" as an addition strategy.	**Fishing for Children: "What's My Rule?"** (Activity 4-14, p. 216)	388
8·5	**Introduction to Function Machines** To introduce and provide practice with function machines. ∞ **Links to the Future** Children will continue to apply rules to numbers using function machines in Grades 1 and beyond.	**Reviewing Coins** (Activities 6-1, 6-2, 6-7, and 7-5, pp. 282, 284, 296, and 342)	390
8·6	**Number Gymnastics Game** To develop children's number sense and ability to manipulate numbers through a mental math game.	**Studying Weather and Temperature Data** (Routines 6 and 7, pp. 24 and 28; *My First Math Book,* p. 23) ∞ **Links to the Past** Children have been collecting weather and temperature data all year as part of the Ongoing Daily Routines.	392
8·7	**Introduction of the $1 Bill** To introduce the $1 bill.	**Reviewing Function Machines** (Activity 8-5, p. 390; *My First Math Book,* p. 24)	394

Core Activities, *continued*

Activity	Objective	Revisit Activity	Page
8·8	**One-Dollar Game** To reinforce penny, dime, and dollar values and exchanges through a game. 🔗 **Links to the Future** In Grade 1, children play a similar game called *One-Dollar Exchange.*	**Making Name Collections** (Activity 7-9, p. 350)	396
8·9	**Name Collection Posters** To reinforce the concept of equivalent names for numbers.	**Number Scrolling** (Activity 7-10, p. 352; *Math Masters,* p. 111)	398
8·10	**"What's My Rule?" with Numbers** To help children identify function rules and generate numbers that follow those rules.	**Using the Hour-Hand Clock** (Activity 8-3, p. 384)	400
8·11	**Hour-Hand, Minute-Hand Story** To introduce the minute hand on the analog clock.	**Playing Dice Addition and Subtraction Games** (Activity 7-6, p. 344)	402
8·12	**Time Match Game** To provide practice with telling time to the hour with digital and analog clocks. 🔗 **Links to the Future** In Grade 1, children will play a similar game using clocks with times on the hour, half-hour, and quarter-hour.	**Dividing Wholes into Halves** (Activity 6-16, p. 314)	404
8·13	**Missing Number Problems** To provide concrete experiences with figuring out missing numbers in equations. 🔗 **Links to the Future** In later grades, children will continue to read, write, and solve open sentences as a foundation for algebra.	**Playing *I Spy*: Shapes and Patterns** (Activities 6-6 and 7-15, pp. 294 and 362) 🔗 **Links to the Past** Children have worked with 2- and 3-dimensional shapes and with repeating sound, movement, and visual patterns throughout Kindergarten.	406
8·14	**Number Stories with Calculators** To introduce how to model number stories on a calculator.	**Playing *Number Gymnastics* with Slates** (Activity 8-6, p. 392)	408
8·15	**Pan Balance with Uniform Weights** To introduce the use of nonstandard units on a pan balance.	**Practicing Number Writing** (Activity 3-1, p. 138; *My First Math Book,* pp. 27–47; *Math Masters,* pp. 13–24)	410
8·16	**Introduction of the $10 Bill** To introduce the $10 bill.	**Measuring in Different Ways** (Activity 5-12, p. 258)	414

Ongoing Learning and Practice

Practice through Games

Games are an essential component of practice in the *Everyday Mathematics* program. Games offer skills practice and promote strategic thinking. These games are introduced in this section:

Activity	Game	Skill Practiced
8◆1	*Ones, Tens, Hundreds Game; Paper Money Exchange Game*	Counting by ones and tens and exchanging ones for tens and tens for hundreds [Number and Numeration Goals 1 and 3]; Exchanging $1, $10, and $100 bills [Number and Numeration Goals 1 and 6]
8◆3	*Walk Around the Clock*	Tracking the hour hand on the clock [Measurement and Reference Frames Goal 4]
8◆4	*High Roller* Games	Comparing numbers and counting on [Operations and Computation Goal 1]
8◆6	*Number Gymnastics*	Adding, subtracting, and manipulating digits mentally [Number and Numeration Goal 3; Operations and Computation Goal 1]
8◆8	*One-Dollar Game*	Making exchanges with pennies, dimes, and dollars [Measurement and Reference Frames Goal 2]
8◆12	*Time Match*	Matching times on digital and analog clocks [Measurement and Reference Frames Goal 4]

Home-School Connection

Home Links provide homework and home communication. The following activities contain Home Links: 8-2, 8-6, 8-8, 8-11, 8-14.

Home Connection Handbook provides more ideas to communicate effectively with parents. ▶

◀ *Mathematics at Home* Books **1–4** provide additional ideas for mathematics activities that families can do together, as well as lists of children's books related to topics in each strand area. Families can do activities from **Book 4** during Section 8.

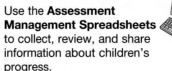

Balanced Assessment

Ongoing Assessment

Recognizing Student Achievement

Opportunities to assess children's progress toward Kindergarten Goals:

Activity	Skill Assessed
8♦1	Exchange ones for tens and tens for a hundred. [Number and Numeration Goal 3]
8♦9	Represent equivalent names for numbers. [Number and Numeration Goal 5]
8♦10	Apply simple addition and subtraction rules to complete a number pair. [Patterns, Functions, and Algebra Goal 1]
8♦11	Add and subtract small numbers. [Operations and Computation Goal 1]
8♦13	Identify shapes. [Geometry Goal 1]
8♦14	Identify addition and subtraction situations. [Operations and Computation Goal 2] Model number stories with numbers and symbols. [Patterns, Functions, and Algebra Goal 2]
8♦15	Generate equivalent names for numbers, including representations with addition and subtraction. [Number and Numeration Goal 5 and Operations and Computation Goal 1]

Informing Instruction

To anticipate common trouble spots and to highlight problem-solving strategies:

Activity 8♦4 Introduce and monitor addition and subtraction strategies	**Activity 8♦16** Make exchanges

Portfolio Opportunities

- Name Collection Posters, **Activity 8-9**
- Number Scrolls, **Activity 8-9**

Assessment Handbook

- Kindergarten Goals, pp. 27–33
- Section 8 Assessment Overview, pp. 64–65
- Assessment Overviews by Strand, pp. 66–75
- End-of-Year Periodic Assessment Tasks, pp. 45–48
- Individual Profile of Progress and Class Checklist (End-of-Year), pp. 91–96
- Individual Profile of Progress and Class Checklist (Sections 7–8), pp. 83–84
- Cumulative Individual Profile of Progress (Sections 5–8), pp. 99–102

Periodic Assessment

End-of-Year assessment tasks will be completed in Section 8.

Differentiated Instruction

Teaching Options

Use optional Part B activities as time permits to meet individual and class needs and to integrate mathematics throughout the Kindergarten classroom and schedule.

ELL SUPPORT

8•2	Ordering time intervals	8•13	Modeling missing-number problems on a walk-on number line
8•3	Drawing daily events		
8•5	Acting as function machines	8•15	Illustrating *heavier* and *lighter*

READINESS

8•1	Practicing making bundles	8•12	Playing *Time Match* with cards faceup
8•6	Playing *Number-Grid Grab*		

CONNECTIONS

Literacy
8•2	Marking time in different ways
8•3	Reading *The Grouchy Ladybug*
8•7	Reading a dollar story
8•8	Reading money stories
8•9	Reading about equivalent names for numbers
8•14	Creating number stories from pictures

Science
8•12	Studying clocks
8•15	Weighing dry or wet sponges

Movement
8•11	Exploring the length of a minute

Snack
8•15	Weighing snack food

TECHNOLOGY

8•1	Making exchanges on the computer	8•16	Adding money on a calculator
8•4	Playing *High Roller* with calculators		

ENRICHMENT

8•1	Playing *Paper Money Exchange Game*	8•12	Playing *Time Match*
		8•13	Using number-model cards
8•5	Applying skip-counting rules		
8•7	Making exchanges	8•16	Playing the Advanced *Paper Money Exchange Game*

EXTRA PRACTICE

8•3	Playing *Walk Around the Clock;* making a human clock	8•10	Solving "What's My Rule?" with a partner; using "What's My Rule?" for facts practice
8•4	Playing *High Roller* with subtraction		
8•5	Using function machines	8•11	Adding clocks to the daily schedule
8•6	Recording *Number Gymnastics* numbers	8•14	Reading the class number story book
8•8	Playing other exchange games	8•15	Using other nonstandard weights
8•9	Finding equivalent dominoes		

CENTERS

Block Center
8•10	Building and using a function machine

Dramatic Play Center
8•7	Playing dollar store

Language Support

Everyday Mathematics provides activity-specific suggestions to help *all* young children develop the language necessary to acquire, process, and express mathematical ideas. Activities that provide additional support for non-native English speakers are marked by ☰☰ ELL SUPPORT ☰☰ and ☰☰ ELL ☰☰.

Connecting Math and Literacy

Activity 8◆3 *The Grouchy Ladybug* by Eric Carle (HarperCollins, 1996)

Activity 8◆7 *The Big Buck Adventure* by Shelley Gill and Deborah Tobola (Charlesbridge, 2000)

Activity 8◆9 *One Is a Snail, Ten Is a Crab* by April Pulley Sayre and Jeff Sayre (Candlewick, 2003)

Activity 8◆14 *More, Fewer, Less* by Tana Hoban (Greenwillow, 1998)

See pages 383 and 397 for more literature suggestions.

Using the Projects

Use Math Outdoors (Project 8, page 416) during or after Section 8 to reinforce skills and concepts related to measurement, spatial relationships, and data collection.

Adjusting the Activity

AUDITORY   ◆   KINESTHETIC   ◆   TACTILE   ◆   VISUAL

Activity 8◆4 Using tally marks; recording sums with number sentences

Activity 8◆6 Using a slower pace or number grid when playing *Number Gymnastics*

Language & Vocabulary

Use these terms informally with children.

add	level
addition sign	minus (take away) sign
all clear	
analog	minute
balance	minute hand
clear	missing number
compare	name collection
count on	number sentence
digit	
digital	number story
dollar	o'clock
dollar sign	one-dollar bill
equal sign	ones
equals	reverse
equivalent names	rule
	slower
exchange	subtract
faster	ten-dollar bill
function machine	tens
halfway between	total
	trade
hour	unit
hour hand	weigh
hundreds	weights
just after	
just before	

Planning Tips

Pacing Pacing depends on a number of factors, such as children's individual needs and how long your school has been using *Everyday Mathematics*. Use the optional Part B activities throughout Section 8 if you have extended mathematics instructional time. See page 376 for a list of these activities.

	← **MOST CLASSROOMS** →	
APRIL	MAY	JUNE

Teaching Resources

Resources for the Kindergarten Classroom provides additional teaching ideas, including suggestions for bringing mathematics into thematic instruction as well as using games, literature, technology, and rhymes to support mathematics learning. ▶

Minute Math provides brief activities for transition times and for spare moments throughout the day. During Section 8, use the activities in Part 3, pages 197–258.

NCTM Standards

Content Standards: 1 Number and Operations, **2** Algebra, **3** Geometry, **4** Measurement, **5** Data Analysis and Probability
Process Standards: 6 Problem Solving, **7** Reasoning and Proof, **8** Communication, **9** Connection, **10** Representation

Section 8 Activities	8•1	8•2	8•3	8•4	8•5	8•6	8•7	8•8	8•9	8•10	8•11	8•12	8•13	8•14	8•15	8•16
NCTM Standards	1	4, 9	4, 9	1	1, 2, 7	1	4, 9	1, 4, 9	1, 8	1, 2, 7, 8	4, 9	4, 9	1, 2, 7, 8	1, 2	1, 4, 7	1, 4

Professional Development

	Teacher's Reference Manual Links					
Activity	**Topic**	**Section**	**Activity**	**Topic**	**Section**
8•5	Functions	15.1.4	**8•13**	Algebra and Uses of Variables	15.2

Materials

Activity	Masters	Materials	
8·1	Game Master, p. 130	• number cubes* with sides marked 1, 3, 5, 10, 10, 10 • craft sticks* (single	sticks, bundles of 10, and a "big bundle" of 100) • small rubber bands*
8·2	Home Link Master, p. 55	• wall clock	• timer* or watch that beeps on the hour
8·3	My First Math Book, p. 22 Teaching Master, p. 56	• scissors • brad fasteners	• cardstock or paper plates (optional)
8·4		• dice*	• counters*
8·5	Teaching Master, p. 57 (optional)	• small box • index cards	• chalkboard and chalk • counters* (optional)
8·6	Home Link Master, p. 59	• Class Number Grid and/or number line*	
8·7	Teaching Aid Masters, pp. 115 and 116	• magnifying lenses	• slates* or paper (optional) • real dollar bills (optional)
8·8	Home Link Master, p. 60 Teaching Aid Masters, pp. 115 and 116	• several cubes labeled 1¢, 1¢, 10¢, 10¢, 10¢, 10¢	• pennies • dimes • quarters (optional)
8·9		• chart paper or poster board • markers or crayons	• manipulatives • tape
8·10		• chalkboard; chalk; eraser	

* Indicates items in the Kindergarten manipulative kit.

Activity	Masters	Materials	
8·11	Home Link Master, p. 61 Teaching Master, p. 56	• scissors • paper clocks from Activity 8–3 • analog clock	• demonstration clock (optional)
8·12	Game Masters, pp. 140–143	• paper clock or demonstration clock	• digital clock and analog clock (optional)
8·13	My First Math Book, p. 25	• bag or box for pocket	• counters* • chalkboard
8·14	Home Link Master, p. 62	• calculators	
8·15	My First Math Book, p. 26 Teaching Master, p. 63	• pan balances* • small objects with uniform weight such as cube counters,* pennies, washers,	or small or large paper clips • assortment of objects to weigh
8·16	Teaching Aid Masters, pp. 113–116	• real $10 bill	• magnifying lenses
End-of-Year Assessment	Assessment Handbook, pp. 45–48	• number line* or Class Number Grid • objects for counting • estimation and reference jar • straws* or craft sticks* • rubber bands* • attribute blocks*; pattern blocks* • measuring tools* (various)	• class calendar and daily schedule • drawing of something symmetrical • crackers • number cards (0–20) • class graph • Minute Math • coins and dollar bill

Technology

Assessment Management Spreadsheets,
Section 8: See the *iTGA.*

Section Opener

Ones, Tens, Hundreds Game

CCSS **Mathematical Practices**
SMP1, SMP2, SMP6,
SMP7, SMP8
Content Standards
K.CC.1, K.CC.4a, K.CC.4b, K.CC.5

🎯 **Objective** To deepen children's understanding of place value through an exchange game.

☐ Whole Group
✔ Small Group
✔ Partners
✔ Center

Key Concepts and Skills
• Count by 10s and 1s. [Number and Numeration Goal 1]
• Use craft sticks to exchange 1s for 10s and 10s for 100s. [Number and Numeration Goal 3]
• Recognize numbers as combinations of 100s, 10s, and 1s. [Number and Numeration Goal 5]

Terms to Use ones, tens, hundreds, equals, trade, exchange

Materials Game Master (*Math Masters,* p. 130); number cubes with sides marked 1, 3, 5, 10, 10, 10; craft sticks (single sticks, bundles of 10, and a "big bundle" of 100); rubber bands

Planning Tip Prepare the number cubes and make bundles of sticks before introducing the game. Each group of 4 children that plays at the same time will need at least 40 single craft sticks, 40 bundles of 10, and 1 "big bundle" of 100. Provide cups, containers, or sheets of different-colored paper to help children keep their bundles and sticks separate, as needed.

A Core Activities

▶ Playing the *Ones, Tens, Hundreds Game* (*Math Masters*, p. 130)

Remind children of how they grouped 10 single craft sticks into bundles of 10 in previous activities. Ask: *How many craft sticks would we have if we had 10 bundles of 10? How can we find out?* After children share their ideas, count 10 bundles (by 10s) and show and explain that 10 bundles of 10 equals 100 craft sticks.

Explain that they will use single and bundled craft sticks to play the *Ones, Tens, Hundreds Game.* Demonstrate the game, which can be played by partners or small groups. Players take turns rolling the number cube and picking up the appropriate number of craft sticks from a pile in the center. When players have 10 sticks, they trade them for a bundle of 10 from the pile. When they have 10 bundles of 10 sticks each, they exchange them for a "big bundle" of 100. Play ends when the first child gets a big bundle of 100. (Play can continue beyond 100 if desired.) At the end of the game, each

NOTE Be sure children understand why they can trade 10 single sticks for a bundle of 10. You might ask: *Has your number of sticks changed?* Have children count their sticks before and after exchanging if they need reinforcement.

player counts his or her craft sticks and records the total on a sheet of paper. Players then compare their totals. Children also can record how many big bundles of 100, bundles of 10, and single sticks they have on *Math Masters,* page 130.

▶ Counting the Class Collection (Revisit Activity 7•2, p. 332; *My First Math Book,* p. 15)

If they haven't done so recently, have the class count the items in the Class Collection they began in Activity 7-2 and update the information on page 15 of their math books, as well as on your class data display(s). If children have lost interest in the original collection, vote on a new item to begin collecting.

B Teaching Options

READINESS

▶ Practicing Making Bundles

To prepare for playing the *Ones, Tens, Hundreds Game,* children can practice making bundles of 10s and 100s by repeating Activity 7-8, page 348.

ENRICHMENT

▶ Playing *Paper Money Exchange Game*

(*Math Masters,* pp. 113, 114, 131, and 132)

Children can play an exchange game with $1, $10, and $100 bills (*Math Masters,* pages 113 and 114). See *Math Masters,* pages 131 and 132 for directions and a gameboard.

TECHNOLOGY

▶ Making Exchanges on the Computer

Children can play a version of the *Paper Money Exchange Game* on the computer using *Everyday Mathematics EM Games.*

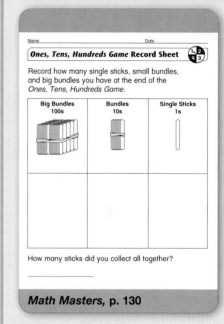

Math Masters, p. 130

Ongoing Assessment:
Recognizing Student Achievement

Use the *Ones, Tens, Hundreds Game* to assess children's ability to exchange 1s for 10s and 10s for 100. Children are making adequate progress if they can accurately make exchanges through 100.

[Number and Numeration Goal 3]

How Long Is an Hour?

ACTIVITY 8·2

CCSS
Mathematical Practices
SMP1, SMP2, **SMP4**
Content Standards
K.MD.3

◎ **Objective** To develop children's sense of the duration of an hour.

☑ Whole Group
☐ Small Group
☐ Partners
☐ Center

Key Concepts and Skills
• Develop a sense of the length of an hour. [Measurement and Reference Frames Goal 4]
• Notice the "o'clock" times on an analog clock. [Measurement and Reference Frames Goal 4]

Terms to Use hour, o'clock

Materials Home Link Master (*Math Masters*, p. 55); wall clock; timer or watch that beeps on the hour

Planning Tip Early in the day, show children the timer and explain that it will beep every hour throughout the day. Establish expectations for what they should do whenever they hear the timer beep.

A Core Activities

 ## Marking Hours

Set a timer or a watch to sound when the classroom wall clock is on the hour (the "o'clock" times). Each time the timer beeps, announce the time and have children look at the wall clock. Have a brief conversation about what they've done during that hour. (You might make a list of things they've done for each hour of the day.) Over the course of the day, children might be interested in comparing the events of one hour to another.

At the end of the day, help the class make a list of things that take about an hour to do. Begin with experiences that are likely to be familiar to most children, such as watching two television shows or going to lunch and recess. Explain Home Link 8-2, and tell children you will add their responses to the class list when they bring their Home Links back to school. Be sure to revisit the list as children return their Home Links.

Home Link 8·2 *(Math Masters, p. 55)*

Children list everyday events that take about an hour.

▶ **Graphing Favorite Math Games** (Revisit games in multiple activities)

With children's input, make a list of their favorite math games that they've played during the year. (You can use the Games Correlation Chart in *Resources for the Kindergarten Classroom* to refresh your memory and theirs, if needed.) Help the class make a bar graph that shows how many children choose each game as their favorite (games on one axis; number of children on the other axis). Post the list in the Math Center and be sure to make children's favorite games available for play during the remainder of the year. (You might feature different games in the Math Center for a few days at a time.)

B **Teaching Options**

ELL SUPPORT

▶ **Ordering Time Intervals**

Engage children in a discussion to order some or all of the following time intervals from shortest to longest: day, year, month, hour, second, minute, week. English language learners can relate this to similar vocabulary in their native languages.

LITERACY CONNECTION

▶ **Marking Time in Different Ways**

Read *My Grandmother's Clock* by Geraldine McCaughrean (Clarion Books, 2002) or *Me: Counting Time* by Joan Sweeney (Dragonfly, 2001). Discuss the different ways people describe, measure, and mark the passage of time.

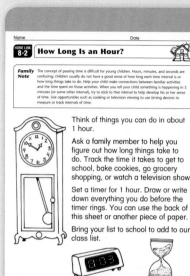

Math Masters, p. 55

384

The Hour-Hand Clock

ACTIVITY
8·3

Objective To introduce the analog clock, focusing on the hour hand.

Mathematical Practices
SMP1, SMP2, **SMP3,** SMP4, **SMP5,** SMP6
Content Standards
K.G.1, K.G.2, K.G.3, K.G.4, K.G.5, **K.G.6**

☑ Whole Group   ☐ Partners
☑ Small Group   ☐ Center

Key Concepts and Skills
• Make and use hour hand clocks. [Measurement and Reference Frames Goal 4]

Terms to Use hour hand, o'clock, just before, just after, halfway between

Materials *My First Math Book,* p. 22; Teaching Master (*Math Masters,* p. 56); scissors; brad fasteners; cardstock or paper plates (optional)

Planning Tip You might have children cut and assemble their clocks in a Center or during a separate session prior to using the clocks. The paper clock is more durable when mounted on cardstock or a paper plate.

A **Core Activities**

▶ Making an Hour-Hand Clock (*My First Math Book,* p. 22; *Math Masters,* p. 56)

Give each child a paper-clock master and have them cut out the clock face and an hour hand. (Explain that the other hand is the minute hand, which they will use later. Collect the minute hands and save them for Activity 8-11.) Help children attach the hour hands

Children can color the hour hand of their clocks to help distinguish hour hands from minute hands later.

Name _____ Date _____
8·3 **Paper Clock**

Math Masters, p. 56

to their clock faces. (Poke a small hole in the center of the clock face and in the center of the dot on the hour hand before inserting the brad.)

When children have finished making their clocks, explain that the hand they added is called the **hour hand,** and it tells the hour of the day or night. Model how to use the hour hand to make various "o'clock" times on your paper clock saying the time you show (*1 o'clock, 5 o'clock,* and so on) each time. Children should match the same time on their clocks. Then, slowly move the hour hand between the numbers on the clock face and use terms such as **just before, just after,** and **halfway between** to describe the approximate time that is shown (just before 10 o'clock, or halfway between 8 o'clock and 9 o'clock, for example). It may come as a surprise to discover how accurate one can be using only the hour hand.

Call out some approximate times for children to show on their hour-hand clocks. Continue to give "just before," "just after," and "halfway between" times, in addition to "o'clock" times. To involve children in generating times, ask questions such as: *What time do you go to bed?* or *When is dinnertime?* If they give times such as 7:15, restate them with approximate language. (*7:15—That's a little after 7 o'clock.*) After they've had ample practice with their clocks, call out three more approximate times and have children draw the hour hand in the correct position on the clocks on page 22 in their math books.

Children should practice reading the hour-hand clocks often. Keep an hour-hand clock in your meeting area or by the classroom door to use during transition times or spare moments. Also place a few extra clocks in the Math Center for continued use.

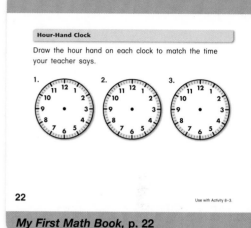

My First Math Book, p. 22

NOTE Reading an analog clock is confusing because there are two hands moving at different rates, with the short, slow hand marking the greater unit of time. In addition, the numerals on the clock have multiple meanings—for instance, the numeral 1 can mean the 1 o'clock hour or 5 minutes after any hour. To reduce confusion and lay groundwork for understanding the minute hand in later grades, it is helpful to begin telling time using only the hour hand.

▶ Making Shapes and Structures (Revisit Activities 1◆15 and 7◆4, pp. 73A and 340)

Place straws and twist ties or pipe cleaners in the Math or Art Center and encourage children to use them to make shapes and structures. Encourage children to combine 2-dimensional shapes to create other 2-dimensional shapes, as well as 3-dimensional shapes. Prompt them to describe what they are doing with shape language (*sides*, *corners*, and so on) and position language (*next to*, *above*, and so on), as well as with 2- and 3-dimensional shape names. Engage children in manipulating their shapes and constructions in different ways, such as rotating them or turning them upside down, to help them realize that the shape is the same regardless of its orientation.

Also remember to use *Minute Math* during spare moments in the day.

B Teaching Options

EXTRA PRACTICE

▶ Playing *Walk Around the Clock* (Math Masters, p. 56)

Children can use game markers to represent the movement of the hour hand around a paper clock. (Use *Math Masters,* p. 56 without the hour or minute hands.) Start with all game markers on the 12. Each player rolls a die (with sides marked 1, 2, 3, 1, 2, 3), moves his or her marker the number of hours ahead as indicated on the die, and then says the time ("2 o'clock" when the marker is on the 2, for example). Play continues until someone rolls the exact number they need to return to 12.

ELL SUPPORT

▶ Drawing Daily Events

Have children draw pictures of events that could possibly take place at specific times of the day (for example, waking up at 7 o'clock in the morning or taking a bath at 7 o'clock at night).

▶ Making a Human Clock

Have 12 children simulate an analog clock by sitting in a circle and holding the numbers 1–12 in order. Say a time, such as *4 o'clock,* or *just before 5 o'clock.* Call on another child to be the hour hand. Have this child stand in the center of the human clock and point or extend an arm toward the correct position. Children can take turns acting as the hour hand.

▶ Reading *The Grouchy Ladybug*

Read *The Grouchy Ladybug* by Eric Carle (HarperCollins, 1996). Point out the clocks on each page and the time each clock shows.

CCSS
Mathematical Practices
SMP1, SMP6, SMP7, **SMP8**
Content Standards
K.CC.7, K.OA.1, K.OA.5

**ACTIVITY
8·4**

High Roller Game

◎ **Objective** To develop "counting on" as an addition strategy.

☐ Whole Group
☑ Small Group
☑ Partners
☑ Center

Key Concepts and Skills
- Compare numbers to decide which is greatest. [Number and Numeration Goal 6]
- Use "counting on" as a strategy to add numbers from dice throws. [Operations and Computation Goal 1]

Terms to Use compare, count on

Materials dice; counters

A **Core Activities**

▶ Playing *High Roller*

Roll two dice and model the strategy of "counting on" from the higher number to get the total. Repeat with a few more dice rolls, calling on children to use the strategy.

Demonstrate the game, which can be played with a partner or in small groups. Each player rolls his or her own pair of dice. Players choose the die in their pair with the larger number (the High Roller) and roll the other die again. Players "count on" from the High Roller to get the sum of their two dice. The player with the highest total takes a counter from the pile. Play ends when one player has 10 counters. For example: Player One rolls 6 and 3, keeps the 6, and rolls the other die again and gets 5 (for a total of 11). Player Two rolls 4 and 2, keeps the 4, and rolls the other die again and gets 6 (for a total of 10). Players determine who has the higher total and that player gets a counter.

Encourage children to play *High Roller* frequently in the Math Center.

**Adjusting
the Activity**

Instead of collecting counters, children can use tally marks to keep track of each round they win. Some children may be interested in recording the sums of their rolls with number sentences
$(6 + 5 = 11$, for example).

AUDITORY ♦ KINESTHETIC ♦ TACTILE ♦ VISUAL

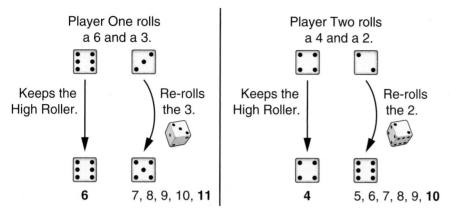

Player One rolls a 6 and a 3.

Keeps the High Roller. | Re-rolls the 3.

6 | 7, 8, 9, 10, **11**

Player Two rolls a 4 and a 2.

Keeps the High Roller. | Re-rolls the 2.

4 | 5, 6, 7, 8, 9, **10**

Player One takes a counter because 11 is higher than 10.

▶ Fishing for Children: "What's My Rule?" (Revisit Activity 4•14, p. 216)

Play several rounds of *"What's My Rule?" Fishing*. For an extra challenge, fish for two attributes, such as shirts that are red and long-sleeved, or hair that is short and brown.

B Teaching Options

EXTRA PRACTICE

▶ Playing *High Roller* with Subtraction

Children can vary *High Roller* by subtracting the lower dice roll from the higher roll. Encourage children to share their subtraction strategies, which may include "counting back," using fingers, using manipulatives, or some combination of these strategies.

TECHNOLOGY

▶ Playing *High Roller* with Calculators

Children can play *High Roller* using dice with higher numbers (marked with numerals, rather than dots) and use a calculator to find the sums.

Ongoing Assessment:

Informing Instruction

Watch what strategies children use to find the sum of the two dice. Many children will have memorized combinations or have very fluent mental strategies, especially for lower numbers.

For children who start at 1 and count the dots on both dice, rather than "counting on" or trying to recall the facts, explain the "counting on" strategy as a shortcut. Help children understand why it works by whispering the numbers as you count the dots on the first dice, saying only the last number out loud. Then continue to count the dots on the second dice out loud. You may wish to wait to introduce this strategy to children who do not seem ready. It is important to allow children to use strategies that make sense to them, so they do not see addition just as a rote process.

Also monitor children's subtraction strategies as they play *High Roller* with Subtraction. Introduce the "counting-back" strategy for those who are ready. (See Teaching Options.)

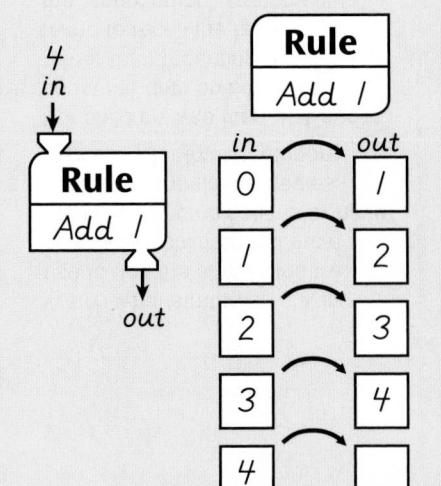

Introduction to Function Machines

CCSS
Mathematical Practices
SMP2, **SMP3,** SMP5, SMP6, **SMP8**
Content Standards
K.CC.4c, **K.OA.5**

ACTIVITY
8·5

🎯 **Objective** To introduce and provide practice with function machines.

☑ Whole Group
☑ Small Group
☐ Partners
☐ Center

Key Concepts and Skills
• Apply addition- and subtraction-based function rules. [Operations and Computation Goal 1]
• Use function rules to generate related pairs of numbers. [Patterns, Functions, and Algebra Goal 1]

Terms to Use function machine, rule

Materials Teaching Master (*Math Masters,* p. 57) (optional); small box; index cards; chalkboard and chalk; counters (optional)

Planning Tip Use a shoe box or other small box to create a concrete function machine. Put a hole on the top labeled *in* and a hole on the bottom or side labeled *out.* Make a pocket on the front of the machine for the rule.

A **Core Activities**

▶ **Introducing the Function Machine** (*Math Masters,* p. 57)

Show the function machine box you created. Tell children this is called a **function machine** and point out the *in, out,* and *Rule* features of the machine. Explain that when a number goes *in* the machine something happens to it, and a new number comes *out* of the machine. The *Rule* tells what will happen to each *in* number. Write "Add 1" on a card and put it in the rule space on the box. Point to the rule and say: *If I put 2 in, what will come* out? *If my* rule *("Add 1") stays the same and I put 3* in, *what will come* out? Record the *in* and *out* numbers for your rule on the board using the system in the margin. Repeat with several examples, then change rules and model the process again. Use subtraction rules, such as "Take away 1," as well as addition rules. Provide counters for children who need them to apply the rule. Children can work with counters on a function machine diagram (*Math Masters,* page 57).

● ●

▶ Reviewing Coins (Revisit Activities 6◆1, 6◆2, 6◆7, and 7◆5, pp. 282, 284, 296, and 342)

Place a penny, nickel, dime, and quarter in a Feely Box. Give clues about a type of coin.
Then call on children to say what the coin is and try to pick it from the Box.

B Teaching Options

ENRICHMENT

▶ Applying Skip-Counting Rules

Use rules such as +2, +5, and +10 for the function machine activities. If you start with
an input number of 0 and use each output number as the next input number, children
will have another way of seeing skip-counting rules and patterns.

EXTRA PRACTICE

▶ Using Function Machines (*Math Masters*, pp. 57 and 58; *Center Activity Cards*, 35)

Place counters and function machine diagrams (*Math Masters*, page 57) or your function
machine box in the Math Center for children to use. They can record their *in* and *out*
numbers on copies of *Math Masters*, page 58.

ELL SUPPORT

▶ Acting as Function Machines

Children can act out the work of a function machine. One child (the *in* person) says a
number out loud (the *in* number) and brings that number of counters to the child with
the *Rule* job. The *Rule* person applies the rule to the counters (adds 1 or takes away 2,
for example) and gives the resulting number of counters to the *out* person. The *out*
person counts the counters and announces the *out* number. The *in* and *out* children can
also record their respective numbers, and the *Rule* child can record the rule. Repeat,
rotating jobs and changing the rule frequently.

Links to the Future

This activity provides early
exposure to applying rules to
numbers and representing
functions using words, symbols,
tables, graphs, and algebraic
notation. These skills are Grades
1–6 Goals. For background
information on functions, see
Chapter 15 in the *Teacher's
Reference Manual*.

Number Gymnastics Game

ACTIVITY 8·6

◎ **Objective** To develop children's number sense and ability to manipulate numbers through a mental math game.

CCSS Mathematical Practices
SMP2, SMP3, **SMP4,**
SMP5, **SMP6**
Content Standards
K.CC.3, K.MD.3

☑ Whole Group
☑ Small Group
☐ Partners
☐ Center

Key Concepts and Skills

• Manipulate digits in numbers. [Number and Numeration Goal 3]

• Use mental math strategies to add and subtract numbers. [Operations and Computation Goal 1]

Terms to Use digit, reverse, add, subtract

Materials Home Link Master (*Math Masters*, p. 59); number grid and/or number line

---

A Core Activities

▶ Playing *Number Gymnastics*

Begin the game with a number clue, such as: *I'm thinking of a number with 2 as its first digit and 3 as its second digit. What is my number?* (23) Give step-by-step instructions for ways to change the number, making one change at a time. Ask children to say the number after each step. (The first time through the game, you may also want to record the number after each step to help children follow along.) For example, the starting number above might be changed with the following steps:

• What is the number if I reverse the digits? (32)

• What number comes before that number? (31)

• Now reverse those digits. (13)

• Now add two. (15)

Adjusting the Activity

This is a quick-paced, playful mental gymnastics game. To simplify the game, allow children more time to answer and point out numbers on the number grid or number line after each step.

AUDITORY ◆ KINESTHETIC ◆ TACTILE ◆ VISUAL

Continue until it seems appropriate to start with fresh digits. It is fun to try to get back to the number with which you started. Encourage children to refer to the number grid or number line to help them track the numbers. After they've played several times, children can give the clues. Play the game frequently.

▶ Studying Weather and Temperature Data

(Revisit Routines 6 and 7, pp. 24 and 28; *My First Math Book,* p. 23)

Review the weather and temperature data the class has collected over the course of the year. Post any graphs, tally charts, or other displays (such as the temperature color strip), and pose questions about the data for children to think about and answer. Children can answer the questions on page 23 of their math books—as well as any other questions that you pose—as a class, individually, or in small groups. Encourage children to pose their own questions that can be answered using the data.

 Home Link 8·6 (*Math Masters,* p. 59)
Children collect data about their families' mail.

B Teaching Options

READINESS

▶ Playing *Number-Grid Grab*

Children can repeat Activity 7-13, page 358 (main activity and/or the Extra Practice activity, *Number-Grid Grab*) to gain additional experience with manipulating digits in 2-digit numbers.

EXTRA PRACTICE

▶ Recording *Number Gymnastics* Numbers

You can use *Number Gymnastics* for number writing practice by having children record each number on a slate or on the writing and drawing pages in their math books.

Weather Graph Questions

Use the class **weather graphs** to answer these questions.

1. What month had the most sunny days? _____

2. What month had the least sunny days? _____

3. Did any months have 0 rainy days? If so, which ones?
   _____

4. Write a question about the weather graphs for someone else to answer.

Use with Activity 8·6.   23

My First Math Book, p. 23

Name _____ Date _____

HOME LINK 8·6 **Collecting Data about Mail**

Family Note Observing and collecting data gives children the opportunity to count and compare numbers and to think about how numbers are used to give information. Help your child collect data about the mail you receive for one week. Also help him or her correctly use and count tallies on the chart.

Ask someone to help you make a tally chart like the one below. Make a tally mark in the correct row for each piece of mail that comes during the week. At the end of the week, count your tallies to find out how much of each type of mail your family received.

How much mail did your family get in a week?

Which was the most common type of mail?

Which was the least common type of mail?

TYPE	OUR MAIL
PERSONAL LETTERS	//
BUSINESS / BILLS	||||-//
MAGAZINES	//
ADS / JUNK MAIL	||||-||||-//

Math Masters, p. 59

Introduction of the $1 Bill

ACTIVITY 8·7

◎ **Objective** To introduce the $1 bill.

CCSS Mathematical Practices
SMP1, SMP2, **SMP4,**
SMP7, **SMP8**
Content Standards
K.OA.5

☑ Whole Group
☑ Small Group
☐ Partners
☐ Center

Key Concepts and Skills
• Explore the characteristics of the $1 bill. [Measurement and Reference Frames Goal 2]
• Learn about the value of a dollar. [Measurement and Reference Frames Goal 2]

Terms to Use one-dollar bill, dollar sign, exchange, equals

Materials Teaching Aid Masters (*Math Masters,* pp. 115 and 116) or real dollar bills; magnifying lenses; slates or paper (optional)

Planning Tip If it is difficult for you to duplicate the masters onto a single sheet of paper so that the fronts and backs align, you can copy the fronts and backs on separate sheets so children will see and use both sides of the dollar. You may want to have children glue the front and back of the bills together. Save the dollar bills to use in later activities.

A Core Activities

▶ Exploring the $1 Bill (*Math Masters,* pp. 115 and 116)

Give a real dollar bill or a dollar bill master to each child. Have children share the magnifying lenses to look closely at both sides of the dollar. Discuss the size, shape, color, and any markings they notice. Note the number 1 in all 4 corners, front and back, and the shapes and content of the pictures. Explain that this is called a one-dollar bill.

Write a dollar sign ($) on the board and tell children that this symbol is used to show dollars. Have children trace the dollar sign in the air or draw it on slates or paper. (You might note that the dollar sign is an *S* with a line through it.) Explain that one dollar can be written as $1.00 or $1. Both mean exactly 100 cents. Prompt discussion by asking: *If a dollar is 100 cents, how many pennies are in a dollar? Does anyone remember how many quarters are in a dollar? What can you buy with $1?* Collect everyone's dollars and count the total. Discuss children's ideas about what they could buy with this much money.

▶ Reviewing Function Machines

(Revisit Activity 8•5, p. 390; *My First Math Book*, p. 24)

Quickly review how to use a function machine and record the *in* and *out* pairs. When the class seems comfortable, introduce page 24 in their math books. On the left side of the page, children apply the rule "Add 1" to find the *out* numbers. Then, children work with a partner to complete the right side of the page. Each child thinks of a rule and writes it in the function machine in his or her own book. They also fill in the *in* numbers. Children then trade books with a partner. Partners must fill in the *out* numbers. Make counters available for children who want them.

Teaching Options

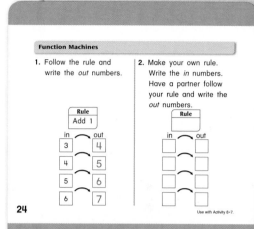

My First Math Book, p. 24

ENRICHMENT

▶ Making Exchanges

Put out a collection of dimes, quarters, and dollars, and invite children to try to make some exchanges. You might ask children to help create a chart to show exchanges.

MATHEMATICS IN THE DRAMATIC PLAY CENTER

▶ Playing Dollar Store

Mark a few items with higher prices and add play dollars to the store in the Dramatic Play Center. (See Activity 6-2, page 284.) If you did not set up a store before, you might wish to do so now.

LITERACY CONNECTION

▶ Reading a Dollar Story

Read *The Big Buck Adventure* by Shelley Gill and Deborah Tobola (Charlesbridge, 2000). Ask children what they would buy if they were the child in the story.

Math Masters, p. 115

Backs of the dollar bills are on *Math Masters*, page 116.

One-Dollar Game

Objective To reinforce penny, dime, and dollar values and exchanges through a game.

CCSS **Mathematical Practices**
SMP1, SMP2, **SMP3,**
SMP6, SMP7, SMP8
Content Standards
K.OA.3

☐ Whole Group
☑ Small Group
☑ Partners
☑ Center

Key Concepts and Skills
• Make exchanges with pennies, dimes, and dollars. [Number and Numeration Goal 3]
• Learn about the value of the dollar. [Measurement and Reference Frames Goal 2]

Terms to Use dollar, exchange, trade

Materials Home Link Master (*Math Masters,* p. 60); Teaching Aid Masters (*Math Masters,* pp. 115 and 116); several cubes labeled 1¢, 1¢, 10¢, 10¢, 10¢, 10¢; pennies; dimes; quarters (optional)

Planning Tip Prepare your money cubes in advance. You will need one cube for each group of 2 to 4 players who play at the same time. Each group will also need about 40 pennies, 40 dimes, and several dollar bills in their bank.

 A **Core Activities**

▶ Playing the *One-Dollar Game* (*Math Masters,* pp. 115 and 116)

Teach children how to play the *One-Dollar Game.* Players take turns rolling the money cube and picking up the appropriate coin from the bank. When players have 10 pennies, they exchange them for 1 dime. When players have 10 dimes, they exchange them for a dollar bill. Play ends when one player reaches $1.

For a more challenging variation of the game, make a money cube labeled 25¢, 25¢, 10¢, 10¢, 10¢, and 1¢, and add about 15 quarters to your bank. Children can exchange pennies for dimes, 2 dimes and 5 pennies for a quarter, and 4 quarters for $1. Introduce this variation only to children who are proficient with the standard version of the game.

Home Link 8·8 (*Math Masters*, p. 60)
Children explore coins at home.

▶ Making Name Collections (Revisit Activity 7·9, p. 350)

Work with the class to generate a collection of equivalent names for the date number on the calendar or another number (perhaps the temperature). Prompt children to include names that involve subtraction, as well as those that involve addition. Also be sure that other representations such as pictures, tallies, Ten Frames, or pictures of bundles of 10 and single sticks are included in the name collection.

B **Teaching Options**

EXTRA PRACTICE

▶ Playing Other Exchange Games

Children can practice coin exchanges by playing *Money Cube* or *Money Grid* (Activity 7-1, pages 330–331). You might also put out *The Raft Game* (Activity 5-10, page 254) for children to play. Discuss how it is similar to the exchange games that involve money.

LITERACY CONNECTION

▶ Reading Money Stories

Read *A Bargain for Frances* by Russell Hoban (HarperCollins, 1992), and talk with children about how Thelma tricked Frances. You might also read *A Chair for My Mother* by Vera B. Williams (Greenwillow, 1998), and talk with children about whether they have ever tried to save money for anything. (Many children may have begun a family penny or coin jar as a result of Home Links 2-13 and 6-8.)

Name		Date

 8·8 **Exploring Coins**

Family Note Children are familiar with money transactions, but many children are unable to distinguish between coins, understand a coin's value, or realize that a coin of greater value can be exchanged for several coins of lesser value. To build your child's familiarity with money, empty your coin purse or pocket and have fun exploring pennies, nickels, dimes, and quarters together.

Ask someone at home to empty a purse or pocket. Explore the coins with them and think about these questions:

• How many pennies are there? Nickels? Dimes? How many coins all together?

• Which coin is the biggest? Which is the smallest? The thickest? The thinnest?

• How many pennies equal a nickel? How many pennies equal a dime?

• Do you think all the coins add up to more or less than $1?

• What else do you notice about the coins?

Math Masters, p. 60

Technology

Children can play a version of the *One-Dollar Game* on the computer using *Everyday Mathematics EM Games*.

Name Collection Posters

◎ **Objective** To reinforce the concept of equivalent names for numbers.

CCSS Mathematical Practices
SMP1, SMP2, SMP3, SMP6, SMP7
Content Standards
K.CC.3, K.OA.1, K.OA.3, K.OA.4

☑ Whole Group
☑ Small Group
☐ Partners
☐ Center

Key Concepts and Skills
- Represent numbers using manipulatives, drawings, tallies, and numerical expressions. [Number and Numeration Goal 3]
- Generate equivalent names for numbers. [Number and Numeration Goal 5]
- Represent numbers with simple addition and subtraction number sentences. [Operations and Computation Goal 1]

Terms to Use equivalent names, name collection

Materials chart paper or poster board; markers or crayons; assorted manipulatives; tape

A Core Activities

▶ Making Name Collection Posters

Write the numeral 10 at the top of a sheet of chart paper. Ask the class to think of other ways they can show the number 10. Record or have children record their ideas on the paper. If necessary, prompt them by mentioning some of the previous activities they've done to make equivalent names for numbers, such as counting different dot combinations on dominoes, using plus and minus signs, and representing numbers with pictures, manipulatives, coins, tally marks, Ten Frames, and craft sticks (bundles of 10 and singles). To include concrete representations, tape the manipulatives to the paper, create a space under the paper to display the manipulative equivalents, or sketch or photograph the manipulatives and add the pictures to the poster. Repeat the activity for a number in the teens.

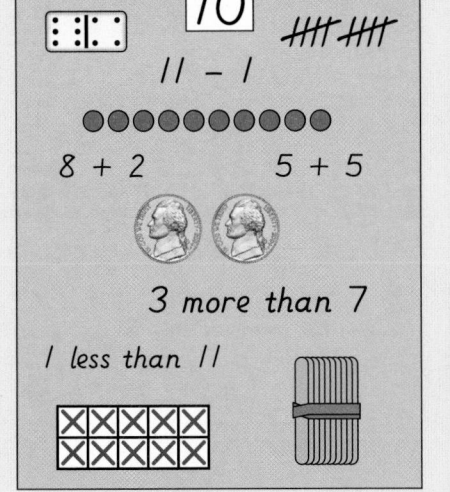

Name Collection Poster for the number 10

Divide the class into small groups. Give each group a large sheet of paper or posterboard and assign them a number. Group members should work together to represent their number on the paper in as many ways as they can.

▶ Number Scrolling (Revisit Activity 7•10, p. 352; *Math Masters*, p. 111)

Give children time to continue work on their number scrolls, especially if they haven't added to their scrolls recently. You may need to pass out new blank grids to children who reach 100 or higher.

Also remember to use *Minute Math* during spare moments in the day.

(EXTRA PRACTICE)

▶ Finding Equivalent Dominoes (*Center Activity Cards*, 36)

Children can use double 9 dominoes to find all the possible domino dot combinations for sums between 0 and 18. (Provide a card for each number between 0 and 18 and have children place the correct dominoes under each sum.) Invite children to think of other possible combinations and draw them.

(LITERACY CONNECTION)

▶ Reading about Equivalent Names for Numbers

Read *One Is a Snail, Ten Is a Crab* by April Pulley Sayre and Jeff Sayre (Candlewick, 2003). Discuss how the authors used different combinations of animals (with different numbers of legs) to represent equivalent names for numbers. You may wish to have children write number models for the situations in the book ($1 + 10 = 11$, for example). Encourage children to figure out number names based on the animals in the story (such as 1 snail and 1 crab for a total of 11 legs) to add to their name collection posters.

Ongoing Assessment: Recognizing Student Achievement

Use **Name Collection Posters** to assess children's ability to represent equivalent names for numbers. Children are making adequate progress if they are able to represent equivalent names for numbers up to 20 using manipulatives, drawings, and simple numerical expressions.

[Number and Numeration Goal 5]

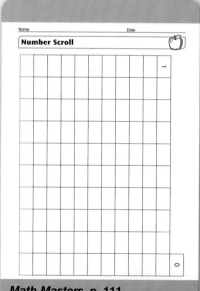

Name _____   Date _____

Number Scroll

Math Masters, p. 111

"What's My Rule?" with Numbers

ACTIVITY 8·10

CCSS Mathematical Practices
SMP1, SMP2, SMP3, SMP4, SMP5, **SMP6**, SMP8
Content Standards
K.OA.1, K.OA.5

◎ **Objective** To help children identify function rules and generate numbers that follow those rules.

☑ Whole Group
☑ Small Group
☐ Partners
☐ Center

Key Concepts and Skills
• Apply addition- and subtraction-based rules. [Operations and Computation Goal 1]
• Explore the difference between addition and subtraction rules. [Operations and Computation Goal 2]
• Use related pairs of numbers to identify function rules. [Patterns, Functions, and Algebra Goal 1]
• Use rules to determine missing numbers in a number pair. [Patterns, Functions, and Algebra Goal 1]

Terms to Use function machine, rule

Materials chalkboard; chalk; eraser

A Core Activities

▶ Solving "What's My Rule?" with Numbers

Draw a function machine and an *in/out* chart on the board. Review the function machine by having children apply a simple rule, such as "Add 3" to compute several *out* numbers.

After children have worked with several examples, explain that you will show them some *in* and *out* numbers, and they should try to figure out what the rule on the function machine is. Think of a rule and write at least three *in* and *out* pairs that follow the rule. (The accompanying diagram shows examples for the rule "Add 2.") Write a question mark in the rule space on your function machine and on your *in/out* chart. Ask: *What's my rule?* After gathering responses, write the correct rule and have children share and discuss how they figured out your rule. Then write another *in* number and ask children what the *out* number should be. Finally, write an *out* number and ask children what the *in* number should be.

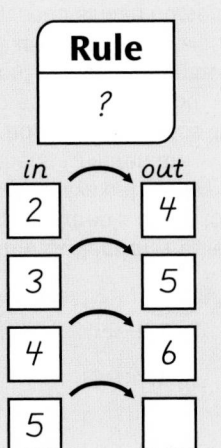

Provide a set of *in* and *out* pairs that follow a different rule, and have children use them to figure out your rule. Also have them apply the rule to figure out missing *in* and *out* numbers. Repeat using both addition and subtraction rules as long as time and interest permit. Gradually increase the difficulty by using more challenging rules, such as "Add 10." Also begin to use higher *in* numbers.

▶ Using the Hour-Hand Clock (Revisit Activity 8•3, p. 384)

Call out several approximate times (*a little past 10 o'clock, half past 4 o'clock, exactly 8 o'clock,* and so on) for children to show on their hour-hand clocks.

B Teaching Options

EXTRA PRACTICE

▶ Solving "What's My Rule?" with a Partner

(*Math Masters,* p. 58)

Partners can solve "What's My Rule?" problems in the Math Center. One child records pairs of *in* and *out* numbers on a slate or a copy of *Math Masters,* page 58. The other child uses the pairs of numbers to guess the rule.

EXTRA PRACTICE

▶ Using "What's My Rule?" for Facts Practice

Provide children with "What's My Rule?" problems that use +0, −0, +1, −1, +2, and −2 as rules. This will help them internalize the patterns for adding and subtracting these small numbers, which will help them build fluency for these facts.

MATHEMATICS IN THE BLOCK CENTER

▶ Building and Using a Function Machine

Children can build a function machine with blocks, add a rule, and then use small blocks or interconnecting links to represent the *in* and *out* numbers.

Ongoing Assessment:
Recognizing Student Achievement

Use **"What's My Rule?" with Numbers** to assess children's ability to complete a number pair by applying a rule. Children are making adequate progress if they can apply simple addition and subtraction rules to complete a number pair.

[Patterns, Functions, and Algebra Goal 1]

Hour-Hand, Minute-Hand Story

ACTIVITY 8·11

◎ **Objective** To introduce the minute hand on the analog clock.

☑ Whole Group
☑ Small Group
☐ Partners
☐ Center

Key Concepts and Skills
- Add the minute hand to paper clocks. [Measurement and Reference Frames Goal 4]
- Recognize the difference between the hour hand and the minute hand. [Measurement and Reference Frames Goal 4]
- Copy clock times on a paper clock. [Measurement and Reference Frames Goal 4]

Terms to Use hour hand, minute hand, hour, minute, slower, faster, o'clock

Materials Home Link Master (*Math Masters*, p. 61); minute hands from Teaching Master (*Math Masters*, p. 56); scissors; paper clocks from Activity 8·3; analog clock; demonstration clock (optional)

A Core Activities

▶ Telling the "Hour-Hand, Minute-Hand Story" (*Math Masters*, p. 56)

Have children look at an analog clock. Ask: *What do you notice? How many hands does the clock have? Are they exactly the same? How are they different?* Tell the following story to give information about the hour and minute hands.

The hour hand is short and slow. It doesn't need to hurry because it has a whole hour to get from one number to the next. When it is pointing right at the 3, the time is 3 o'clock. When it is pointing between the 2 and the 3, the time is somewhere between 2 and 3 o'clock.

The minute hand is longer and faster than the hour hand. It moves more quickly because it needs to touch all of the numbers around the clock in one hour! When the time says "o'clock," the minute hand points straight up. Then it moves around this way (circle your finger clockwise from 12 to 12) *until the next "o'clock" time.*

NOTE As you tell the story, move the hands of a demonstration clock or paper clock to illustrate the action.

Links to the Future

Expect that children will be able to estimate time focusing only on the position of the hour hand. This activity provides an early exposure to the minute hand. Learning how to use the minute hand to tell time is a Grades 1–3 Goal.

Help children cut out and attach the minute hands to their paper clocks from Activity 8-3. When their clocks are assembled, have children look at the classroom clock and set the time on their paper clocks. Children also might use their arms to match the hands on the classroom clock. Repeat frequently to help children notice the position of both hands on the clock.

 Home Link 8·11 (*Math Masters*, p. 61)
Children investigate the length of a minute.

▶ **Playing Dice Addition and Subtraction Games** (Revisit Activity 7◆6, p. 344)
Have children play Dice Addition and Subtraction Games in the Math Center. You might have children record number sentences for each turn. Consider using some of the variations suggested in the Teaching Options on page 345 for children who are ready.

 **Teaching Options**

(EXTRA PRACTICE)
▶ **Adding Clocks to the Daily Schedule** (*Math Masters*, p. 112)
Children can help you create paper clocks to represent the times on your daily schedule. Use copies of a blank analog clock (*Math Masters,* page 112).

(MOVEMENT CONNECTION)
▶ **Exploring the Length of a Minute**
Give a start signal and tell children to raise their hands when they think a minute has passed. After a minute, discuss whether it seemed longer or shorter than they thought it would. You might have children try jumping or standing on one foot for one minute. To support English language learners, discuss the meaning of the expression, "Just a minute."

 Ongoing Assessment: Recognizing Student Achievement

Use **Dice Addition and Subtraction Games** to assess children's ability to fluently add and subtract small numbers. Children are making adequate progress if they can quickly solve or recall the sums and differences.

[Operations and Computation Goal 1]

Name _____ Date _____

HOME LINK 8·11 **Timing Yourself**

Family Note As children learn about time, they may have difficulty understanding how long a minute is. In this activity, your child will think about what he or she is able to do in a minute.

Guess how long a minute lasts. Ask someone to help you check the clock and tell you when to start timing. Clap your hands when you think a minute has passed. How close were you?

How many sit-ups, leg raises, arm raises, or jumping jacks can you do in one minute?

Think of other activities that you can do in one minute. Can you touch your toes 10 times, do 5 jumping jacks, and spin around 3 times in one minute?

Math Masters, p. 61

Time Match Game

Objective To provide practice with telling time to the hour with digital and analog clocks.

CCSS

Mathematical Practices
SMP1, SMP2, SMP4, SMP5, **SMP6**

✔ Whole Group
✔ Small Group
✔ Partners
✔ Center

Key Concepts and Skills

• Read clocks to the hour. [Measurement and Reference Frames Goal 4]

• Match times shown on digital and analog clocks. [Measurement and Reference Frames Goal 4]

Terms to Use analog, digital

Materials Game Masters (*Math Masters*, pp. 140–143); paper clock or demonstration clock; digital clock and analog clock (optional)

Planning Tip Copy and cut out the clock faces from the Game Masters to create several game decks before the lesson. You might want to color-code the decks to keep them separate.

A Core Activities

▶ **Playing** *Time Match* (*Math Masters*, pp. 140–143)

Show children an analog clock (or a picture of one) and say: *We've been talking a lot about this type of clock. Are there other types of clocks?* After children share their ideas, show a digital clock (actual or picture). Explain that, although they show the time differently, both types of clocks tell time. Hold up a paper clock or a demonstration analog clock and set the hands to show 1 o'clock. Ask whether anyone knows what time it shows. Prompt children to look at the hour hand and notice that it is pointing exactly at the 1. Ask: *Where is the minute hand pointing?* Explain that on the "o'clock" times, the minute hand always points straight up. Repeat for several o'clock times. Then ask: *Does anyone know what the o'clock times look like on a digital clock?* After gathering responses, show several of the digital clock masters and explain that these show o'clock times on a digital clock. Ask: *What is the same about them?* Point out that o'clock times on the digital clock always end in :00.

NOTE You might explain that "o'clock" means exactly on the hour (0 minutes before or after). The digital clock shows "o'clock" by showing :00 (or 0) in the minutes section of the clock display. The analog clock shows "o'clock" by having the minute hand point straight up.

To prepare for playing the matching game, hold up both a digital and an analog clock card and discuss whether they show the same time. Repeat for several pairs, using some that show the same time and some that do not. Help children arrange the cards facedown in rows to play a matching game. Players take turns turning over two cards to look for a digital and an analog clock that show the same time. If they get a pair, they keep it. If the cards don't match, they turn the cards back over. Children can play with partners or in small groups.

▶ Dividing Wholes into Halves (Revisit Activity 6•16, p. 314)

Draw shapes on the board and have children draw lines to divide them in half. Remind them that halves must be equal in size. You might include nonsymmetrical shapes and discuss why it is difficult to divide them exactly in half.

B Teaching Options

READINESS
▶ Playing *Time Match* with Cards Faceup

Children can begin by keeping the clocks faceup to practice finding matches.

ENRICHMENT
▶ Playing with Advanced Cards (*Math Masters*, p. 112)

Children who are ready can play with cards that show half- or quarter-hour times. Make new cards using blank clocks from *Math Masters,* page 112.

SCIENCE CONNECTION
▶ Studying Clocks

Start a collection of clocks for observation. Invite families to loan clocks for the collection. You might also bring in old clocks and allow children to take them apart.

Math Masters, p. 140

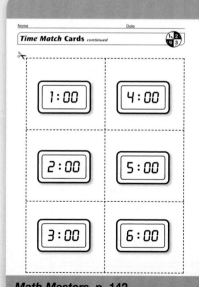

Math Masters, p. 142

ACTIVITY 8·13

Missing Number Problems

Objective To provide concrete experiences with figuring out missing numbers in equations.

☑ Whole Group
☑ Small Group
☐ Partners
☐ Center

Key Concepts and Skills
- Solve missing number problems using concrete objects. [Operations and Computation Goal 1]
- Identify addition and subtraction situations. [Operations and Computation Goal 2]
- Write number sentences. [Patterns, Functions, and Algebra Goal 2]

Terms to Use total, number sentence, missing number, add, subtract

Materials *My First Math Book,* p. 25; bag or box for pocket; counters; chalkboard

Planning Tip You can use the pocket from Activity 3-8, Pocket Problems, page 156 if desired.

NOTE *Minute Math* includes many missing number problems.

A Core Activities

▶ Solving Missing Number Pocket Problems (*My First Math Book,* p. 25)

With the class watching and counting out loud, put 4 objects into a bag or box (the pocket). Write a 4 on the board to help children remember the starting number. Tell children to close their eyes while you change the number of objects in the pocket. Explain that they will be detectives and figure out how many objects you added to or subtracted from the pocket. While children's eyes are closed, add 2 objects to the pocket; then have children open their eyes. Empty the pocket and have the class count the objects. Record the total (6) on the board. Ask:

- Did I add or subtract objects? How do you know?

- How many did I add? How did you figure it out?

Invite children to help you write a number sentence that shows the action you took to get from the starting number to the ending number (write "+ 2 =" between the

4 and the 6 in the example above). You may need to talk through each step with children and reinforce the meaning of the +, −, and = symbols.

Do several more examples with the group (include both addition and subtraction). Then help children complete page 25 in their math books.

▶ Playing *I Spy:* Shapes and Patterns

(Revisit Activities 6•6 and 7•15, pp. 294 and 362)

Play several rounds of *I Spy* to review 2-dimensional and 3-dimensional shapes. Use clues that require children to identify shapes as 2- or 3-dimensional. For example, *I spy a 3-dimensional shape with no corners.* You can also review patterns and patterning rules by incorporating clues such as: *I spy a pattern that follows the same rule as this.* (Show a color or movement pattern and describe its rule.)

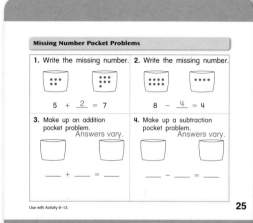

My First Math Book, p. 25

B Teaching Options

ENRICHMENT

▶ Using Number-Model Cards (*Center Activity Cards,* 37)

Write equations with missing numbers on strips of cardstock. Children can solve the missing-number problems (using manipulatives if needed) and show their answers with craft sticks, counters, number cards, or wipe-off markers (if the cards are laminated).

ELL SUPPORT

▶ Modeling Missing-Number Problems on a Walk-On Number Line

Pose missing-number problems for children to act out and solve on a walk-on number line, such as: *If you stand on 5, how many forward steps will it take to get to 9?* Write number models for the problems (5 + ? = 9), and help children see the connection between the number-line problems and missing-number pocket problems.

| $3+4=$___ | $5=$___$+3$ |
| $5+$___$=7$ | $7-2=$___ |

 Ongoing Assessment:

Recognizing Student Achievement

Use *I Spy* to assess children's recognition of 2- and 3-dimensional shapes. Children are making adequate progress if they can identify circles, squares, triangles, rectangles, spheres and cubes.

[Geometry Goal 1]

ACTIVITY 8·14

Number Stories with Calculators

Mathematical Practices
SMP1, **SMP2, SMP5,** SMP6

Content Standards
K.OA.1, K.OA.2

◎ **Objective** To introduce how to model number stories on a calculator.

☑ Whole Group
☑ Small Group
☑ Partners
☐ Center

Key Concepts and Skills
- Use calculators to model and solve number stories. [Operations and Computation Goal 1]
- Recognize number stories as addition or subtraction stories. [Operations and Computation Goal 2]
- Use +, −, and = symbols to create number models for number stories.
  [Patterns, Functions, and Algebra Goal 2]

Terms to Use number story, addition sign, minus (take away) sign, equals, equal sign, clear, all clear

Materials Home Link Master (*Math Masters*, p. 62); calculators

A Core Activities

▶ Telling Number Stories with Calculators

Children can use calculators to model addition or subtraction number stories. Remind them to press Ⓐ or Ⓒ before each new story. Tell an addition number story or ask a child to tell one. For example, *I had 6 lollipops. I got 4 more. Then I had 10 lollipops.* Accompany the story by recording both the numbers and symbols on the board: 6 + 4 = 10. Children follow along by pressing the appropriate keys on their calculators. After children have told a few addition stories and modeled them on calculators, tell (or ask a child to tell) a subtraction (take away) story. For example, *I had 10 lollipops. I ate 2. How many did I have left?* (10 − 2 = 8). Write the story on the board with numbers and symbols as children press the appropriate keys on their calculators.

✔ Ongoing Assessment:
Recognizing Student Achievement

Use **Number Stories with Calculators** to assess children's ability to tell a simple number story and model it with numbers and symbols. Children are making adequate progress with identifying addition and subtraction situations if they correctly choose the + or − symbol on their calculators.

[Operations and Computation Goal 2]

They are making adequate progress with writing number sentences if they correctly enter the numbers and symbols on their calculators to match the story.

[Patterns, Functions, and Algebra Goal 2]

Children also can use their calculators to help them figure out solutions. For example, you might ask: *If I had 8 apples and got 4 more, how many apples would I have all together?* Have children press the appropriate keys on their calculators, then press $=$ to find the solution. They can compare answers. Children may want to double check the calculator answer with manipulatives or other aids. Always encourage children to think about whether the answers they get on a calculator make sense.

Home Link 8·14 (*Math Masters*, p. 62)

Children and family members tell number stories at home.

▶ Playing *Number Gymnastics* with Slates (Revisit Activity 8∗6, p. 392)

Play several rounds of *Number Gymnastics,* and have children record each number on slates or on the writing and drawing pages in their math books to practice writing 2-digit numbers.

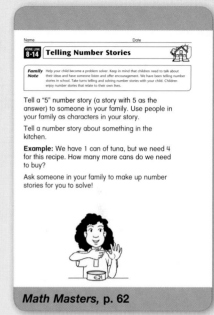

Math Masters, p. 62

B Teaching Options

EXTRA PRACTICE

▶ Reading the Class Number Story Book

Children can use calculators to model some of the stories in the Class Number Story Book from Activity 7-3, page 336.

LITERACY CONNECTION

▶ Creating Number Stories from Pictures

Use the photographs in the book *More, Fewer, Less* by Tana Hoban (Greenwillow, 1998) as the source for a variety of number stories that children can solve using calculators or other tools and strategies.

Pan Balance with Uniform Weights

CCSS Mathematical Practices
SMP2, SMP3, SMP4,
SMP5, SMP6
Content Standards
K.CC.3, K.MD.1, K.MD.2

ACTIVITY 8·15

⊙ **Objective** To introduce the use of nonstandard units on a pan balance.

☐ Whole Group
☑ Small Group
☐ Partners
☑ Center

Key Concepts and Skills

- Count the number of nonstandard units used to weigh an object. [Number and Numeration Goal 2]
- Compare the weight of two or more objects using nonstandard units. [Number and Numeration Goal 6]
- Use nonstandard units to weigh objects on a pan balance. [Measurement and Reference Frames Goal 1]

Terms to Use level, weigh, weights, unit, balance

Materials *My First Math Book,* p. 26; Teaching Master (*Math Masters,* p. 63); pan balances; small objects with uniform weight such as cube counters, pennies, washers, or small or large paper clips; assortment of objects to weigh

Planning Tip Choose one type of uniform-weight object to use during the core activity. You might add other types of objects to serve as weights as children continue to explore in the Math Center and/or to use as part of the Mathematics Extension in the Teaching Options.

 A **Core Activities**

▶ Weighing Objects (*My First Math Book,* p. 26; *Math Masters,* p. 63)

Show a pan balance and briefly review what it looks like and what it means when the pans are level (the objects on both sides weigh the same). Show children a lightweight object that fits in the pan (a marker, small block, or pair of scissors, for example). Also show the uniform weights you chose for the activity (pennies, washers, or paper clips, for example) and explain that they will use these items to weigh different objects in the pan balance.

Pass around the object you want to weigh and one of the uniform weights. Ask children to estimate how many of the weights they think it will take to balance the object. Then, place the object you want to weigh in one pan and add uniform weights, one at a time, to the other pan as the children count each weight out loud. When the pans are level, count and record the number of weights it took to balance the object. (For example, 1 marker weighs about the same as 8 pennies.) Compare the number with children's predictions. Choose another object to weigh with the same type of weights. Prompt discussion with questions such as: *Which object is heavier? How do you know? Would we get different results if we put a different type of weight in the other pan?*

Leave the pan balance(s), various objects to weigh, and some uniform weights in the Math Center. Children should work to balance at least one item with the weights and use pictures, numbers, and words to record their findings on page 26 of their math books. Also place copies of *Math Masters,* page 63 (a duplicate of *My First Math Book,* page 26) in the center for children to use to show their results as they weigh other objects.

NOTE Exact balance may be rare with a single unit of weight, especially with relatively heavyweight units. Lighter weights, such as small paper clips, are more likely to result in balanced pans, but it will take more of them. Explain that children should try to get the pans as close to level as possible, but it may not be possible to level them exactly.

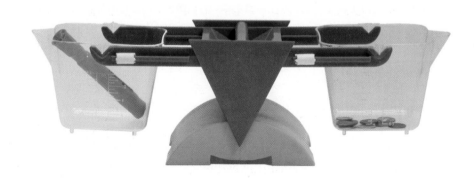

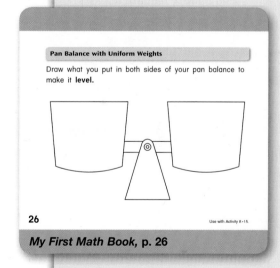

Pan Balance with Uniform Weights

Draw what you put in both sides of your pan balance to make it **level.**

26

Use with Activity 8·15.

My First Math Book, p. 26

▶ Practicing Number Writing

(Revisit Activity 3•1, p. 138; *My First Math Book,* pp. 27–47; *Math Masters,* pp. 13–24)

Portfolio Ideas Have children work on pages 27–47 in their math books. These pages are similar to the Number Book pages children completed in Activity 3-1, but the numbers go up through 20. On these pages, children should show different ways to represent each number in the box at the bottom of each page. Encourage them to use pictures, numbers and symbols (3 + 2), tallies, Ten Frames, words, and other representations to show each number.

This project should extend over several days, so that children can take their time and work carefully and thoroughly. Children will enjoy seeing their progress from earlier in the year! If desired, you can substitute *Math Masters,* pages 13–24 (using the blank page for numbers beyond 10) and use the pages to make new number books.

Also remember to use *Minute Math* during spare moments in the day.

B Teaching Options

EXTRA PRACTICE

▶ Using Other Nonstandard Weights

Children can weigh the same object using different uniform weights, then record and compare the results. (For example, 1 marker weighs about the same as 11 counting cubes; 1 marker weighs about the same as 8 pennies). Ask: *Why did it take different numbers of weights to level the pan balance? Which weight unit do you think is heavier? Why?*

Number Writing (1)
Name _____

28   Use with Activity 8•15.

My First Math Book, p. 28

Ongoing Assessment:

Recognizing Student Achievement

Use the **Number Writing** pages to assess children's ability to represent numbers in different ways. Children are making adequate progress with the concept of equivalent number names if they include a variety of representations on each page.

[Number and Numeration Goal 5]

Children are making adequate progress with understanding and applying addition and subtraction concepts if they include equivalent names that involve addition and subtraction.

[Operations and Computation Goal 1]

▶ Illustrating Heavier and Lighter

Ask children to draw pictures that show the meanings of *heavier* and *lighter*.

▶ Weighing Snack Food *(Center Activity Cards, 38)*

Provide a pan balance and have children weigh a specified amount of food for a snack. For example, each child can weigh out 10 paper clips worth of goldfish crackers.

▶ Weighing Dry or Wet Sponges

Children can compare the weights of wet and dry sponges on a pan balance. Have them predict the results, then use a pan balance to check their predictions. Children can directly compare two sponges by putting them on opposite sides of the balance. They can also use a uniform weight unit to determine the weights of the dry sponge and the wet sponge. Ask: *Which is heavier? How many more units did it take to balance the wet sponge? Why do you think the wet sponge is heavier?*

Introduction of the $10 Bill

ACTIVITY 8·16

🎯 **Objective** To introduce the $10 bill.

☑ Whole Group ☐ Partners
☑ Small Group ☐ Center

Key Concepts and Skills

- Practice making exchanges with $1 and $10 bills. [Number and Numeration Goal 3]
- Explore the characteristics of the $10 bill. [Measurement and Reference Frames Goal 2]
- Learn about the value of the $10 bill. [Measurement and Reference Frames Goal 2]

Terms to Use one dollar bill, ten dollar bill, trade, exchange, equals, dollar sign

Materials Teaching Aid Masters (*Math Masters,* pp. 113–116); real $10 bill; magnifying lenses

Planning Tip See the Planning Tip in Activity 8-7, page 394 about photocopying the bill masters so that children can see both the fronts and the backs of each type of bill.

A **Core Activities**

▶ Exploring the $10 Bill (*Math Masters,* pp. 113–116)

Show a real $10 bill and discuss what might be purchased with $10. Give each child a $10 bill from *Math Masters,* pages 113 and 114. Have them share the magnifying lenses to look closely at both sides of the bill. Discuss the size, shape, color, and any markings children notice. Note the number 10 in all 4 corners (front and back) and the shapes and contents of the pictures. Demonstrate how to write $10 using the dollar sign and the number 10.

Distribute $1 bill masters and discuss similarities and differences between the $1 bill and the $10 bill. Then give partners a pile of play $1 bills. Ask them whether they have enough $1 bills to exchange for a $10 bill. Have them work together to put the $1 bills into piles of 10. Act as the class banker and call on children to exchange each of their piles of ten $1 bills for one $10 bill. When all the piles of $1 bills have been traded in,

⭐ Ongoing Assessment:

Informing Instruction

Watch for children who do not understand why you can exchange ten $1 bills for one $10 bill. Remind these children of their experiences with exchanging ten single craft sticks for a bundle of 10 craft sticks (in the Concrete Number Count Routine and in Activities 7-8 and 8-1). Explain that the $1 bills are similar to the single craft sticks and the $10 bills are similar to the bundles of 10 craft sticks. Allow children to practice making exchanges with craft sticks as needed to build their comfort with this concept.

partners count how many $10 bills and how many leftover $1 bills they have. Then they count by 10s and 1s to determine their total amount of dollars.

Ask if anyone can figure out how many $10 bills can be exchanged for a $100 bill. Have them share strategies and reasons for their responses. Collect ten $10 bills from the groups (counting by 10s as you go) and exchange them for a $100 bill. Pass around the $100 bill for children to see.

▶ Measuring in Different Ways (Revisit Activity 5•12, p. 258)

Set out measuring tools such as rulers, tape measures, foot cutouts (children's and standard), and connecting cubes. Invite children to use the tools to measure items in the classroom and to record their findings with drawings and numbers. They can use the writing and drawing pages in their math books to record their measures.

B Teaching Options

ENRICHMENT

▶ Playing the *Paper Money Exchange Game* (Advanced)

(*Math Masters*, pp. 132, 133, and 134)

Children can play an advanced version of the *Paper Money Exchange Game* (Activity 8-1 Teaching Option, page 381). In this version, play continues until a player reaches $1,000. See *Math Masters*, pages 132, 133, and 134 for instructions, a gameboard, and a $1,000 bank draft.

TECHNOLOGY

▶ Adding Dollar Amounts on a Calculator

Children can use a calculator to find the total dollar amount of a mixed collection of $10 and $1 bills. They can double-check the sum by counting by 10s and 1s. Add $100 bills for children who are ready.

Math Masters, p. 113

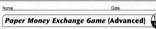

Math Masters, p. 133

Math Outdoors

CCSS Mathematical Practices
SMP2, SMP4, SMP5, SMP6

Content Standards
K.G.1

◎ **Objective** To provide practice with measurement, spatial relationships, and collecting and tracking data through a variety of outdoor activities.

Terms to Use estimate, measure, compare, height, length, over, under, near, far, left, right

Materials

Obstacle Courses
☐ measuring tools
☐ stopwatch or other timing devices

Shadow Mathematics
☐ chalk
☐ ruler
☐ scarves, ribbons, colored transparencies or other items to enhance shadow exploration
☐ paper and markers (optional)

Planting Seeds
☐ bean seeds
☐ dowel rods or sticks, at least 14 inches long
☐ twist ties for supporting the growing vines
☐ rulers
☐ foam cups or half-pint milk cartons and potting soil (for inside garden)
☐ measurement tools; chart paper, calendar, or journal for recording growth

Introduction

Take advantage of the rich mathematical opportunities that are available as children explore the outdoors. Spring is an ideal time of year to incorporate mathematics into the outdoor environment. The activities in this project include measuring length and time, describing position and spatial relationships, and collecting and tracking data. The activities offer meaningful connections with other curricular areas, especially science and physical education. (You may want to ask the P.E. teacher to get involved with the Obstacle Course activity.) As with other projects, choose the topics and activities that most interest you and your class.

Activity Options

▶ Obstacle Courses   ✔ Whole Group ✔ Small Group ✔ Partners

Many children love the fun and challenge of completing obstacle courses. Creating such courses and describing them for others to follow is also very engaging for children. The following activities can be done with any obstacle course that you or children create:

▷ Measure the distance from one point on the course to the next.

▷ Draw a map of the obstacle course.

▷ Describe the course using language that refers to spatial location and directionality (*over, under, near, far, left, right,* and so on).

▷ Use a stopwatch or other timing device to measure the amount of time it takes to complete the obstacle course.

▷ Repeat the course, then compare and try to better the time.

▷ Collect data by recording individual times on a chart or table.

▷ Use ordinal numbers to describe the course; then describe it in the reverse order.

▷ Predict and estimate the time it will take to complete the obstacle course in reverse order. Try it and compare the actual time with the estimate.

▷ Compare the time it takes to complete the course forward and in reverse order.

▶ Shadow Mathematics ✔ Whole Group ✔ Small Group ✔ Partners ✔ Center

Shadow explorations provide rich science and mathematics experiences for children. Some teachers conduct shadow units that span several weeks or longer. You might use the following ideas alone or as starting points for a more extensive study.

Shadow Dancing On a sunny day, have children move about to make shadows, observing the changes in their own and other's shadows. Transparencies, scarves, ribbons, and other similar materials are fun to dance with, and they make the shadows even more interesting. Encourage children to describe their shadows. Prompt with questions such as: *How big is your shadow? Which way is your shadow pointing? Is everyone's shadow pointing the same way? Does the shape of the shadow match the shape of what is making the shadow? What happens to your shadow when you move? Can you make your shadow bigger? Smaller?*

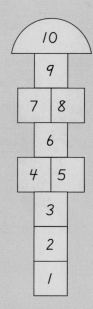

Shadow Tracing Shadows change size and shape depending on the angle of the sun at different times of the day. Children can trace their shadows early in the morning, and then, standing in the same place, trace their shadows closer to noon to determine the changes in size and shape. Have children work with partners, tracing their first and second shadows in different-colored chalk. They can estimate, then measure the difference between the two shadows. You can initiate interesting discussions with questions such as: *What makes the shadows? Why do all of the shadows stretch in the same direction? Why do you think the lengths of the shadows changed?* As they gain experience, you might encourage children to think about the changing angle of the sun relative to their own positions.

Shadow Walk Take children on a walk on a sunny day. Encourage them to observe the shadows of different objects they pass—trees, buildings, fences, as well as their own moving shadows. Ask children to compare and describe the size and orientation of the shadows relative to the objects, as well as to the position of the sun. Ask and discuss: *What happens to your shadow when you walk in the shadow of a large building?*

Literature Link *What Makes a Shadow?* by Clyde Robert Bulla (HarperCollins, 1994) is one of many excellent non-fiction children's books about shadows.

My Shadow by Robert Louis Stevenson

I have a little shadow that goes in and out with me,
And what can be the use of him is more than I can see.
He is very, very like me from the heels up to the head;
And I see him jump before me, when I jump into my bed.

The funniest thing about him is the way he likes to grow—
Not at all like proper children, which is always very slow;
For he sometimes shoots up taller like an India-rubber ball,
And he sometimes gets so little that there's none of him at all.

He hasn't got a notion of how children ought to play,
And can only make a fool of me in every sort of way.
He stays so close beside me, he's a coward you can see;
I'd think shame to stick to nursie as that shadow sticks to me!

One morning very early, before the sun was up,
I rose and found the shining dew on every buttercup;
But my lazy little shadow, like an arrant sleepy-head,
Had stayed at home behind me and was fast asleep in bed.

(from *A Child's Garden of Verses*, Simon & Schuster, 1999)

NOTE Children should be cautioned to protect their eyes by never looking directly at the sun.

▶ Planting Seeds

✔ Whole Group ✔ Small Group ✔ Partners

Growing plants provides children with new opportunities to observe and measure changes over time. Create a small garden in the school courtyard, outside a classroom door, or near a sunny window in the classroom. Read or tell the story of "Jack and the Beanstalk" to the class. Then, individually or as partners, children can plant seeds. To help measure growth, push a dowel into the soil and use a permanent marker to mark where the dowel meets the soil (the "zero growth point"). The dowel also serves as a support and keeps the vines growing fairly straight. Children can mark the growth point on the dowel each day or two. They can also measure the plant's growth using rulers or other measuring devices.

Help children record the date of planting, sprouting, and subsequent growth measurements. They might record measurements on a growth chart or table and/or draw and label a picture of the plant at various intervals on a calendar or in a journal. Discuss their findings, prompting with questions such as: *How tall is your plant? How much did your plant grow since the last time you measured it? How tall do you think it will be after the weekend? How many leaves does it have now? How many new leaves has it grown since the last time we counted?*

Home Link Suggestions

Children can take their plants home. They can also grow other plants with their families. Encourage children to find ways to monitor the growth of their plants.

Literature Link The following books about planting are fun to share with children: *Anno's Magic Seeds* by Mitsumasa Anno (Philomel Books, 1995); *Planting a Rainbow* by Lois Ehlert (Harcourt Brace, 1988); *Tops and Bottoms* by Janet Stevens (Harcourt Brace, 1995).

Planting Tips:

▷ Plan for this activity to span 5 to 6 weeks.

▷ Plant a few extra seeds—not all will germinate!

▷ Invite a few parents to assist on planting day.

▷ Cover indoor pots with plastic wrap to keep the soil moist until the seeds germinate.

▷ Use a spray bottle to water indoor plants.

Index

A

B

C

Bold entries indicate activity names and their page numbers.

Bold entries indicate activity names and their page numbers.

Bold entries indicate activity names and their page numbers.

Bold entries indicate activity names and their page numbers.

Bold entries indicate activity names and their page numbers.

Bold entries indicate activity names and their page numbers.

Notes

Notes

Notes

Notes